ENCYCLOPEDIA OF
GERMAN TANKS
OF WORLD WAR TWO

A complete illustrated directory of German battle tanks, armoured cars, self-propelled guns and semi-tracked vehicles, 1933-1945. By Peter Chamberlain and Hilary L. Doyle.

ARMS AND
ARMOUR

Arms and Armour Press
A Cassell Imprint
Villiers House, 41-47 Strand, London WC2N 5JE.

Distributed in the USA by Sterling Publishing Co. Inc., 387
Park Avenue South, New York, NY 10016-8810.
Distributed in Australia by Capricorn Link (Australia) Pty.
Ltd, P.O. Box 665, Lane Cove, New South Wales 2066.
First published 1978; this revised edition published 1993.
© Peter Chamberlain and Hilary Doyle, 1978, 1993

British Library Cataloguing-in-Publication Data: a catalogue
record for this book is available from the British Library
ISBN 1-85409-214-6
Printed and bound in Great Britain by
Butler & Tanner Ltd, Frome and London
Edited by Michael Boxall; designed by David Gibbons;

Photograph credits: B. Benvenuti, Bundesarchiv (Koblenz),
P. Chamberlain, J. Cunev, B. L. Davis, P. Decker,
H. L. Doyle, E. C. A. (France), C. Ellis, T. Gander,
I. V. Hogg, R. Hunnicutt, Col. R. J. Icks, Imperial War
Museum (London), T. Jentz, J. Milsom, K. R. Pawlas,
W. J. Spielberger, U.S. Official, B. Vanderveen,
C. H. Yust, S. Zaloga.
Jacket illustrations: Front cover shows a Sturmgeschütz III
Ausf G assault gun/tank destroyer armed with a 7.5cm
StuK40 L/48 gun (data page 84). Back cover: top row left,
captured French Somua medium tank in use by the German
Army as Pz Kpfw 35-S (data page 215); top row right, Pz
Kpfw III (Fl) flame-thrower tank in action (data page 69);
second row left, Pz Kpfw V Ausf A (Panther I) tanks
advance under fire in Russia (data page 122); second row
right, Pz Kpfw III Ausf L medium tank (data page 66); third
row left, German troops watch action in Russia in 1941 from
an le gep Beob Wg (Sd Kfz 253) semi-tracked observation
post (data page 168); third row right, the 12.8cm-gunned
Jagdtiger (data page 144); bottom row left, Pz Bef Wg 38(t)
command tank (data page 44); bottom right, Pz Kpfw V
Ausf A (Panther I) heavy medium tank (data page 122).
Half-title page (Plate 1). Pz Kpfw IV Ausf E medium support
tanks in action on the Russian Front in 1941 (data page 93).

Title page (Plate 2). Rear view of StuG III Ausf C or D
assault gun (data page 80).
Below: Plates 3-8.
Plate 3. Pz Kpfw 35(t) in France (data page 42).
Plate 4. An early production Pz Kpfw IV Ausf G (data page
97), the vision ports on the turret sides and on the loader's
side of the turret front having been eliminated. The gun is
equipped with the early globular muzzle brake.
Plate 5. One of the nine self-propelled anti-tank guns that
the Germans created by mounting captured Russian M1936
field guns on five ton semi-tracks (data text 183).
Designated 7.62cm FK36(r) auf Pz Jag Sf Zgkw 5t (Sd Kfz
6), they were sent to North Africa in early 1942.
Plate 6. The heavily-armoured reconnaissance tank Pz Kpfw
II Ausf J (or VK1601) in service as a training vehicle (data
page 35).
Plate 7. StuIG33B assault infantry guns in Russia (data page
86).
Plate 8. Grille, 15cm sIG33(Sf) auf Pz Kpfw 38(t) Ausf H,
passing through a Belgian town in the spring of 1943 (data
page 47).
Opposite page (Plate 9). Karlgerät 60cm self-propelled
heavy siege mortar ready for action on the Russian Front
(data page 158).

3

4

5

6

7

8

Contents

Contents
list of vehicle types

10

11

12

15

13

14

Contents
list of vehicle types

Panzerkampfwagen VI (Tiger) and variants, 134

16

Miscellaneous fully-tracked vehicles, 146

17

Semi-tracked vehicles, 162

18

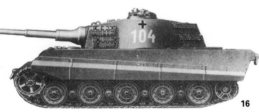

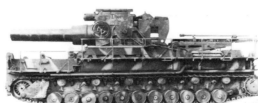

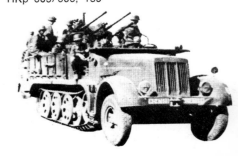

Chapter illustrations:
Plate 16. Pz Kpfw VI (Tiger II) Ausf B.
Plate 17. Karlgerät heavy siege mortar 'Thor'.
Plate 18. M Zgkw 8t mit 2cm Flakvierling (Sd Kfz 7/1).
Plate 19. S Pz Sp Wg Sd Kfz 231 (8-Rad).
Plate 20. Pz Kpfw B–2 740(f).

19

20

Introduction

By the early seventies, most publications dealing with German armoured vehicles were forced to repeat information which had remained unchanged for many years. During this period, the many new photographs which had become available were presented again and again without any new information.

The authors and technical editor of *Encyclopedia of German Tanks of World War Two* and such experts as Walter J. Spielberger concentrated research on the more technical aspects of German vehicles; this, in turn, led to increased interest in German armoured units. Study of these units, their equipment and where they served, provided new information. In the final analysis, technical study of armoured vehicles requires foolproof identification of a particular model or variant. The only identification of this kind is the vehicle chassis number.

Chassis numbers were found in the reports on captured vehicles tested by the Allies, on museum exhibits, and on photographs. But these reports and existing vehicles are few, and it was necessary to examine huge numbers of photographs in an attempt to spot required numbers. The practice of painting chassis numbers on German tanks and armoured vehicles was by no means universal, and depended on the period, the vehicle and the manufacturer. Obviously, overpainting eliminated any trace of numbers. At a later date, the isolated examples of chassis numbers

proved invaluable, in clarifying external features of each model. However, even when chassis numbers had been found, it was often impossible to trace the changes which occurred during the production of each series, particularly where several manufacturers were producing the same model. While a broad band of chassis numbers was issued for a particular model, each manufacturer was allocated a range of chassis numbers within an overall band. Thus, a high chassis number did not always mean a late production vehicle. In the case of mass-produced vehicles like tanks, with the exception of the Pz Kpfw Tiger, no fewer than three and sometimes as many as eight firms were delivering the same model during the same period. Depending upon their capacity, and the size of the original order, different firms were building different Marks of the same tank at the same time. As a result, external features of later models appeared on earlier ones, and vice versa, because they were built during the same period.

The missing link in all this research was clearly the manufacturers' records. Inevitably, this led to the investigation of German wartime industrial history, and other areas not formerly frequented by armoured vehicle researchers. Industrial information has never been correlated in a fashion useful to the tank enthusiast, but production reports for each area, for each monthly period and industrial category, yielded small amounts of data

Plates 21-23 (below). Left: le gep Beob Wg semi-tracked light armoured observation post (data page 168). Centre: a self-propelled anti-aircraft gun created by mounting a 2cm FlaK38 on a standard medium 6 x 4 truck, here in use against ground targets (data page 209). Right: Pz Sp Wg Panhard 178-P204(f), a captured French armoured car, operating on the Russian Front in 1942 (data page 226).

which led eventually to a complete picture. Acceptance and strength reports of the OKH (General Staff, Army) provided the final pieces of the jigsaw.

In *Encyclopedia of German Tanks of World War Two*, we are proud to present the result of this research. For the first time, enthusiasts will know just how many of each model were available to the German Army and, again for the first time, each model is accurately dated. Description and data are more accurate than has been possible hitherto. The photographs clearly identify features more comprehensively than would have been possible without this new data.

The book is intended to be an up-to-date reference directory which clearly identifies each vehicle and variant. The data, history and description have been prepared, to show the combat potential of the model, without giving too many details. The section on combat service gives an indication of the unit or type of unit with which the vehicles served. In cases where a particular vehicle was issued to a limited number of units, the units are identified. Mass-produced vehicles were delivered to many units and more comprehensive coverage of these is impossible within the confines of this book. The amount of information which we have collected on the types and numbers of vehicles delivered to every unit throughout the war is worthy of a future publication. The information

given in this book supersedes anything published in any earlier work by the authors. It is hoped that accuracy of the data contained in *Encyclopedia of German Tanks of World War Two* will go far to eliminate the generalities and part-truths which have formed the basis of so many past publications devoted to German armour.

The authors and the technical editor would like to express their thanks and appreciation to their many friends and associates who helped in the production of this book; especially Walter J. Spielberger, for allowing access to the material researched for his series of books – *Militaerfahrzeuge* (Military Vehicles), published in Germany by Motorbuch Verlag, Charles Kliment for information concerning armour production in Czechoslovakia during the war, which has been taken from material in his book on Czech armour; the staffs of the U.S. Archives, Bundesarchiv, and Imperial War Museum, and finally, our publisher for bearing with us until all the pieces of the jigsaw fitted together.

The authors and technical editor welcome constructive comment and information which could be included in future editions of the *Encyclopedia of German Tanks of World War Two*.

Peter Chamberlain, Hilary Louis Doyle,
Tom Jentz, 1978.

24

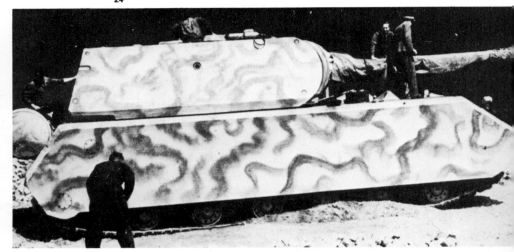

26

28

30

31

Explanatory notes

34

35

37

38

Designation: The designation used is the one found most frequently in OKH documents, which were the source of much of the material presented in this book. The originals included full, abbreviated and mixed terms, explanations of which are given in the Glossary on pages 14–17.

Other designations: These are alternative designations differing substantially from the OKH nomenclature, and include manufacturers' names, code names and, for foreign or captured equipment, the original designations in the country of origin.

Manufacturer: The Glossary on pages 14–17 includes the names and locations of the manufacturers listed on the data pages.

Chassis Nos: These figures represent the maximum and minimum of the chassis-number band; not all of the intervening numbers were used, as each manufacturer was allocated part of the band.

Engine: Full details of engine capacity, fuel, coolant, etc. are given in an Appendix on page 256. 1 PS = approximately 1 HP.

Gearbox: Number of gears, forward and reverse.

Speed and Range: Both figures relate to performance on roads.

Radio: Full details of each type of equipment are given in an Appendix on page 254.

Armament: Performance details are presented in an Appendix on page 244, and notes on related optical equipment are given in an Appendix on page 255. An equals sign (=) has been used as a horizontal ditto mark, and indicates data identical to that given in the column to its immediate left.

Armour: Thicknesses are given in millimetres; for angles, 0° means vertical, 90° horizontal.

History, Specific features, Combat service: These sections provide a brief account of each vehicle's development history, technical characteristics that identify the particular model, its significant service history, and the type of unit operating it.

Plate 24. A Pz Kpfw III Ausf J converted to a repair and recovery vehicle (data page 76). **Plate 25.** Flakpanzer 38(t) Ausf L in action, with upper superstructure folded down (data page 50). **Plate 26.** Flammwagen auf Pz Kpfw B-2(f) testing the flame-projector (data page 214). **Plate 27.** 'Maus' prototype on trials with turret and armament (data page 148). **Plate 28.** 12.8cm Selbstfahrlafette L/61 in Russia (data page 135). **Plate 29.** A Pz Kpfw 38(t) workshop vehicle removing the main armament of a Pz Kpfw/IV Ausf G. **Plate 30.** 2cm KwK38 auf Steyr s gl Pkw — a North African field modification mounting the 2cm KwK and MG34 combination mounting from the Sd Kfz 222 on the Steyr heavy 4 × 4 personnel car. **Plate 31.** Pz Kpfw IV/70(V) in action during the Ardennes offensive (data page 104). **Plate 32.** Pz Bef Wg 38(t) based on the E or F vehicle (data page 44). **Plate 33.** Loading ammunition for the 38cm Sturmmörser (data page 138). **Plate 34.** Neubaufahrzeug in Norway, 1940 (data page 147). **Plate 35.** The Büssing-NAG prototype for MTW I (data page 198). **Plate 36.** VK7001. A wooden model of 'Löwe' or 'Tiger-Maus', the Krupp project to build a replacement for the Tiger II; this was to utilize Tiger II components, and to have the engine at the front of the vehicle. **Plate 37.** R2, one of a projected series of self-propelled coast guns sponsored by the German Navy from 1939. Ranging in calibre from 15cm to 38cm, they were to be fired from tracked carriages on a 360° turntable. **Plate 38.** Mörser Zugmittel 35(t) (data page 43).

Glossary
of technical terms

Abbreviation	Full Term	English Translation
Abt; Abtlg	Abteilung	Battalion; detachment; department
Abshn	Abschnitt	Section
ARW	Achtradwagen	8-wheeled vehicle
	achse	Axle
	Adler	Vehicle manufacturer in Frankfurt
	Alkett	AFV manufacturer in Berlin
	als	As
	Alt/Alte	Old
	Alter	Older
(a)	Amerikanisch	American
Anh	Anhänger	Trailer
	Antenne	Aerial
	Ardelt	AFV development company
	Armee	Army; field army
Art	Artillerie, Typ	Artillery, Type
Art Pz Beob Wg	Artillerie Panzerbeo-bachtungswagen	Armoured artillery observation vehicle
	Antrieb	Drive
	Argus	AFV development company
	auf	Upon; on
	Aufbau	Vehicle body; superstructure
Aufkl	Aufklärung/Aufklärer	Reconnaissance; reconnaissance vehicle
	Ausbildung	Training
Ausf	Ausführung	Model; mark; design
	Auto-Union	Vehicle manufacturer in Chemnitz
	Ballistik-Messfahrzeug	Gunnery survey vehicle
	Barbarossa	Redbeard (code name for the invasion of the Soviet Union)
BW	Bataillonswagen	Battalion vehicle (code name for Pz Kpfw IV series)
	Batterie/Batterien	Battery; batteries (artillery)
BMW	Bayerische Motoren Werke	Vehicle manufacturer in Munich
	Becker, Alfred	Engineering works in Krefeld
Bef Wg	Befehlswagen	Command vehicle
(b)	belgisch	Belgian
Beob Wg	Beobachtungswagen	Observation vehicle
	Beobachtungspanzer-wagen	Armoured observation vehicle
	Bergeanker	Recovery anchor
	Bergegerät	Recovery equipment
Pz Berge Wg	Bergepanzer/Berge-Panzerwagen	Armoured recovery vehicle
	Beute	Booty; captured equipment
	Bewaffnung	Armament
	bis	To
BMM	Böhmisch-Mährische Maschinenfabrik	AFV manufacturer in Prague, Czechoslovakia (formerly CKD or Praga)
	Bord	Intercom
	Borgward	Vehicle manufacturer in Bremen
Brig	Brigade	Brigade (unit)
BL	Brückenleger	Bridge-laying vehicle
	Brückenkampfwagen	Tank bridge-carrier
	Brummbär	Grizzly Bear (SP gun)
	Büssing-NAG	Vehicle manufacturer in Berlin, Elbe and Leipzig
cm	zentimeter	Centimetre (0.3937 inches) used to define gun calibres
DB	Daimler-Benz	AFV manufacturer in Berlin
(d)	Deutsche	German
DAK	Deutsche Afrika Korps	German (North) Africa Corps
DEW	Deutsche-Eisenwerke	AFV manufacturer in Duisburg and Teplitz Schonau
	Deutsche Werke	Vehicle manufacturer in Kiel
DEMAG		AFV manufacturer in Dusseldorf and Berlin
	Doppel	Double
	Drilling	Triple
DW	Durchbruchwagen	Breakthrough vehicle (code name for Pz Kpfw V and VI)
Einh	Einheits	Universal (standardized)
	Einheitswaffenträger	Universal weapon carrier (tracked SP carriage)
	Eisenwerke	Steel works
	Elefant	Elephant (SP gun) formerly the Ferdinand
(e)	englisch	English
	Ente	Duck (code name for light tracked vehicle)
E	Entwicklung	Project (development)
Ers	Ersatz	Replacement; substitute
	Fahrerblende	Driver's visor
	Fahrersehklappe	Driver's visor
Fgst	Fahrgestell	Chassis
F Boote	Fahrprammboote	Tank landing craft
	Fahrschulefahrzeug	Driving school vehicle
	Fahrschulwanne	Driving school chassis (turret removed)
Fz	Fahrzeug	Vehicle
FAMO	Fahrzeug und Motorenbau, GmbH	AFV manufacturer in Breslau and Warsaw, Poland (formerly Ursus)
	Falke	Falcon (code name for APC)
	Fallschirmtruppen	Parachute troops
F H	Feldhaubitze	Field howitzer
F K	Feldkanone	Field gun
F	Fernrohr	Telescope
Fernschr	Fernschreiber	Teletype apparatus
Fsp Pz Wg	Fernsprechpanzerwagen	Telephone communications AFV
	Fernsprechbetriebspanzer-wagen	Telephone exchange vehicle
	Feuerleitpanzerfahrzeug	Fire control AFV
Fla Pz	Flakpanzer	Anti-aircraft vehicle
Flak Pz Wg	Flakpanzerwagen	Anti-aircraft tank
	Flakvierling	Four-barrelled anti-aircraft gun
	Flakvisier	Anti-aircraft gun sight
	Flakzwilling	Double-barrelled anti-aircraft gun
Flw; Fl W	Flammenwerfer	Flame-thrower
	Flammenwerfer Anlagen	Flame-thrower attachment
	Flammgranate	Incendiary shell
(Fl)	Flammpanzer	Flame-throwing tank
	Flammpanzerwagen	Flame-throwing AFV
	Fliegerabwehr	Anti-aircraft
Flak	Flugerabwehrkanone	Anti-aircraft gun
	Flugabwehrzug	Anti-aircraft platoon
(f)	französisch	French
	früher	Formerly
	für	For
Fu	Funk	Radio
FuG	Funkgerät	Radio equipment
Fkl	Funklenk	Radio-controlled
	Funklenkwagen	Radio-controlled vehicle
Fu Pz Wg	Funkpanzerwagen	Radio-controlled AFV
Fu Spr G; Fu Spr	Funksprechgerät	Radio-telephone equipment
Fu Wg	Funkwagen	Radio vehicle
	Geheim	Secret
gl	Geländegangiger	Cross-country travelling ability
gep	gepanzerte	Armoured
gep LKW	gepanzerter Lastkraftwagen	Armoured vehicle
gep Mannschaft Tr Wg	gepanzerter Mannschaft-stransportwagen	APC
gep Mun Schl	gepanzerter Munitionssch-lepper	Armoured ammunition tractor

Abbreviation	Full Term	English Translation
gep Sf fürstug	gepanzerter Selbstfahrlafette fur Stürmgeschütz	Armoured self-propelled carriage for assault gun
	Gerät	Equipment (generally refers to equipment number)
Gesch	Geschütz	Gun
Gw	Geschützwagen	Gun motor carriage (SP gun)
Gr	Granate	Shell
GrW	Granatwerfer	Mortar
	Grille	Cricket (SP gun)
gr Pz Bef Wg	Grosse Panzer Befehlswagen	Heavy armoured command vehicle
	Grosstraktor	Large tractor (code name for heavy tank project)
	Gummi	Rubber
Hb	Halb	Semi; half
HK	Halbkettenfahrzeug	Halftrack vehicle
	Hängelafette	Suspended mounting (armoured car turret)
	Hansa-Loyd-Goliath	Vehicle manufacturer in Bremen
Hanomag	Hanoversche Maschinenbau AG	Vehicle manufacturer in Hannover
H	Heer	Army
HWA; HWaA	Heereswaffenamt	Army Ordnance Office
(H)	Henschel	AFV manufacturer in Kassel
	Hetzer	Baiter (tank destroyer)
	Heuschrecke	Grasshopper (SP gun)
HL	Hochleistung	High performance (engine)
HL	Hohlladung	Hollow charge (HEAT)
	Horch	Vehicle manufacturer in Zwickau
	Hornisse	Hornet (SP gun)
	Hummel	Bumble Bee (SP gun)
Inf	Infanterie	Infantry
I G; IGesch	Infanteriegeschütz	Infantry howitzer
IR	Infrarot	Infra-red
In	Inspektion	Inspectorate
	Instandsetzungskraftwagen	Maintenance vehicle
(i)	Italienisch	Italian
Jäg	Jäger	Hunter
Jgd Pz	Jagdpanzer	Tank destroyer
	Jagdpanther	Tank destroyer (Panther chassis)
	Jagdtiger	Tank destroyer (Tiger chassis)
	Kätzchen	Kitten (code name for tracked APC)
	Karlgerät	Code name for heavy SP siege gun
Kpfw; Kw	Kampfwagen	Tank; armoured vehicle
Kal	Kaliber	Calibre
KFF	Kampfwagen Fahrer Fernrohr	Tank driver's episcope
KwK	Kampfwagenkanone	Tank gun
K	Kanone	Cannon, Gun
	Kavallerie	Cavalry
Kl	Klein	Small
Km	Kilometer	Kilometre (0.6214 miles)
Kmdo; KDO	Kommando	Command
	Kommandopanzerwagen	Armoured headquarters vehicle
	Korps	Corps (unit)
Kfz	Kraftfahrzeug	Motor vehicle
	Kraftfahrlehrkommando	Driver training command
Kw Werkst Z	Kraftwagenwerkstattzug	Vehicle workshop troop
Kr Pz Wg	Krankenpanzerwagen	Armoured ambulance
(KM)	Krauss-Maffei	Vehicle manufacturer in Munich
(K)	Krupp/Krupp-Gruson	AFV manufacturer in Essen and Madgeburg
	Kugelblitz	Ball lightning (anti-aircraft tank)
Kg ZF; KZF	Kugelzielfehrnrohr	Ball mounted telescope
Laf	Kurz	short
	Lafette	Gun carriage
	Ladungsleger	Explosives-carrier (layer)
	Ladungsträger	Explosives-carrier
LWS	Land-Wasser-Schlepper	Land and water tractor
LaS	Landwirtschaftlicher Schlepper	Agricultural tractor (code designation for Pz Kpfw I and II series)
	Lang	Long
	Lange	Length
Lkw	Lastkraftwagen	Truck, load-carrying vehicle
L	Kaliberlange	Length of gun barrel in calibres
	Laufwerk	Suspension, Running gear
	Lehr	Training
	Leibstandarte	Bodyguard
le SPW	Leichter Schützenpanzerwagen	Light armoured personnel carrier
le	leicht/leichte	Light
leFH; IFH	leichte Feldhaubitze	Light field howitzer
LG	Leichter Geschütz	Light gun (recoilless)
Le IG	Leichtes Infanterie Geschütz	Light infantry gun
LIG		
	Leichtertraktor	Light tractor (code name for light tank project)
Le WS	Leichter Wehrmacht Schlepper	Armed forces light carrier
	Lichtauswertepanzerwagen	Flash spotter AFV
L spur	Leucht spur	Tracer ammunition
LrS	Lorraine Schlepper	Lorraine tractor
	Luftwaffe	Air Force
	Luchs	Lynx (light reconnaissance vehicle)
	Magirus	Vehicle manufacturer in Ulm
MTW	Mannschaftstransportwagen	Troop transport vehicle
	Marder	Marten (Sp gun)
MAN	Maschinenfabrik Augsburg Nürnberg	AFV manufacturer in Nürnberg
MNH	Maschinenfabrik Niedersachen Hannover	AFV manufacturer in Hanover
MG	Maschinengewehr	Machine-gun
MK	Maschinenkanone	Machine cannon
MP	Maschinen pistole	Machine combine
	Maultier	Mule (semi-track carrier)
	Maus	Mouse (heavy tank)
	Maybach	Motor manufacturer in Berlin
	Mechanische Werke	Vehicle manufacturer in Cottbus
MB	Mercedes-Benz	AFV manufacturer in Berlin
	Messtruppanzerwagen	Survey troop AFV
m	meter	3.2808 feet
	millimeter	0.03937 inches
	Minenräum	Mine-clearance
	Minenrollern	Minerollers
	mit	With
	mitte	Middle (centre)
	mittlerer	Medium
	Möbelwagen	Furniture van (anti-aircraft tank)
Mrs	Mörser	Heavy mortar
Mrs tr	Mörserträger	Heavy mortar carrier
MIAG	Muhlenbau-Industrie AG	AFV manufacturer in Braunschweig
Mun	Munition	Ammunition
	Munitionskraftwagen	Ammunition vehicle
Mun Pz	Munitions panzer	Armoured ammunition vehicle

Glossary
of technical terms

Abbreviation	Full Term	English Translation
Mun Schl	Munitionsschlepper	Ammunition carrier
	Nachrichten Abteilung	Communication battalion
	Nahverteidigungswaffe	Close-in defence weapon
	Nashorn	Rhinoceros (SP gun) formerly Hornet
NbW	Nebel	Smoke
	Nebelwerfer	Rocket launcher
NSU	Neckarsulm	Vehicle manufacturer in Neckarsulm
	Neu	New
nA	Neue Art/Ausführung	New type or pattern
NbFz	Neubaufahrzeug	New construction vehicle
Ni-werke	Nibelungenwerke	AFV manufacturer in Linz (Austria)
	Nordbau	Motor manufacturer
	Notek	Lighting equipment manufacturer
	Nummer	Number
OKH	Oberkommando des Heeres	High Command of the Army
OKW	Oberkommando der Wehrmacht	High Command of the Armed Forces
	oder	Or; alternatively
	offen	Open
O	ohne	Without
	Opel	Vehicle manufacturer in Russelheim
OT	Organisation Todt	Work Corps under direction of Todt
O-serie	Nul serie	Pre-production run
	Ostbau	AFV manufacturer in Sagan
	Ostkette	East track (wide tracks for soft ground)
	Ostwind	Eastwind (anti-aircraft tank)
(ö)	östereichische	Austrian
Pz	Panzer	Armour; tank
Pz Abt	Panzerabteilung	Tank detachment; battalion
Pz Abw Abt	Panzerabwehrabteilung	Anti-tank gun battalion
Pak	Panzerabwehrkanone	Anti-tank gun
Pz Art	Panzerartillerie	Armoured artillery
Pz Aufkl Abt	Panzer Aufklärungs Abteilung	Armoured reconnaissance battalion
Pz Bef Wg	Panzerbefehlswagen	Command tank
Pz Beob Wg	Panzerbeobachtungswagen	Tank used for artillery observation
	Panzerbergeanker	Tank recovery anchor (used to assist recovery of AFVs)
Pz Berge Wg	Panzerbergewagen	Armoured Recovery Vehicle (ARV)
Pz B	Panzerbrigade	Tank brigade; armoured brigade
Pz B	Panzerbüchse	Anti-tank rifle
Pz D	Panzerdivision	Tank division; armoured division
PzF	Panzerfähre	Armoured ferry
Pz Fu Wg	Panzerfunkwagen	Armoured radio-car
Pz Gr; Pzgr	Panzergranate	Solid shot; armour-piercing shell
	Panzergrenadier	Private in armoured infantry brigade
	Panzergrenadier Division	Armoured motorized division
Pz H	Panzerhaubitze	Howitzer adapted for fitting in armoured vehicle
Pz Jäg	Panzerjäger	Tank destroyer; tank hunter
Pz Jäg Abt	Panzerjägerabteilung (Sf)	Anti-tank battalion (mobile troops)
Pz Kpfw	Panzerkampfwagen	Tank; armoured fighting vehicle
Pz K	Panzerkanone	Tank gun
Pz Kp	Panzerkompanie	Tank company
	Panzerkorps	Armoured corps
Pz K	Panzerkraftwagen	Armoured vehicle

Abbreviation	Full Term	English Translation
Pz Rgt	Panzerregiment	Tank regiment; armoured regiment (mixed)
Pz Sf; Pz Sfl	Panzer Selbstfahrlafette	Armoured self-propelled mount
Pz Sp Wg	Panzerspähwagen	Armoured scout car
	Panzer Truppen	Armoured troops; armoured units; tank forces
	Panzerwagen	Armoured vehicle
	Panzerwerfer	Armoured rocket-launcher
Pz Zug	Panzerzug	Tank troop
	Patrone	Round (ammunition)
	Periskop	Periscope
PKW	Personenkraftwagen	Passenger car
Pi	Pionier	Engineer
Pi Pz Wg	Pionierpanzerwagen	Engineers armoured vehicle
	Polizei Panzerwagen	Police AFV
(p)	polnisch	Polish
(P)	Porsche	AFV development company in Stuttgart
	Protectorate	Occupied Czech states of Bohemia and Moravia
	Protze	Limber
	Prüfung	Testing
RA		Rocket launcher sight
	Rad	Wheel
	Radfahrzeug	Wheeled vehicle
R PzB	Rakete Panzerbüsche	Anti-tank rocket launcher
RW	Raketenwerfer	Rocket projector
	Raümen	Clearer (minefield)
	Raupe	Caterpillar track
RR	Raupen Rader	Wheel-cum-track
RSO	Raupenschlepper Ost	Tracked carrier, East (Steyr)
RaupFzg	Raupenfahrzeug	Self-propelled full tracked vehicle
	Regiment	Regiment
	Reich	Republic
	Reihenwerfer	A series of mortars mounted on a frame
RhB	Rheinmetall-Borsig	AFV manufacturer in Dusseldorf
	Ringhoffen-Tatra	(See Tatra)
	Ritscher	Vehicle manufacturer in Hamburg
	Rot	Red
RSO	Raupenschlepper Ost	Tracked Tractor East
Rblf	Rundblickfernrohr	Panoramic telescope
(r)	russische	Russian
	R-Vielfachwerfer	Multiple Rocket launcher used by the Waffen SS only
Saukopf	Saukopfblende	Boars head (cast) gun mantlet
	Saurer	Vehicle manufacturer in Vienna
	Schachtellaufwerk	Interleaved running gear
	Schallaufnahmepanzerwagen	Sound recording armoured vehicle
	Schallauswertepanzerwagen	Armoured sound ranging vehicle
	Schichau	Vehicle manufacturer in Elbing
	Schienen-Ketten Fahrzeug	Railway tracked vehicle
	Schildkröte	Turtle (code name for amphibious armoured car project)
	Schlepper	Tractor
	Schmal	Narrow
	Schürze	Armoured apron, skirting plate
SPW; Spzwg	Schützenpanzerwagen	Armoured infantry vehicle (APC)
SS	Schütz Staffeln	SS (Protection Squads)
	Schwadron	Troop

Abbreviation	Full Term	English Translation	Abbreviation	Full Term	English Translation
s	schwere	Heavy		Traktor	Tractor
sFH	schwere Feldhaubitze	Heavy field howitzer		Trippel	Vehicle development company
sIG	schwere Infanteriege- schütz	Heavy infantry gun	(Tp)	Tropen ausführung	Tropical version
				Truppenluftschütz	Anti-aircraft
sIG Kp	schwere Infanterieg- schütz Kompanie	Heavy infantry gun company		Truppenversuch	Troop trials
				Turm	Turret
SMK	schwere Maschinen Karbine	Heavy machine-gun (ammunition)	TBF	Turmblickfernrohr	Turret panoramic telescope
			TZF	Turmzielfernrohr	Turret telescope
sPzB 41	schwere Panzerbüchse 41	Heavy anti-tank rifle 41		Typ	Type
s Pz Sp Wg	schwere Panzerspähwagen	Heavy armoured reconnaissance car	UHU		Eagle Owl (code name for infra-red searchlight vehicle)
SW	Schwere Wagen	Code name for heavy tank project	u	und	And
			(V)	Vomag	AFV manufacturer in Plauen
sWS	Schwere Wehrmacht Schlepper	Heavy army tractor	Verl	Verlangert	Lengthened
			V	Versuchs	Experimental
	Schwimmkampfwagen	Amphibious tank	V serie	Versuchs serie	Experimental series, prototype series
	Schwimmkorper	Amphibious body			
	Schwimmpanzer	Amphibious AFV	Vs Kfz	Versuchs Kraftfahrzeug	Experimental vehicle
	Seelöwe	Sealion (code name for the invasion of Britain)	Verst	Verstärkt	Strengthened, re-inforced
			VK	Versuchskonstruktion	Experimental prototype
Sf; Sfl	Selbstfahrlafette	Self-propelled (gun mount) SP gun		Vielfache	Multiple
				Vielfachwerfer (Raketen)	Multiple rocket launcher
	Serie	Series		Vierling	Quadruple
	Skoda	AFV manufacturer in Pilsen, Czechoslovakia	VK	Vollkettenfahrzeuge	Fully-tracked vehicle
				Vollkettenaufklärer	Fully-tracked reconnaissance vehicle
	Sockellafette	Pivot or pedestal mounting for gun			
				Vorsatz P	Device P (ball mount for curved barrel weapon)
Sd	Sonder	Special purpose			
Sd Anh	Sonder Anhänger	Special purpose trailer		Waffe	Weapon
	Sonderausführung	Special model		Waffen	Arms; weapons; ordnance
Sd Fgst	Sonderfahrgestell	Special purpose chassis		Waffen SS	Military wing of the SS
SGer	Sondergerät	Special purpose equipment	Wa	Waffenamt	Ordnance (Department)
Sd Kfz	Sonderkraftfahrzeug	Special purpose vehicle	Wa A	Waffenamt Abteilung	Ordnance Department
Sp W, Sp Wg	Spähwagen	Reconnaissance vehicle	Wa Prüf	Waffenprüfungsamt	Ordnance Test Officer Dept
	Sprengdienst Kraftfahrzeug	Demolition vehicle (Goliath)		Waffentrager	Weapons carrier (SP gun)
			Wg	Wagen	Wagon; vehicle
Sprgr/Spgr	Sprenggranate	High-explosive shell		Wanze	Bug (code name for one-man tank project)
SprLdg	Sprengladung	Explosive load (charge)			
	Stoewer	Vehicle manufacturer		Wehrmacht	Armed Forces
	Stab	Headquarters	WH	Wehrmacht Heer	Armed Forces Army
	Stabskompanie	Headquarters Company	WL	Wehrmacht Luftwaffe	Armed Forces Air Force
	Starr	Rigid (gun mounted without recoil gear)	WM	Wehrmacht Marine	Armed Forces Navy
				Wegmann	AFV manufacturer in Kassel
	Stielgranate	Hollow-charge stick round (muzzle loader)	Werf, W	Werfer	Projector
				Werkstatt Kompanie	Workshop company
Steyr	Steyr-Daimler-Puch	Vehicle manufacturer in Austria		Weserhütte	Vehicle manufacturer in Bad Oeynhausen
StuA	Sturmartillerie	Assault artillery		Wespe	Wasp (SP gun)
StuG	Sturmgeschütz	Assault gun (SP gun)	WZF	Winkelzielfernrohr	Angled telescope
StuG Abt	Sturmgeschütz Abteilung	Assault gun battalion		Wirblewind	Whirlwind (anti-aircraft tank)
StuH	Sturmhaubitze	Assault howitzer (SP gun)		Wumag	Vehicle manufacturer in Gorlitz
StuIG	Sturm Infanterie Geschütz	Assault infantry gun (SP)			
				Wurfgerät	Rocket equipment
StuK	Sturmkanone	Assault cannon (SP gun)		Wurfrahmen	Rocket launcher frame
Stu Mrs	Sturmmörser	Assault mortar (SP gun)		Zerstörer	Destroyer
	Sturmpanther	Assault Panther	ZRW	Zehnradwagen	10-wheeled vehicle
Stu Pz	Sturmpanzer	Assault armoured vehicle	ZF	Zielfernrohr	Telescope sight
				Zahnradfabrik, Friedrich- shaven	Gearbox manufacturer
	Sturmsteg	Infantry assault footbridge			
	Sturmtiger	Assault Tiger		Zug	Platoon
	Süd	South	ZW	Zugführerwagen	Platoon commander's vehicle (code name for the Pz III series)
	Taifun	Typhoon (code name for remote-controlled demolition unit)			
			Zgkw	Zugkraftwagen	Prime mover; semi-tracked vehicle
	Tatra	Engine manufacturer in Czechoslovakia			
				Zugmittel	Tractor
	Tauchpanzer	Submersible tank	Zw	Zwilling	Twin; dual
(t)	Tschechoslowakisch	Czechoslovakian (i.e. of Czech origin)		Zwillingslafette	Twin mounting
				Zwischenlösung	Interim development
ton	tonne	Metric ton (0.9842 long tons)		Zwitterfahrzeug	Semi-tracked vehicle
	Träger	Transport; carrier	zbV		For special employment

Panzerkampfwagen I
and variants

Panzerkampfwagen I Ausf A ohne Aufbau

Other designation: Krupp Traktor LaS
Type: Light armoured tracked vehicle for training use

Manufacturer: Henschel, MAN, Daimler-Benz, Rheinmetall-Borsig, Krupp-Gruson
Chassis Nos.: 8011–9000
15 produced from February to April 1934

Crew: 2	Engine: Krupp M305
Weight (tons): 3.5	Gearbox: 5 forward, 1 reverse
Length (metres): 4.02	Speed (km/hr): 37
Width (metres): 2.06	Range (km): 145
Height (metres): 1.15	

Armour (mm/angle):	Front	Side	Rear	Top/Bottom
Hull:	13/27°	13/0°	13/15°	6/90°

History: Prevented by the Treaty of Versailles from possessing or manufacturing tanks or similarly designed armoured fighting vehicles, Germany skirted the treaty restrictions by producing 15 tank hulls without superstructures, turrets or armament. To spread production experience as far as possible, five companies had been selected in 1933 to produce three vehicles each. The official designation, 'Landwirtschaftlicher Schlepper' (agricultural tractor), helped disguise the fact that any type of tracked armoured vehicle was being manufactured.

Specific features: This vehicle had a fully-tracked armoured hull. The suspension consisted of a sprocket, 4 road wheels, a fifth, larger road wheel (also acting as the idler) and 3 return rollers. The forward road wheel was cushioned by a coil spring and hydraulic shock absorber. The other 4 road wheels were mounted in pairs, cushioned by leaf springs supported by a girder. This girder was all that remained of a suspension design which related back to development from a Carden-Loyd design.

Combat service: Designed as a training vehicle, the turretless Krupp Traktor was not intended for combat. In the Spring of 1934, it was issued to the first two Panzer regiments, Kraftfahrlehrkommando (Motorization Instructional Command) Zossen und Ohrdruf to give the troops their first experience of driving a fully-tracked armoured vehicle.

Plate 39 (top). The Krupp 1937 prototype LKA export tank.
Plate 40. Krupp's 'Landwirtschaftlicher Schlepper'.
Plate 41 (below). Fahrschulwanne—the LaS in use as driving school vehicles.

Panzerkampfwagen I Ausf A (Sd Kfz 101)

Other designation: LaS (Vs Kfz 617)
Type: Machine-gun armed light tank

Manufacturer: Henschel, MAN, Krupp-Gruson, Daimler-Benz
Chassis Nos.: 9001–10477
818 produced from July 1934 to June 1936

Crew: 2	Engine: Krupp M305
Weight (tons): 5.4	Gearbox: 5 forward, 1 reverse
Length (metres): 4.02	Speed (km/hr): 37
Width (metres): 2.06	Range (km): 145
Height (metres): 1.72	Radio: FuG2

Armament: Two 7.92mm MG13
Traverse: 360° (hand)
Elevation: −12° +18°
Sight: TZF2
Ammunition: 2,250 Patr SmK

Armour (mm/angle):	Front	Side	Rear	Top/Bottom
Turret:	13/10°	13/22°	13/22°	8/82°−90°
Superstructure:	13/22°	13/22°	13/17°	6/82°−90°
Hull:	13/27°	13/0°	13/15°	6/90°
Gun mantlet:	13/round			

History: Originally known as the MG Panzerwagen (armoured MG tank) (Vs Kfz 617), the Pz Kpfw I Ausf A was the first German tank to go into mass-production. An initial order for 135, given to Krupp, was quickly expanded by orders for an additional 450 in January 1934.

Specific features: The Pz Kpfw I Ausf A had the same hull and suspension as the Ausf A o Aufbau. The superstructure was built out over the tracks with the turret mounted offset to the right side. This allowed room for the driver's access hatch in the left side and roof of the superstructure. Both machine-guns were mounted coaxially in the turret front in an internal moving gun mantlet. Although there were only two crew members, five vision ports were provided in the superstructure and six in the turret. The original design did not provide adequate ventilation with the result that the air-cooled engine overheated. To reduce this problem, an 'air-scoop' type of louvre was added to the rear deck, and two scoops were added to the rear to deflect the exhaust air.

Combat service: The first complete Pz Kpfw I Ausf A were issued in September 1934. By July 1935, the Kraftfahrlehrkommando had received 475. As new Panzer units were formed around cadres drawn from older units, and because the cadres took their Pz Kpfw I Ausf A with them as training vehicles, by the beginning of the war, the Ausf A was scattered throughout all the Panzer units. It was used extensively in Poland and France, and was issued to Pz-Abt 40 which took part in the invasion of Denmark and Norway. From late 1940 until 1941, the Ausf A was withdrawn from units in the main combat areas. Its final service was in Finland in 1941, and in North Africa.

42

Plates 42-43. Pz Kpfw I Ausf A on pre-war manoeuvres (below) and in France during 1940 (above).
Plate 10 (Page 6). Kpfw I Ausf A.

Panzerkampfwagen I Ausf B (Sd Kfz 101)

Other designation: LaS Maybach
Type: Machine-gun armed light tank

Manufacturer: Henschel, MAN, Daimler-Benz, Krupp-Gruson, Wegmann
Chassis Nos.: 10478–16500
675 produced from August 1935 to June 1937

Crew: 2	Engine: Maybach NL38TR
Weight (tons): 5.8	Gearbox: 5 forward, 1 reverse
Length (metres): 4.42	Speed (km/hr): 40
Width (metres): 2.06	Range (km): 170
Height (metres): 1.72	Radio: FuG2

Armament: Two 7.92mm MG13
Traverse: 360° (hand)
Elevation: −12° +18°
Sight: TZF2
Ammunition: 2,250 Patr SmK

Armour (mm/angle):	Front	Side	Rear	Top/Bottom
Turret:	13/10°	13/22°	13/22°	8/82°–90°
Superstructure:	13/22°	13/22°	13/0°	6/83°–90°
Hull:	13/27°	13/0°	13/19°	6/90°
Gun mantlet:	13/round			

44

History: When the Ausf A proved to be underpowered, and its engine was found to overheat, the turret and superstructure were mounted on the longer chassis designed for the kl Pz Bef Wg.

Specific features: The Ausf B had a longer chassis than the Ausf A, having taken over the chassis designed for the kl Pz Bef Wg. The suspension was modified and resulted in 5 road wheels, 4 return rollers and the idler wheel elevated so that it was no longer in use as a road wheel. The rear deck was also redesigned with louvres so arranged as to supply and exhaust air for the water-cooled engine and its radiator. The turret and superstructure were identical with those on the Ausf A.

Combat service: The Ausf B was issued to all existing Panzer units from 1935 until 1940. From the latter half of 1940 until early 1941, it was phased out of service and when the Germans invaded Russia in June 1941, only 74 were serving with Panzer Regiments. The Ausf B was issued as an armoured vehicle for company and battalion commanders of the Panzerjägerabteilung–(Sf) (tank-hunter batallion which was equipped with self-propelled anti-tank guns mounted on German-designed armoured vehicles). Late in 1943, the commanders of the Pz Jäg Abt registered a complaint that the Ausf B was completely inadequate as a command vehicle.

Plates 44-46. Pz Kpfw I Ausf B: top, in France, 1940; above, the experimental vehicle LKB2 powered by an air-cooled Krupp M601 diesel engine; below, the Ausf B in Poland in 1939.

Panzerkampfwagen I Ausf B ohne Aufbau

Other designation: Instandsetzungskraftwagen I
Type: Light armoured tracked vehicle for maintenance equipment

Manufacturer: Henschel, MAN, Daimler-Benz, Krupp-Gruson,
  Wegmann
Chassis Nos.: 10478–16500
164 produced from 1936 to November 1938

Crew: 2	Engine: Maybach NL38TR
Weight (tons): 4.0	Gearbox: 5 forward, 1 reverse
Length (metres): 4.42	Speed (km/hr): 40
Width (metres): 2.06	Range (km): 170
Height (metres): 1.35	

Armour (mm/angle):	Front	Side	Rear	Top/Bottom
Hull:	13/27°	13/0°	13/19°	6/90°

History: The Pz Kpfw I Ausf B o Aufbau was produced to provide each armoured company with a fully-tracked repair and maintenance vehicle.

Specific features: This vehicle consisted of the hull of the Ausf B minus its turret and superstructure. The rear deck remained in place to protect the engine from the elements and to funnel the ventilation.

Combat service: Issued to the repair and recovery sections of armoured companies until 1941, when it was found to be too small to perform in a recovery role. From mid 1940, it served mainly as a training vehicle.

48

49

50

Plates 47-48. The modified driving school vehicle based on the Pz Kpfw I Ausf B and driven by gas.
Plate 49. Instandsetzungskraftwagen repair and recovery vehicle.
Plate 50. LKB1 fitted (like the LKB2 in Plate 45) with the M601 diesel engine.

Kleine Panzerbefehlswagen (Sd Kfz 265)

Type: Light armoured tracked command vehicle

Manufacturer: Daimler-Benz
Chassis Nos.: 9406–9430, 10478–15200
184 produced from 1935 to 1937 plus 6 based upon Pz Kpfw I Ausf A
  chassis

Crew: 3	Engine: Maybach NL38TR
Weight (tons): 5.9	Gearbox: 5 forward, 1 reverse
Length (metres): 4.42	Speed (km/hr): 40
Width (metres): 2.06	Range (km): 170
Height (metres): 1.99	Radio: FuG6 and FuG2

Armament: One 7.92mm MG13 or 34
Traverse: hand
Sight: KgZF2
Ammunition: 900 Patr SmK
Turret: fixed

Armour (mm/angle):	Front	Side	Rear	Top/Bottom
Superstructure:	13/23°	13/23°	13/20°	8/90°
Hull:	13/25°	13/0°	13/20°	6/90°

51

52

History: The kleiner Panzerbefehlswagen was developed as an armoured command vehicle. The Pz Kpfw I had room for a radio receiver only, and had to be modified to accommodate a transmitter and its operator. Several of these vehicles were produced by modifying Pz Kpfw I Ausf A. The production series was based on the lengthened chassis which had been developed for the kl Pz Bef Wg, and later utilized for the Pz Kpfw I Ausf B.

Specific features: The kl Pz Bef Wg had the same hull and rear deck as the Pz Kpfw I Ausf B. The size of the superstructure was increased by heightening the sides. Both transmitting and receiving sets were mounted in this superstructure. The only armament was provided by a machine-gun in a hull mount in the superstructure front. Early production vehicles only had a split hatch in the superstructure roof. This was later replaced by a stationary cupola with slits for all-round vision. After the campaign in Poland, 15mm armour was added to hull, superstructure and cupola front, and 12mm armour was added to the glacis plate of some vehicles.

Combat service: Issued to company, battalion, regimental and brigade headquarters of Panzer units from 1935 until 1940. In late 1940/early 1941, it was withdrawn from companies and remained in service only with higher headquarters until late 1942. From 1940 it was also issued to the signals battalion and observation batteries of artillery regiments in the Panzer divisions.

Plate 51. Early version of the kl Pz Bef Wg based on the Ausf A.
Plate 52. A modified version based on the Ausf B.
Plate 53. A kl Pz Bef Wg converted to an ambulance.
Plate 54. The command vehicle equipped with extra radio equipment and a frame aerial.
Plate 55 (opposite page). Kl Pz Bef Wg operating in Poland.

53

54

Munitionsschlepper auf Panzerkampfwagen I Ausf A (Sd Kfz 111)

Other designation: Gerät 35
Type: Light armoured tracked ammunition carrier

51 converted in September 1939
Chassis Nos.: 8011–10477

Crew: 2	Engine: Krupp M305	
Weight (tons): 5.0	Gearbox: 5 forward, 1 reverse	
Length (metres): 4.02	Speed (km/hr): 37	
Width (metres): 2.06	Range (km): 95	
Height (metres): 1.4		

Armour (mm/angle):	Front	Side	Rear	Top/Bottom
Superstructure:	13/22°	13/22°	13/17°	6/82°–90°
Hull:	13/27°	13/0°	13/15°	6/90°

History: The Munitionsschlepper was developed to provide the Panzer Regiments with an armoured vehicle for supplying ammunition to front-line tanks under enemy fire.
Specific features: The turret of the Ausf A was removed and the opening was covered with a segmented armour plate hatch to provide overhead protection for the driver and his cargo.
Combat service: The Sd Kfz 111 vehicle was issued to the supply companies of Panzer regiments and served in Poland and France.

Plates 56-57. Mun Schl auf Pz Kpfw I Ausf A: the rear view (right) shows the armour plate hatch on the top of the hull.

15cm sIG33(Sf) auf Panzerkampfwagen I Ausf B

Type: Self-propelled heavy infantry gun on tank chassis

Manufacturer: Alkett
Chassis Nos.: 10478–16500
38 converted in February 1940

Crew: 4
Weight (tons): 8.5
Length (metres): 4.67
Width (metres): 2.06
Height (metres): 2.8

Engine: Maybach NL38TR
Gearbox: 5 forward, 1 reverse
Speed (km/hr): 40
Range (km): 140

Armament: One 15cm sIG33 L/11
Traverse: 12½° left 12½° right (hand)
Elevation: −4° +75°
Sight: Rblf36

Armour (mm/angle):	Front	Side	Rear	Top/Bottom
Superstructure:	13/22°	13/22°	13/0°	6/83°–90°
Hull:	13/27°	13/0°	13/19°	6/90°
Gun shield:	10/0°-25°	10/0°	open	open

History: Developed to provide armoured infantry with immediate fire support from a self-propelled armoured platform which could follow them closely into action.

Specific features: The turret and superstructure were removed from the Pz Kpfw I Ausf B, and a large box-shaped gun shield, open at top and rear, was built on the hull. The 15cm sIG (heavy infantry gun) on its normal field carriage was mounted in this enclosure.

Combat service: Used to equip sIG(Sf) Kompanien (Heavy Infantry Gun (SP) Companies) 701–706, which were allocated to six Panzer divisions before the campaigns in Belgium, Holland and France in May–June 1940. Several were still in service in mid 1943 with the 704th schwere Infanteriegeschütz Abteilung of the 5th Panzer Division in Russia.

58

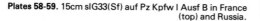

Plates 58-59. 15cm sIG33(Sf) auf Pz Kpfw I Ausf B in France (top) and Russia.

59

Panzerkampfwagen I Ausf C

Other designation: Pz Kpfw I nA (VK601)
Type: Light tracked reconnaissance vehicle

Manufacturer: Krauss-Maffei
Chassis Nos.: 150101–150140
40 produced from July to December 1942

Crew: 2
Weight (tons): 8.0
Length (metres): 4.19
Width (metres): 1.92
Height (metres): 1.94

Engine: Maybach HL45P
Gearbox: 8 forward, 2 reverse
Speed (km/hr): 79
Range (km): 300
Radio: FuG 5

Armament: One EW141 MG
Traverse: 360° (hand)
Elevation: −10° +20°
Sight: TZF10

One 7.92mm MG34
hand

Armour (mm/angle):	Front	Side	Rear	Top/Bottom
Turret:	30/13°	20/24°	20/6½°	10/80°–90°
Superstructure:	30/10°	20/0°	20/15°	10/82½°–90°
Hull:	30/20°	20/0°	20/30°	10/90°
Gun mantlet:	30/round			

History: A further development of the Pz Kpfw I to provide a fast reconnaissance vehicle with increased armour protection, for use in airborne operations. Krauss-Maffei received the order to develop the chassis on 15 September 1939, while Daimler-Benz were ordered to design the superstructure and turret. A single prototype was built and extensively tested. The wheel and track arrangements underwent considerable modification. Initially, the trial production series of 40

Plates 60-61. Pz Kpfw I Ausf C. Left, undergoing trials.

61

vehicles were to have been fitted with self-lubricating tracks, but these were dropped in favour of dry pin tracks before the VK601 was issued to combat units in 1943. A more powerful motor, the Maybach HL61, was fitted in the final development vehicle, the VK602.

Specific features: The Pz Kpfw I Ausf C was a completely different design from the Ausf A & B. The suspension had overlapping road wheels sprung with a torsion bar, which allowed the vehicle to attain the high speed of 65 kilometres per hour. The armour thickness was double that of previous Pz Kpfw I models. The driver's vision was limited to a visor in the front plate and a second visor immediately to his left. A cupola was fitted with 8 periscopes to allow all-round vision for the commander, whose only other vision was provided by the sighting telescope. The main armament was a large-calibre machine-gun, the EW141, which was coaxially mounted with the MG34.

Combat service: Two were issued to the 1st Panzer Division early in 1943 and taken to Russia for combat evaluation. The other 38 had been issued to reserve units of LVIII Pz Res Korps (Reserve Tank Corps) in 1943.

4.7cm PaK(t) (Sf) auf Panzerkampfwagen I Ausf B

Other designation: Panzerjäger
Type: Self-propelled anti-tank gun on tank chassis

Manufacturer: Daimler-Benz, Skoda
Chassis Nos.: 10478–16500
202 converted from Pz Kpfw I Ausf B from March 1940 to February 1941

Crew: 3	Engine: Maybach NL38TR
Weight (tons): 6.4	Gearbox: 5 forward, 1 reverse
Length (metres): 4.42	Speed (km/hr): 40
Width (metres): 2.06	Range (km): 140
Height (metres): 2.25	Radio: FuG2

Armament: One 4.7cm PaK(t) L/43.4
Traverse: $17\frac{1}{2}°$ left $17\frac{1}{2}°$ right (hand)
Elevation: $-8°$ $+12°$
Sight: ZF2 × 30°
Ammunition: 86 Patr

Armour (mm/angle):	Front	Side	Rear	Top/Bottom
Superstructure:	13/22°	13/22°	13/0°	6/90°
Hull:	13/27°	13/0°	13/17°	6/90°
Gun shield:	14.5/27°	14.5/27°	open	open

History: Developed to provide self-propelled anti-tank guns with armour protection. First of the many German conversions of standard Panzer chassis, to give the Panzerjäger mobility by utilizing otherwise obsolescent vehicles.

Specific features: The basic Pz Kpfw I Ausf B was modified by removing the turret and superstructure roof and altering the air intake at the front of the rear deck. A gun shield, with rear and top left open, was built up around the superstructure. The 4.7cm PaK (anti-tank gun) was mounted within the shield on a pivoting mount supported by girders.

Combat service: Issued to five Heeres Pz Jäg Abt. It first saw service in 1940 in Belgium and France. After serving in all the major campaigns, it was phased out late in 1943.

Plates 62-63. 4.7cm PaK(t) (Sf) auf Pz Kpfw I Ausf B in North Africa (above) and in action during the 1940 campaign.

62

Panzerkampfwagen I Ausf F

Other designation: Pz Kpfw I nA Verstärkt (VK1801)
Type: Heavily armoured infantry assault tank (machine-gun armed)

Manufacturer: Krauss-Maffei
Chassis Nos.: 150301–150330
30 produced from April to December 1942

Crew: 2	Engine: Maybach HL45P
Weight (tons): 21.0	Gearbox: 4 forward, 1 reverse
Length (metres): 4.38	Speed (km/hr): 25
Width (metres): 2.64	Range (km): 150
Height (metres): 2.05	Radio: FuG5

Armament: Two 7.92mm MG34
Traverse: 360° (hand)
Elevation: −10° +20°
Sight: TZF8

Armour (mm/angle):	Front	Side	Rear	Top/Bottom
Turret:	80/0°	50/10°	50/10°	25/90°
Superstructure:	80/10°	50/0°	50/10°	25/90°
Hull:	80/20°	50/0°	50/14°	25/90°
Gun mantlet:	80/round			

History: Further development of the Pz Kpfw I, with the heaviest possible armour as the main design feature. The initial order of 30, given on 22 December 1939, was filled, but an additional order for 100 was cancelled before production began. The final development vehicle, the VK1802, was built with the VG15319 pre-selector gearbox.

Specific features: The Ausf F had a 'Schachtellaufwerk' (interleaved suspension) with overlapping road wheels and a torsion bar suspension. Its 80mm frontal armour was inpenetrable by most anti-tank guns of the period. The commander had 5 periscopes set in the turret roof for vision to the front and sides, plus a binocular telescope for sighting the machine-guns. Vision for the driver was provided by a sliding shutter visor in the superstructure front, and a periscope mounted in the hull roof, on the driver's left side.

Combat service: Eight were issued to the 1st Panzer Division early in 1943. The 12th Panzer Division reported 3 operational of a total of 7 on 1 July 1943.

64

65

Plates 64-66. Pz Kpfw I Ausf F: Plate 65 shows the 5 periscopes in the turret roof.

66

Plates 67-68. Ladungsleger auf Pz Kpfw I Ausf B. The version shown in Plate 67 had a cable-operated arm to drop the charge behind the vehicle, while that in Plate 68 deposited the charge from a slide at the vehicle rear.
Plate 69. Brükenleger auf Fgst Pz Kpfw I Ausf A.
Plate 70. Flammenwerfer auf Pz Kpfw I Ausf A.
Plate 71. Munitionsschlepper auf Pz Kpfw Ia und Ib.

67

68

69

71

Ladungsleger auf Panzerkampfwagen I Ausf B

Type: Demolition charge-laying tank

History: The Ladungsleger were devices fitted to the rear deck of the Pz Kpfw I to allow a charge to be placed near obstacles and defences in order to clear a path for assault troops. Two versions existed. The first allowed the charge to fall behind the tank; the second had a cable-operated arm which pivoted over the tank to place the 50kg charge behind the vehicle.

Combat service: The Ladungsleger device was mounted on ten Pz Kpfw I Ausf B of the 3 Pz Pioniere Kp (3rd Armoured Engineers Company) of each Pioneer Battalion in the Panzer Divisions.

Brückenleger auf Panzerkampfwagen I Ausf A

Type: Armoured bridgelayer

History: The Brükenleger auf Fgst Pz Kpfw I used the Ausf A chassis, but inadequate suspension of these vehicles made the idea impracticable. The bridges were later used for similar vehicles based on the Pz Kpfw II.

Flammenwerfer auf Panzerkampfwagen I Ausf A

Type: Flame-thrower tank

History: In preparation for the assault on Tobruk, the Engineers of 5 le Division (5th Light Division) of the Deutsche Afrika Korps, converted PZ Kpfw I Ausf A to flame-thrower tanks. The portable Flammenwerfer replaced the right-hand machine-gun in the turret. Fuel capacity allowed between 10 and 12 one-second bursts, with a maximum range of 25 metres. A similar conversion on an Ausf B had been used in Spain during the Civil War.

Munitionsschlepper Auf Panzerkampfwagen Ia und Ib (Sd Kf3 III)

Type: Ammunition carrier

History: From the spring of 1942, obsolete Pz Kpfw I were converted to load-carriers by the fitting of a large steel box in place of the turret. This box was covered by a canvas tilt. From early 1943, however, an order was issued that all remaining Pz Kpfw I be converted to 'Munitionsschlepper ohne Aufbau' (ammunition tractors without superstructure). These were often created by removing only the turret and not the superstructure as indicated in the order. The turrets removed from these vehicles, and from the earlier self-propelled gun conversions, were used for permanent fortifications. In May 1944, of the 611 Pz Kpfw I turrets available, 511 had already been released for this purpose. The Munitionsschlepper converted in 1942 were issued to various Pz formations including 1 SS Leibstandarte Adolf Hitler. From 1943, the Pz divisions converted the tanks still in their possession.

Panzerkampfwagen II
and variants

Panzerkampfwagen II Ausf a/1, a/2 und a/3 (Sd Kfz 121)

Other designation: 1 Serie LaS 100
Type: Light tank

Manufacturer: MAN, Daimler-Benz
Chassis Nos.: 20001–20075
75 produced from May 1936 to February 1937
Crew: 3
Weight (tons): 7.6
Length (metres): 4.38
Width (metres): 2.14
Height (metres): 1.95

Engine: Maybach HL57TR
Gearbox: 6 forward, 1 reverse
Speed (km/hr): 40
Range (km): 200
Radio: FuG5

Armament:	One 2cm KwK30 L/55	One 7.92mm MG34
Traverse:	360° (hand)	=
Elevation:	−9½° +20°	=
Sight:	TZF4	=
	180 Pzgr & Sprgr	2,250

Armour (mm/angle):	Front	Side	Rear	Top/Bottom
Turret:	13/round	13/22°	13/22°	8/86°–90°
Superstructure:	13/9°	13/0°	13/9°	8/90° & 10/70°
Hull:	13/round	13/0°	13/0°	5/90°
Gun mantlet:	15/round			

History: Originally identified as the '2cm MG Panzerwagen' (Vs Kfz 622), the Pz Kpfw II was designed to supplement the Pz Kpfw I by providing an automatic weapon capable of firing both a high-explosive round and an armour-piercing round. The design period was very short: the initial order for a tank design in the 10-ton class was issued by the Waffenamt (Ordnance Department) in July 1934, and the first complete soft steel prototype was put through its paces in October 1935. Many of the teething problems had not been worked out when rapid expansion of the armoured units (and international politics) forced the decision to order the comparatively large number of twenty-five in each of the experimental, development series, instead of the usual two or three.

Specific features: After production of the first ten Ausf a/1, a welded rear idler replaced the original rubber-tyred, cast rear idler. An improvement was made with the Ausf a/2 by designing the fireproof engine compartment wall so that it could be removed from the crew compartment, and a large port was installed under the motor for access to the fuel pump and oil filter. The Ausf a/3 had a larger radiator installed, and the springs for the suspension were improved.

Combat service: The Pz Kpfw II were first issued to Panzer units in the spring of 1936. Assigned to platoon and company commanders, they were also used to equip a full platoon in each company, for tank-versus-tank engagements. They retained their main combat tank status in Poland, but were finally relegated to a reconnaissance/exploitation role during the campaign in the West. When the Russian campaign started, each Panzer Regiment, Panzer Detachment and Panzer Company had a platoon of Pz Kpfw II assigned for reconnaissance. In 1942, these platoons were withdrawn from tank companies. The Pz Kpfw II was phased out of service with tank regiments late in 1943 but remained in service with various Panzer units on secondary fronts until the end of the war.

72

73

Plate 72. Krupp's prototype export vehicle similar to the Pz Kpfw II specification, which bore Krupp's own designation LKA II. It was developed from the LKA I, by fitting a larger turret.
Plate 73. Pz Kpfw II Ausf a/1, a/2 and a/3, showing the split hatch and dummy commander's periscope cover characteristic of models preceding Ausf C.

Panzerkampfwagen II Ausf b (Sd Kfz 121)

Other designation: 2 Serie LaS 100
Type: Light tank

Manufacturer: MAN, Daimler-Benz
Chassis Nos.: 21001–21025
25 produced from February to March 1937

Crew: 3
Weight (tons): 7.9
Length (metres): 4.76
Width (metres): 2.14
Height (metres): 1.96

Engine: Maybach HL62TR
Gearbox: 6 forward, 1 reverse
Speed (km/hr): 40
Range (km): 200
Radio: FuG5

Armament: One 2cm KwK30 L/55   One 7.92mm MG34
Traverse: 360° (hand)   =
Elevation: −9½° +20°   =
Sight: TZF4   =
Ammunition: 180 Pzgr & Spgr   2,250

Armour (mm/angle):	Front	Side	Rear	Top/Bottom
Turret:	13/round	13/21°	13/21°	10/84 −90°
Superstructure:	13/10°	13/0°	13/0°	12/90° & 10/82°
Hull:	13/round	13/0°	13/7°	5/90°
Gun mantlet:	15/round			

History: The Ausf b was the second model in the development series for the Pz Kpfw II.

Specific features: An entire series of modifications was made to improve the Pz Kpfw II, and these were incorporated in the Ausf b. The mountings for the final drives, transmission and larger motor were strengthened. A new drive sprocket, wider/smaller return rollers and wider road wheels along with a wider track were added. The springs for the suspension were modified to prevent slipping and breakage, and brackets were added to strengthen the support for each pair of road wheels. The rear section of each fender was hinged so that it could be raised to prevent the buildup of mud and other debris. The ventilation and cooling of the engine compartment was improved, and a different style of exhaust muffler was installed.

Combat service: The Ausf b was employed in the same fashion as the Pz Kpfw II Ausf a/1–a/3.

Plates 74-75. Pz Kpfw II Ausf b: note that the vehicle shown below is equipped with large smoke-dischargers at the rear.

74

75

Panzerkampfwagen II Ausf c, A, B und C (Sd Kfz 121)

Other designation: 2, 3, 4, 5, 6 und 7 Serie LaS 100
Type: Light tank

Manufacturer: MAN, Daimler-Benz, Henschel, Wegmann, Alkett, MIAG, FAMO
Chassis Nos.: 21101–27000
1,113 produced from March 1937 to April 1940

Crew: 3	Engine: Maybach HL62TR
Weight (tons): 8.9	Gearbox: 6 forward, 1 reverse
Length (metres): 4.81	Speed (km/hr): 40
Width (metres): 2.22	Range (km): 200
Height (metres): 1.99	Radio: FuG5

Armament: One 2cm KwK30 L/55 One 7.92mm MG34
Traverse: 360° (hand) =
Elevation: $-9\frac{1}{2}°$ $+20°$ =
Sight: TZF4 (Ausf c) =

Ammunition: 180 Pzgr & Sprgr

Armour (mm/angle):	Front	Side	Rear	Top/Bottom
Turret:	14.5/round	14.5/22°	14.5/22°	10/86°–90°
Superstructure:	14.5/9°	14.5/0°	14.5/9°	10/81°–90°
Hull:	14.5/round	14.5/0°	14.5/6°	14.5/73°–63° + 5/90°
Gun mantlet:	16/round			

76

History: The final model of the development series was the Ausf c, which bore the external features that came to be recognized as the standard design for the Pz Kpfw II. The Ausf c retained the 13mm armour of the Ausf b. The Ausf A was the first production series and was built from July 1937. The Ausf B was produced from December 1937, the Ausf C, from June 1938.

Specific features: With the Ausf c, the suspension was changed from six small road wheels to five independently sprung larger diameter road wheels, and the number of return rollers was increased from three to four. The track design was changed (which meant that the drive sprockets had to be modified) and wider fenders and idler wheels were installed. The ventilation and cooling of the engine compartment was again improved. The final drives and epicyclic steering system on 25 of the Ausf c were manufactured from an 'ersatz (substitute) molybdenum' steel.

The last major change in the Pz Kpfw II series was the introduction of an improved transmission in the Ausf A. There were only minor differences (mainly changes to the vision ports) between the Ausf A, B and C. As originally produced, all the Pz Kpfw II Ausf c, A to C had a split hatch on the turret roof for the commander, and a rounded hull front. The Polish anti-tank rifle could easily penetrate the 15mm armour of the Pz Kpfw II and the troops requested that it be strengthened. By May 1940, additional 20mm armour plates had been bolted to the front of the turret, superstructure and hull front of approximately 70 per cent of the Pz Kpfw II Ausf c to C, and the armour of the remainder had been increased before the invasion of Russia.

During the campaign in Poland, commanders had complained of limited vision, and had registered the same complaint during the campaign in the West. From October 1940, this defect was remedied by the provision of a kit with eight periscopes for the commander's cupola.

Combat service: The Ausf c, A, B and C were employed in the same way as the earlier Ausf a and b.

Plate 11 (Page 6). Pz Kpfw II Ausf A.
Plate 950 (Page 247). Pz Kpfw II Ausf C turret.

Plates 76-77. A comparison of hull fronts: the top photograph shows the rounded shape of the early models, Ausf c, A, B and C, while the lower view shows the Ausf c with additional armour plate bolted to the hull front. The second vehicle in this lower photograph is an Ausf A, with different driver's visor and vision ports.
Plate 78. A side view showing the new suspension introduced with the Ausf c.
Plate 79. Pz Kpfw II Ausf A or B.
Plate 80. Pz Kpfw II Ausf B, with re-worked hull front.
Plate 81. The new commander's cupola and additional armour bolted to the turret and hull front on the Ausf A, B and C.
Plate 82. The Pz Beob Wg (artillery observation) conversion of the Pz Kpfw II.

7

81

82

Panzerkampfwagen II Ausf D und E (Sd Kfz 121)

Other designation: 8 Serie LaS 138
Type: Light tank for cavalry units

Manufacturer: MAN
Chassis Nos.: 27001–28000
43 produced from May 1938 to August 1939

Crew: 3	Engine: Maybach HL62TRM
Weight (tons): 10.0	Gearbox: 7 forward, 1 reverse
Length (metres): 4.65	Speed (km/hr): 55
Width (metres): 2.3	Range (km): 200
Height (metres): 2.06	Radio: FuG5

Armament: One 2cm KwK30 L/55	One 7.92mm MG34
Traverse: 360° (hand)	=
Elevation: $-9\frac{1}{2}°$ $+20°$	=
Sight: TZF4/36	=
Ammunition: 180 Pzgr & Sprgr	2,250

Armour (mm/angle):	Front	Side	Rear	Top/Bottom
Turret:	14.5/round	14.5/22°	14.5/22°	10/76°–90°
Superstructure:	30/9°	14.5/0°	14.5/20°	10/90°–79°
Hull:	30/9°	14.5/0°	14.5/0°	5/90°
Gun mantlet:	16/round			

History: The Pz Kpfw II Ausf D and E were developed to give the cavalry a light tank for pursuit and reconnaissance, with a top speed of 55km/hr instead of the normal speed of 40km/hr.

Specific features: The entire hull, superstructure and suspension were of a different design from the normal Pz Kpfw II series, but the turret remained the same. The superstructure front was in one straight piece and had two double-shuttered visors, one on the left for the driver and one on the right for the radio operator. This was the first Pz Kpfw to use a torsion-bar suspension and a pre-selective gearbox. Instead of the five single-tyred road wheels and four return rollers of the normal Pz Kpfw II series, the Ausf D and E had four large double-tyred road wheels which also served to return the track. The latter was also redesigned, with centre guides replacing the double horn guides. The dry pin track of the Ausf D was replaced by a lubricated pin track which necessitated the use of newly-designed drive sprockets, idlers and road wheels.

Combat service: The Pz Kpfw II Ausf D and E were to be issued to the tank detachments of the leichter (light) Divisionen. Only sufficient to equip a single Panzerabteilung were completed, and these saw action in Poland. In March 1940, they were withdrawn for conversion to Pz Kpfw II Flamm (flame-throwers).

Plates 83-84. Pz Kpfw II Ausf D: above, being loaded on to light tank transporters.

Panzerkampfwagen II Ausf F (Sd Kfz 121)

Other designation: 9 Serie LaS 100
Type: Light reconnaissance tank

Manufacturer: FAMO
Chassis Nos.: 28001–28834
524 produced from March 1941 to December 1942

Crew: 3	Engine: Maybach HL62TR
Weight (tons): 9.5	Gearbox: 6 forward, 1 reverse
Length (metres): 4.81	Speed (km/hr): 40
Width (metres): 2.28	Range (km): 200
Height (metres): 2.15	Radio: FuG5

Armament: One 2cm KwK30 L/55	One 7.92mm MG34
Traverse: 360° (hand)	=
Elevation: −9½° +20°	=
Sight: TZF4	=
Ammunition: 180 Pzgr & Spgr	2,700

Armour (mm/angle):	Front	Side	Rear	Top/Bottom
Turret:	30/round	15/21°	15/21°	10/77°–90°
Superstructure:	30/10°	15/0°	15/9°	15/90°–10/82°
Hull:	35/13°	15/0°	15/7°	5/90°
Gun mantlet:	30/round			

History: The Ausf F was the final model of the normal Pz Kpfw II series. It was to have been in production by mid 1940, but delays in design set production back until March 1941. Early in June 1942, it was decided to mount the 7.5cm PaK40 on the Pz Kpfw II chassis, with the result that an order of 20 June 1942 stated that 50 per cent of the Pz Kpfw II production was to be 7.5cm PaK40 (Sf). In July 1942, a further directive decreed that with effect from August 1942, all Pz Kpfw II production was to be as chassis for the 7.5cm PaK40 (Sf). This was circumvented when FAMO produced the last fifteen Pz Kpfw II Ausf F in December 1942, which completed the original order of Ausf F as Pz Kpfw II.

Special features: Instead of the rounded hull of the previous models of the normal series, the front hull of the Ausf F was made from one flat 35mm plate. The front of the superstructure was also redesigned as one flat 30mm plate extending across the width of the hull, and a dummy visor of aluminium was fitted on the right-hand side of the driver's double-shuttered visor. The only change to the suspension was the new conical design of the idler wheel. The thickness of the turret front plates and gun mantlet was increased to 30mm, which maintained the same basic design as the earlier series. The commander's eight-periscope cupola was installed as a standard production item.

Combat service: The Pz Kpfw II Ausf F was employed in the same way as the Pz Kpfw II Ausf a/1 to a/3.

85

86

Plates 85-87. Pz Kpfw II Ausf F: above right, arriving in North Africa; below, at the head of an armoured column on the Russian Front.

87

Panzerkampfwagen II Flamm Ausf A und B (Sd Kfz 122)

Other designation: Flamingo
Type: Light flame-thrower tank

Chassis Nos.: 27001–28000
112 from direct production plus 43 converted from Pz Kpfw II Ausf D
& E from January 1940 to March 1942

Crew: 3	Engine: Maybach HL62TRM
Weight (tons): 12.0	Gearbox: 7 forward, 3 reverse
Length (metres): 4.9	Speed (km/hr): 55
Width (metres): 2.4	Range (km): 250
Height (metres): 1.85	Radio: FuG2

Armament: Two Flammenwerfer-Anlagen	One 7.92mm MG34
Traverse: 180° (hand)	360° (hand)
Elevation:	−10° +10°
Sight: direct	KgZF2
Ammunition: 320 litres fuel	1,800

Armour (mm/angle):	Front	Side	Rear	Top/Bottom
Turret:	30/0°	20/21°	20/30°	10/84°–90°
Superstructure:	30/9°	14.5–25 +15/0°	14.5/15°	10/79°–90°
Hull:	30/9°	14.5/0°	14.5/0°	5/90°

History: Early in 1939, the Waffenamt realised the need of an armoured vehicle mounting flame-throwers which could flush an enemy from bunkers and other fortified positions. On 21 January 1939, an order was placed for an 0-Serie (pre-production series) of 90 flame-throwers on the Pz Kpfw II. Ausf D chassis were completed for this purpose as early as April 1939, and a soft steel prototype was completed in July 1939. Final production of the 0-Serie started in May 1940, and the last three of this series were completed in February 1941. A second order for 150 was begun in August 1941, but only 65 had been completed by March 1942, when production ceased, and the chassis were utilized to produce the Pz Sf I für 7.62cm PaK36(r) (Armoured SP Mounting I for 7.62cm anti-tank gun 36 (Russian).

Specific features: The Pz Kpfw II (Fl) had the same basic chassis as the Pz Kpfw II Ausf D & E. The Pz Kpfw II turret was replaced by a smaller turret mounting a single MG34, and two flame-thrower units were mounted on the front corners of the superstructure over the tracks. The fuel for the flame-throwers was stored internally, and armoured compartments were added to the sides of the superstructure to hold four tanks of compressed nitrogen. The second series, identified as Ausf B, had a new sprocket design and further minor improvements in the suspension.

Combat service: The Pz Kpfw II (Fl) first saw service in June 1941 in Russia, with Panzerabteilungen which had been trained in their use as close-support vehicles. The battalion-sized unit proved too large for optimum employment of the vehicle, and the relatively thin armour and highly-flammable fuel caused many casualties. These considerations led to the reorganization of the two flame-thrower battalions as normal Panzer units early in 1942, and the Pz Kpfw II (Fl) were returned to Ordnance for conversion to 7.62cm PaK(r) (Sf).

Plates 88-89. Pz Kpfw II (Fl). Plate 88 provides a clear view of the two flame-projectors mounted on the front corners of the vehicle.
Plates 90-91. Comparative views of the Pz Kpfw II (Fl) based on the Ausf E (text, page 32). This vehicle has been captured, and is shown being tested, by the Russians. Note also the smoke-dischargers visible in Plate 91.

Panzerkampfwagen II Ausf G

Other designation: Pz Kpfw II nA (VK901)
Type: Light reconnaissance tank

Manufacturer: MAN
Chassis Nos.: 150001–150075
12 produced from April 1941 to February 1942

Crew: 3	Engine: Maybach HL66P
Weight (tons): 10.5	Gearbox: 5 forward, 1 reverse
Length (metres): 4.24	Speed (km/hr): 50
Width (metres): 2.38	Range (km): 200
Height (metres): 2.05	

Armament: One EW141 MG   One 7.92mm MG34
Traverse: 360° (hand)   =
Sight: TZF10   =

Armour (mm/angle):	Front	Side	Rear
Turret:	30/	15/	15/
Superstructure:	30/10°	15/0°	15/
Hull:	30/20°	15/0°	15/
Gun mantlet:	30/round		

History: The VK901 was a further development of the Pz Kpfw II series, the main design objective being an increase in speed. The order was issued on 18 June 1938 for MAN to develop the chassis, and Daimler-Benz to develop the superstructure and turret. The order was for an '0-Serie' of 75, with production to start in October 1940. The prototype of the chassis was completed late in 1939, but the many modifications delayed production, and of the entire order, only twelve were completed.

Panzerkampfwagen II Ausf J

Other designation: Pz Kpfw II nA Verstärkt (VK1601)
Type: Heavily-armoured reconnaissance tank

Manufacturer: MAN
Chassis Nos.: 150201–150222
22 produced from April to December 1942

Crew: 3	Engine: Maybach HL45P
Weight (tons): 18.0	Gearbox: 5 forward, 1 reverse
	Speed (km/hr): 31

Armament: One 2cm KwK38 L/55   One 7.92mm MG42
Traverse: 360° (hand)   =
Sight: TZF4/38   =

Armour (mm).	Front	Side	Rear	Top
Turret:	80	50	50	25
Superstructure:	80	50	50	25
Hull:	80	50	50	25
Gun mantlet:	80/round			

History: The VK1601 was a further development of the Pz Kpfw II series, the main objective being the provision of maximum possible armour protection, while retaining the original weight. The develop-

Plate 92. Pz Kpfw II Ausf G.

Specific features: The VK901 had a completely redesigned suspension, with five pairs of overlapping road wheels, sprung on torsion bars. As in the previous Ausf D, E and F, the hull front was box-shaped, but devoid of hatches. The driver and radio operator entered through the superstructure roof hatches, and were provided with vision ports to their front and sides. The turret, mounted centrally, was devoid of vision ports. The commander's vision was supplied by the periscopes in the cupola, and by the gun sight.
Combat service: No evidence has been found of the VK901 having been issued to units for front-line service. Twenty-seven of the VK901 turrets were released for use in fortified emplacements as stationary pillboxes.

ment order for an '0-Serie' was issued on 22 December 1939. Development of the chassis was entrusted to MAN, and of the turret, to Daimler-Benz. The prototype was completed in June 1940, and production was to have started in December of that year. Various delays were encountered, however, and only twenty-two VK1601 were completed.
Specific features: The VK1601 had a Schachtellaufwerk (interleaved suspension) of similar design to that of the VK901, but more strongly built in order to support the additional weight. The hull and superstructure were built as one unit—a departure from the normal German practice up to this time, of a superstructure bolted to the hull. Access for the driver and radio operator was facilitated by circular hatches in the hull sides. The commander's access was through the turret roof, via a cupola which was equipped with periscopes.
Combat service: Seven VK1601 were issued to 12th Panzer Division, which saw service on the Eastern Front during 1943. In 1944, a VK1601 was found minus its turret, and with a jib fitted, to create a rudimentary Berge-Panzerwagen (Armoured Recovery Vehicle).

Plate 6 (Page 4). Pz Kpfw II Ausf J being used as a training vehicle.
Plate 93 (above). Pz Kpfw II Ausf J.
Plate 94 (right). Bergepanzer II, an armoured recovery vehicle conversion of the Pz Kpfw II Ausf J.

Panzerkampfwagen II neuer Art Ausf H und M

Other designations: VK903, VK1301
Type: Light reconnaissance tank

Manufacturer: MAN
Chassis Nos.: 200001–200004 (VK1301)
4 VK1301 produced in August 1942; VK903 prototypes only

Crew: 3	Engine: Maybach HL66P
Weight (tons): 10.5	Gearbox: 4 forward, 1 reverse
	Speed (km/hr): 65

Armament: One Gerät	One 2cm KwK38 L/55	One 7.92mm MG34
8202 or		
Traverse:	360°	=
Sight:	TZF4/38	=

Armour (mm):	Front	Side	Rear	Top
Turret:	30			
Superstructure:	30	20	20	10
Hull:	30	20	20	5
Gun mantlet:	30/round			

Plate 95. Pz Kpfw II nA Ausf M.
Plate 96. Pz Sfl 1c/5cm Pak 38 auf Pz Kpfw II (VK901) (see text Page 41).

History: The VK903 was to have been the production version of the earlier VK901 (Pz Kpfw II nA Ausf G), having increased side armour, different transmission and a higher speed. In March 1942, it was decided to replace the SSG 48 gearbox by the transmission of the Pz Kpfw 38(t) nA in production models. The total order was for 200 vehicles, with 120 to be built between April and December 1942. Delays set the projected production start date back to September 1942, but by this time, the project had been cancelled.
The VK1301 was intended as a heavier reconnaissance vehicle to be built alongside the VK903. It was to have had the 5cm KwK39/1, but, fitted with the 2cm KwK38, it was the forerunner of the Ausf L (VK1303).
Specific features: Both vehicles were similar in appearance to the Pz Kpfw II Ausf L (VK1303), differing only in armour thickness.
Combat service: None.

Panzerkampfwagen II Ausf L (Sd Kfz 123)

Other designations: Pz Sp Wg II, VK1303, Pz Sp Wg Luchs
Type: Light reconnaissance tank

Manufacturer: MAN
Chassis Nos.: 200101–200200
100 produced from September 1943 to January 1944 plus 4 converted from VK1301

Plates 97-98. Pz Kpfw II Ausf L: Plate 97 shows the vehicle in service on the Russian Front. (Note the additional armour on the nose plate.)

Crew: 4	Engine: Maybach HL66P
Weight (tons): 13.0	Gearbox: 6 forward, 1 reverse
Length (metres): 4.63	Speed (km/hr): 60
Width (metres): 2.48	Range (km): 290
Height (metres): 2.21	Radio: FuG12 + FuG Spr a

Armament: One 2cm KwK38 L/55	One 7.92mm MG34
Traverse: 360° (hand)	=
Elevation: −9° +18°	=
Sight: TZF6/38	=
Ammunition: 330	2,250

Armour (mm/angle):	Front	Side	Rear	Top/Bottom
Turret:	30/10°	20/21°	20/21°	12/79°−90°
Superstructure:	30/10°	20/0°	20/28°	10/86°−90°
Hull:	30/22°	20/0°	20/28°	10/90°
Gun mantlet:	30/round			

History: The Luchs (Lynx) was developed as a fully-tracked armoured reconnaissance vehicle. The development order was issued on 15 April 1939, with production to begin in August 1942. MAN developed the chassis and Daimler-Benz, the superstructure and turret. The first trial vehicle was completed in April 1942. The initial order was for 800 Luchs, the first 100 with the 2cm KwK38 and the remainder with the 5cm KwK 39/1 L/60 (designated Leopard). However, the 5cm KwK 39/1 version was never produced, because an order issued in January 1943 decreed that production cease after the first 100 Luchs had been completed.
Specific features: The VK1303 retained the same suspension and hull design as its predecessor, the VK901. The superstructure was widened, extending over the tracks to allow a larger turret to be mounted. The turret lacked a cupola and vision ports. In their place, two revolving periscopes were fitted to the turret roof to provide vision for the gunner and commander.

Combat service: Issued to the Panzer-Aufklärungs-Abteilungen (Armoured Reconnaissance Detachments) of the Panzer divisions, it served on the Eastern and Western fronts until the end of the war.

15cm sIG33 auf Fahrgestell Panzerkampfwagen II (Sf)

Type: Self-propelled heavy infantry gun on tracked carriage

12 produced in November and December 1941

Crew: 4	Engine: Maybach HL62TRM
Weight (tons): 11.2	Gearbox: 6 forward, 1 reverse
Length (metres): 5.41	Speed (km/hr): 40
Width (metres): 2.6	Range (km): 160
Height (metres): 1.9	Radio: FuG Spr f

Armament: One 15cm sIG33 L/12 One 7.92mm MG34
Traverse: 10° (hand) loose
Sight: Rblf36 direct
Ammunition: 30

Armour (mm/angle):	Front	Side	Rear	Top/Bottom
Superstructure:	30/9°	15/30°	15/10°	5/90°
Hull:	30/15°	15/0°	15/15°	5/90°
Gun mantlet: none				
Gun shield:	15/10°	15/30°	open	open

History: After the success of the 15cm sIG33 auf Fgst Pz Kpfw I (Sf) in France in 1940, plans were made to mount this heavy infantry gun on a more suitable chassis, and to drastically lower its height. A prototype was built on a Pz Kpfw Ausf B chassis in February 1941 when it was realised that the normal chassis did not provide sufficient room for the large gun. A new chassis was planned using basic Pz Kpfw II components and was to have been ready for production in July 1941. Because of design problems and delays, however, the twelve 15cm sIG33 (Sf) were not delivered until late 1941.

Specific features: The chassis for this vehicle was basically a Pz Kpfw II chassis which had been widened by 32cm and lengthened by 60cm to accommodate the 15cm sIG33 and maintain a low silhouette. This lengthening required the addition of a sixth road wheel on each side, but no further suspension changes were required. The fighting compartment was formed by 15mm plates on the front and sides, but was open on top and at the rear. The engine cooling was greatly increased by large hatches on the rear deck which could be braced open to allow a large volume of cooling air to circulate.

Combat service: All twelve 15cm sIG Sfl auf Pz II were shipped to North Africa early in 1942, with the 707 and 708 sIG Kp (Sf) (Heavy Infantry Gun Companies (SP). They took part in the spring offensive at Gazala, and all further major offensives in North Africa with the Deutsches Afrika Korps until the last of them were eliminated in the spring of 1943.

Plates 99-101. 15cm sIG33 auf Fgst Pz Kpfw II (Sf): Plate 101 shows the prototype vehicle.

99

100

Gefechts Aufklärer VK1602

Other designation: Leopard
Type: Medium reconnaissance tank

Prototypes incomplete when project was cancelled in 1942

Crew: 4	Engine: Maybach HL157P
Weight (tons): 21.9	Gearbox: 8 forward, 1 reverse
Length (metres): 4.74	Speed (km/hr): 60
Width (metres): 3.1	Radio: FuG2 or FuG5 + FuG8
Height (metres): 2.6	

Armament: One 5cm KwK39/1 One 7.92mm MG34
Traverse: 360° (hand) =
Elevation: −10° +20° =
Sight: TZF =
Ammunition: 50 2,400

Armour (mm/angle):	Front	Side	Rear	Top/Bottom
Turret:	50/20°	30/25°	30/25°	30/
Superstructure:	50/50°	30/0°	30/	20
Hull:	50/	30/0°	30/	20-25/90°
Gun mantlet:	Saukopfblende			

History: Intended as a heavy armoured reconnaissance vehicle, its development was discussed by Hitler in March 1942. MIAG were entrusted with the chassis construction and Daimler-Benz, the turret. All design work was to have been ready by the end of October 1942. Production was to have started in April 1943 with projected output of 105 Leopards by December 1943, and 150 in spring 1944. A full-size mock-up had been prepared by the end of May 1942. The project was cancelled even before the prototypes were ready because of changing requirements as the war progressed. A competing design known as the VK1601 was issued to Porsche and Skoda.

Specific features: Suspension layout was similar to that of the Pz Kpfw II Ausf L. Frontal armour was sloped in a similar fashion to the Panther. The turret developed for this vehicle was subsequently utilized on the heavy 8–rad (8–wheeled armoured car) Sd Kfz 234/2 'Puma'.

Combat service: None.

See Plate 531 (Page 157) Mock up of Leopard chassis as a Waffenträger.

101

Panzer Selbstfahrlafette 1 für 7.62cm PaK36(r) auf Fahrgestell Panzerkampfwagen II Ausf D¹ und D² (Sd Kfz 132)

Other designation: LaS 762
Type: Self-propelled captured anti-tank gun on tank chassis

Manufacturer: Alkett, Wegmann
Chassis Nos.: 27001–28000
201 converted from April 1942 to June 1943

Crew: 4	Engine: Maybach HL62TRM
Weight (tons): 11.5	Gearbox: 7 forward, 3 reverse
Length (metres): 5.65	Speed (km/hr): 55
Width (metres): 2.3	Range (km): 220
Height (metres): 2.6	Radio: FuG Spr d

Armament: One 7.62cm PaK36 L/51.5	One 7.92mm MG34
Traverse: 50° (hand)	loose
Elevation: −5° +16°	loose
Sight: ZF3×8	direct
Ammunition: 30	900

Armour (mm/angle):	Front	Side	Rear	Top/Bottom
Superstructure:	30/9°	14.5/20°	14.5/15°	open
Hull:	30/9°	14.5/0°	14.5/0°	5/90°
Gun shield:	14.5/30°	14.5/15°	open	open

102

History: On 20 December 1941, an order was given to Alkett to develop a self-propelled anti-tank gun by mounting the captured 7.62cm on the LaS 138 chassis. The initial order for 150 was completed by 12 May 1942, and an additional 60 superstructures were ordered so that further Pz Sf 1 (Armoured SP Mounting .1) could be produced from the chassis of Pz Kpfw II (F) returned for repair. The turrets of the Pz Kpfw II (F) were later used in permanent fortifications. By May 1944, a total of 88 such turrets had been released for this purpose.
Specific features: The hull and superstructure remained unchanged from those designed for the Pz Kpfw II Ausf D, E and Flamm. The height of the superstructure front and sides was increased to form a fighting compartment. The 7.62cm PaK36(r) was mounted in this enclosure on a modified field carriage which incorporated a gun shield to protect the crew during combat.
Combat service: The 7.62cm PaK(r) auf Fgst Pz Kpfw II (Sf) were issued to the Panzerjägerabteilungen (Sf) (Tank-Hunter Detachments (SP)) of the Panzer- and Panzer-Grenadier (Armoured and Armoured Infantry) divisions from April 1942, and to units which fought mainly in Russia. Phased out of front-line service early in 1944, the 7.62cm PaK(r) (Sf) had accomplished its role as a stop-gap until better designs could be fielded.

Plates 102-104. The three versions of 7.62cm PaK(r) auf Fgst Pz Kpfw II (Sf), which varied in gun shield and superstructure.

103

104

7.5cm PaK40/2 auf Fahrgestell Panzerkampfwagen II (Sf) (Sd Kfz 131)

Other designation: Marder II
Type: Self-propelled anti-tank gun on tank chassis

Manufacturer: FAMO, MAN, Daimler-Benz
Chassis Nos.: 28001–29550
576 produced from June 1942 to June 1943
75 converted from Pz Kpfw II from July 1943 to March 1944

Crew: 3	Engine: Maybach HL62TRM
Weight (tons): 10.8	Gearbox: 6 forward, 1 reverse
Length (metres): 6.36	Speed (km/hr): 40
Width (metres): 2.28	Range (km): 190
Height (metres): 2.2	Radio: FuG Spr d

Armament: One 7.5cm PaK40/2	One 7.92mm MG34
Traverse: 32° left 25° right (hand)	loose
Elevation: −8° +10°	loose
Sight: ZF3×8	direct
Ammunition: 37	600

Armour (mm/angle):	Front	Side	Rear	Top/Bottom
Superstructure:	30/10°	10/8°	10/0° +open	10/ +open
Hull:	35/13°	15/0°	15/7°	5/90°
Gun shield:	4+4/30°			

History: On 13 May 1942, it was questioned whether the Pz Kpfw II, then in production at a rate of 50 per month, was still adequate in a combat role, or whether it should be replaced by the 7.5cm PaK40 mounted on the Pz Kpfw II chassis. Early in June, it was decided to produce 50 per cent of the series as 7.5cm PaK Sf, and later in the month, it was decided that at least 75 per cent (100 per cent, if the Army so desired) of all new production was to be 7.5cm PaK40. Production was cut short in June 1943, to give all of the Pz Kpfw II Fgst to Wespe (Wasp) production. From July 1943 to March 1944, an additional seventy-five PaK40/2 were mounted on converted Pz Kpfw II Ausf c, A, B, C and F chassis.
Specific features: The hull and superstructure front remained the same as the basic Pz Kpfw II Ausf F. A superstructure was built to form a fighting compartment. The upper half of the field-carriage mount for the 7.5cm PaK40 was retained, but modified with girders to form the support for the anti-tank gun.
Combat service: The Sd Kfz 131 was issued to Panzerjäger detachments (SP) from July 1942. It remained in active service until the end of the war, serving on all major fronts.

105   106

Leichte Feldhaubitze 18/2 auf Fahrgestell Panzerkampfwagen II (Sf) (Sd Kfz 124)

Other designations: Wespe, Gerät 803
Type: Self-propelled light field howitzer on tracked carriage

Manufacturer: FAMO
Chassis Nos.: 31001–32190
676 produced from February 1943 to July 1944
159 munitions vehicles built during the same period

Crew: 5	Engine: HL62TR
Weight (tons): 11	Gearbox: 6 forward, 1 reverse
Length (metres): 4.81	Speed (km/hr): 40
Width (metres): 2.28	Range (km): 220
Height (metres): 2.3	Radio: FuG Spr f

Armament: One 10.5cm leFH18M   One 7.92mm MG34
  L/28

Traverse: 17° left 17° right (hand)	loose
Elevation: −5° +42°	loose
Sight: Rblf36	direct
Ammunition: 32	

Armour (mm/angle):	Front:	Side	Rear	Top/Bottom
Superstructure:	20/30°	15/0°	8/0°	10/90°
Hull:	30/15°	15/0°	15/10°	5/90°
Gun shield:	10/24°	10/17°	10/16°	open

History: The Wespe was designed by Alkett early in 1942, and was chosen as the most practical self-propelled mount for the leFH18 over the Pz Kpfw III and Pz Kpfw IV. As an interim measure, the Wespe proved a great success and in February 1943, all further Pz Kpfw II chassis were ordered to be used for its production. The initial order for 1,000 was cut back to 835 late in 1943. This total included 159 (without leFH18/2) designated Munitions-Sf auf Fgst Pz Kpfw II (Ammunition-SP on chassis (of) AFV II) which carried 90 rounds with a crew of three.

Specific features: The Wespe was built on a modified Pz Kpfw II chassis with the hull slightly lengthened, the engine moved forward, the glacis extended and the cooling-system louvres completely re-designed. The suspension was altered slightly by reducing the number of return rollers from four to three, and by adding spring bumper stops for the road wheels to absorb the recoil loadings. The driver occupied a small compartment forward, next to the transmission, and separated from the remainder of the crew who were located in the rear fighting compartment which was built up from sloping plates. The design of the Munitions-Sf version still allowed the installation of the leFH18/2 by Field Maintenance as replacement for unserviceable Wespe.

Combat service: The Wespe was issued to SP detachments of the Panzerartillerie regiments in Panzer and Panzergrenadier divisions. Its first major action was at Kursk in Russia, and it saw active service in the east, west and south-west until the end of the war.

107

Plate 107. Prototype leFH18/2 auf Fgst Pz Kpfw II (Sf).
Plate 108. LeFH18/2 auf Fgst Pz Kpfw II (Sf).

108

Plates 109-110. Wespe and its ammunition carrier (right), Munitions-Sf auf Fgst Pz Kpfw II.

109

110

Panzerkampfwagen II mit Schwimmkörper

Type: Amphibious tank

History: This amphibious tank was developed as a result of requirements for the proposed invasion of England late in 1940. The firm of Gebr Sachsenberg in Roslau was responsible for the flotation devices which were attached to the sides and front of the Pz Kpfw II. Water propulsion was transferred from the drive sprocket, and the floats were attached on extensions to the track support rollers. Afloat, it was capable of 10km/hr.

Combat Service: These tanks were used as normal Pz Kpfw II by the 18th Panzer Regiment which was formed in October 1940. They were used in action in the central sector of the Russian front from June 1941.

111

Plates 111-114. Pz Kpfw II Ausf C mit Schwimmkörper on trials (Plates 111-113), and Pz Kpfw II fitted with boat-shaped flotation equipment with a hollow centre (Plate 114).

113

Opposite page.
Plate 115. Brükenleger auf Pz Kpfw II, with the bridge ready to be launched.
Plate 116. The turretless tracked carrier Pi Kpfw II.
Plates 117-118. 5cm PaK38 L/60 auf Fgst Pz Kpfw II (Sf).

Brückenleger auf Panzerkampfwagen II

Type: Armoured bridgelayer

History: Magirus of Ulm experimented with a Brückenleger auf Pz Kpfw II Ausf b which featured a pivoting bridge, but the Bruckenleger which was in service in 1940 was fitted with a two-part sliding bridge, designed for scaling obstacles. This had formerly been mounted on the Pz Kpfw I. The number of these Brückenleger produced is not known, but four were in service with the Engineers of the 7th Panzer Division in Belgium and France in 1940.

Panzerkampfwagen II ohne Aufbau

Other designation: Pionier-Kampfwagen, II, Pi Kpfw II
Type: Tracked carrier

History: From 1942, a number of the older Pz Kpfw II, returned for overhaul, were converted to carrier vehicles for the Engineers, by removing their turrets. The turrets removed from these and other self-propelled gun conversions were issued for building into permanent fortifications. In May 1944, 739 Pz Kpfw II turrets were available and of these, 485 had already been released.

5cm PaK38 L/60 auf Fahrgestell Panzerkampfwagen II (Sf)

Type: Self-propelled anti-tank gun

History: Improvised self-propelled gun, similar to the 7.5cm PaK40 auf Fgst Pz Kpfw II (Sf) (Sd Kfz 131). The chassis was that of a Pz Kpfw II Ausf A, B or C.

Panzer Selbstfahrlafette 1c / 5cm PaK38 auf Panzerkampfwagen II (VK901)

Other designation: Leichte Panzerjäger
Type: Self-propelled anti-tank gun

History: In July 1940, the Wäffenamt placed an order with MAN for two prototypes of this light anti-tank vehicle. Rheinmetall-Borsig supplied the gun and superstructure. The two vehicles were delivered in January 1942 and were sent to the front. The total weight was 10.5 tons. No further orders were placed because of the unsuitability of the 5cm PaK38 in the conditions prevailing in 1942.

115

116

117

118

Panzerkampfwagen 35(t) and 38(t)
plus variants

Panzerkampfwagen 35(t)

Other designations: S-IIa, T-11
Type: Captured light tank

Manufacturer: Skoda (80%), CKD (20%)
Chassis Nos.: 50001–50424
424 produced between 1935 and 1938
219 confiscated from Czech Army in March 1939

Crew: 4	Engine: Skoda T11
Weight (tons): 10.5	Gearbox: 6 forward, 6 reverse
Length (metres): 4.9	Speed (km/hr): 35
Width (metres): 2.1	Range (km): 190
Height (metres): 2.35	Radio: FuG37(t)

Armament:	One 3.7cm KwK34(t) L/40	One 7.92mm MG37(t)	One 7.92mm MG37(t)
Traverse:	360° (hand)	10° left 10° right	35° left 11° right
Elevation:	−10° +25°	−14° +25°	=
Sight:	TZF(t)	MGZF(t)	=
Ammunition:	72 Pzgr & Sprgr	1,800	

Armour (mm/angle):	Front	Side	Rear	Top/Bottom
Turret:	25/10°	15/14°	15/15°	8/81° +90°
Superstructure:	25/17°	16/0°	15/60°	8/85° +90°
Hull:	25/30°	16/0°	16/0°	8/90°
Gun mantlet:	25/round			

History: The Panzerkampfwagen 35(t) was the main battle tank of the Czech Army during the years immediately preceding the German annexation of Bohemia and Moravia in March 1939. Initially, this tank was unreliable and although this problem was eventually solved, its bad reputation remained. After it had been taken into German service it was systematically rebuilt, and remained in service for more than three years. At the time of its development it represented a very advanced design, with more than adequate armour and fire power, but its technical specification included too many complex features, notably a pneumatically operated transmission.

Specific features: Rear sprocket drive, small road wheels and particularly wide tracks were the identifying features. The armour was riveted in the contemporary style. The main gun was developed from the Skoda anti-tank gun of the same calibre, and was renowned for its accuracy. The pneumatically controlled gearbox, which was designed to ease driving, proved a great weakness and gave trouble during the Russian winter of 1941.

Combat service: Of the Pz Kpfw 35(t) taken from the Czech Army in 1939, scarcely more than fifty per cent were ready for action, and these served with the 1st Light Division in Poland. In October 1939, the 11th Panzer Regiment and the 65th Panzerabteilung of that division were renamed the 6th Panzer Division which continued to use these tanks, both in France in 1940 and on the North front in Russia until late 1941, by which time, the bulk of the division's armour had been lost.

The Pz Kpfw 35(t) also served with the Army of Bulgaria, 26 being exported by Germany in February 1940 and 10 being supplied direct by Skoda in the summer of 1940. The Armies of Rumania and Slovakia had considerable numbers of these tanks in service throughout the war, having been supplied by Skoda prior to 1939.

119

120

121

Plate 3 (Page 4) Pz Kpfw 35(t).
Plates 119-121. Pz Kpfw 35(t). Plate 121 shows the Pz Bef Wg (Command) version.

Artillerie Schlepper 35(t)

Other designation: Mörser Zugmittel 35(t)
Type: Artillery tractor

History: At least 12 of the surviving Pz Kpfw (35(t) were converted to tractors by removing the turret and fitting a canvas cover in its place. The tow bar fitted to the rear allowed 12 tonne to be pulled. Turrets from these tanks and others returned for repair, were used for fixed fortifications. Of the 38 turrets available, 36 had been issued by May 1944.

Plate 38 (Page 13). Mörser Zugmittel 35(t).
Plate 122. Mörser Zugmittel 35(t).

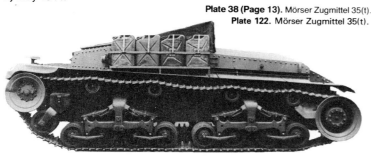

Panzerkampfwagen 38(t) Ausf A

Other designations: I Serie TNHPS, LT Vz 38
Type: Light tank

Manufacturer: BMM
Chassis Nos.: 0001–0150
150 produced from May to November 1939

Crew: 4	Engine: Praga EPA
Weight (tons): 9.4	Gearbox: 5 forward, 1 reverse
Length (metres): 4.6	Speed (km/hr): 42
Width (metres): 2.12	Range (km): 250
Height (metres): 2.4	Radio: FuG37(t)

Armament:	One 3.7cm KwK38(t) L/48.7	One 7.92mm MG37(t)	One 7.92mm MG37(t)
Traverse:	360° (hand)	10° left 10° right	35° left 11° right
Elevation:	−10° +25°	−14° +25°	=
Sight:	TZF(t)	MGZF(t)	=
Ammunition:	72	2,400 (inc 900 AP)	

Armour (mm/angle):	Front	Side	Rear	Top/Bottom
Turret:	25/10°	15/10°	15/10°	10/90°
Superstructure:	25/17°	15/0°	10/60°	8/90°
Hull:	25/16°	15/0°	15/12°	8/90°
Gun mantlet:	25/round			

History: The Pz Kpfw 38(t) was, in fact, the Czech LT Vz 38 which was produced for the Wehrmacht after the annexation of the Czechoslovakian provinces of Bohemia and Moravia in March 1939. Ordered as a prototype from CKD (Praga) in 1937, the Vz 38 was outright winner of competitive tests held in 1938. In July, an order was placed for 150 tanks to be manufactured immediately. The Munich Agreement forced the slow-down of this order and no production vehicles were delivered before March 1939. After the German occupation, an order was placed for the 150 incomplete tanks to be completed for the Wehrmacht as the Pz Kpfw 38(t) Ausf A.

Specific features: Externally similar to the model ordered by the Czech Army in 1938, the Ausf A can be readily identified by the 'battle' aerial in the form of a pipe along the left side of the tank. The Germans increased the crew by a gun loader, thus relieving the commander of this task. The amount of 37mm ammunition was reduced by 3 bins containing 18 rounds, to make space for the additional crewman.

Combat service: Fifty-nine Pz Kpfw 38(t) Ausf A served in the 67th Panzerabteilung of the 3rd Light Division in Poland, and 15 served in Norway in 1940. Thereafter, this tank served in most theatres of war except Africa.

Panzerspähwagen T-15

Other designation: Skoda T-15
Type: Reconnaissance tank

History: In 1942, Skoda built a prototype reconnaissance tank for OKW (Wehrmacht High Command) trials. This 10 ton vehicle was armed with a 3.7cm gun and an MG. The armour was 20mm to 8mm and the vehicle was powered by a V-8 10.8lit engine developing 220PS at 2,800rpm. A crew of 4 was accommodated. The T-15 was unsuccessful in competition with the VK1303.

Plate 123. Wooden mock-up of the Skoda T-15 with improved sloped armour on the hull front. The prototype was shaped like the Pz Kpfw 35(t).

Panzerkampfwagen T-25

Other designation: Skoda T-25

History: Despite considerable political pressure this design never went further than a mock-up. The medium tank was to have had sloped armour similar to the Soviet T-34. A Skoda A-18 7.5cm KwK with semi automatic loading and a 450 PS engine were to have been used.

See Plate 532 (Page 157). Mock up of T-25 chassis as a Waffenträger.

124

Plates 124-125. Pz Kpfw 38(t) Ausf A. The lower photograph shows the curve of the driver's plate and the hull-mounted machine-gun.

125

Panzerkampfwagen 38(t) Ausf B, C und D

Other designation: II, III, IV Serie TNHPS
Type: Light tank

Manufacturer: BMM
Chassis Nos.: 0151–0260, 0261–0370, 0371–0475
325 produced from January to November 1940

Crew: 4	Engine: Praga EPA
Weight (tons): 9.5	Gearbox: 5 forward, 1 reverse
Length (metres): 4.61	Speed (km/hr): 42
Width (metres): 2.14	Range (km): 250
Height (metres): 2.4	Radio: FuG37(t)

Armament: One 3.7cm One 7.92mm MG37(t) One 7.92mm MG37(t)
  KwK38(t) L/47.8

Traverse: 360° (hand)	10° left 10° right	35° left 11° right
Elevation: −10° +25°	−14° +25°	=
Sight: TZF(t)	MGZF(t)	=

Armour (mm/angle):	Front	Side	Rear	Top/Bottom
Turret:	25/10°	15/10°	15/10°	10/90°
Superstructure:	25/17°	15/0°	10/60°	8/90°
Hull:	25/16°	15/0°	15/12°	8/90°
Gun mantlet:	25/round			

History: The Pz Kpfw 38(t) Ausf A ordered in May 1939, was a completion of the tanks already ordered for the Czech Army. The success of tests with the prototypes and the first production vehicles led the Waffenamt to order a further 325. Three series were envisaged, Series II, III and IV, being basically similar apart from minor detail changes to suit German use.
Specific features: Externally similar to Ausf A, both Ausf B and C had the driver's curved plate. The battle aerial was deleted. Smoke-dispensers and the German 'Notek' lighting system were added. The

Plate 126. Pz Kpfw 38(t) Ausf B or C.
Plate 127 (right). Pz Kpfw 38(t) Ausf C with the hull machine-gun removed and the port plated over.

anti-splash protection for the turret ring was introduced on the Ausf D.
Combat service: Both Ausf B and C served in France in 1940 with the 7th and 8th Panzer Divisions, and with the 8th Panzer Division in Greece in 1941. The Ausf D was introduced in September 1940.

Panzerkampfwagen 38(t) Ausf E und F

Other designation: V und VI Serie TNHPS
Type: Light tank

Manufacturer: BMM
Chassis Nos.: 0476–0750, 0751–1000
525 produced from November 1940 to October 1941

Crew: 4	Engine: Praga EPA
Weight (tons): 9.85	Gearbox: 5 forward, 1 reverse
Length (metres): 4.61	Speed (km/hr): 42
Width (metres): 2.14	Range (km): 250
Height (metres): 2.4	Radio: FuG5

Armament: One 3.7cm One 7.92mm MG37(t) One 7.92mm MG37(t)
  KwK38(t) L/47.8

Traverse: 360° (hand)	10° left 10° right	35° left 11° right
Elevation: −10° +25°	−14° +25°	=
Sight: TZF(t)	MGZF(t)	=
Ammunition: 42 Pzgr	2,400	
& Sprgr		

Armour (mm/angle):	Front	Side	Rear	Top/Bottom
Turret:	25+25/10°	30/10°	22/10°	15/90°
Superstructure:	25+25/17°	15+15/0°	10/60°	8/90°
Hull:	25+25/16°	15/0°	15/12°	8/90°
Gun mantlet:	25/round			

History: As a result of experience in Poland, greater protection was demanded, and from November 1940 the frontal armour of these tanks was increased to 50mm by riveting two 25mm plates together on all frontal surfaces. The armour on the turret sides and on the upper sides of the fighting compartment was also increased.
Specific features: New visors—Sehklappe 50 (Observation Port 50) —were fitted for driver and operator, riveting was reduced on frontal plates and the turret machine-gun ball mount was located internally.
Combat service: All models of the Pz Kpfw 38(t) served in Russia from July 1941. The Ausf D, E and F served mainly with the more recently formed 12th, 19th and 20th Panzer Divisions, as well as with the 7th and 8th Panzer Divisions which were the first divisions to be equipped with these tanks.

128

129

Plate 32 (Page 13) Pz Bef Wg 38(t) Ausf E or F.
Plates 946-947 (Page 246) M9 37(t) Hull and turret mounts from Pc Kpfw 38(t) Ausf E.
Plate 128. Pz Kpfw 38(t) Ausf E.
Plate 129. Pz Kpfw 38(t) Ausf E or F.

Panzerkampfwagen 38(t) Ausf S

Other designation: TNH-SV
Type: Light tank

Manufacturer: BMM
Chassis Nos.: 1001–1090
90 produced from May to December 1941

Crew: 4	Engine: Praga EPA
Weight (tons): 9.5	Gearbox: 5 forward, 1 reverse
Length (metres): 4.61	Speed (km/hr): 42
Width (metres): 2.14	Range (km): 250
Height (metres): 2.4	

Armament: One 3.7cm KwK38(t) L/47.8	One 7.92mm MG37(t)	One 7.92mm MG37(t)
Traverse: 360° (hand)	10° left 10° right	35° left 11° right
Elevation: −10° +25°	−14° +25°	=
Sight: TZF(t)	MGZF(t)	=

Armour (mm/angle):	Front	Side	Rear	Top/Bottom
Turret:	25/10°	15/10°	15/10°	10/90°
Superstructure:	25/17°	15/0°	10/60°	8/90°
Hull:	25/16°	15/0°	15/12°	8/90°
Gun mantlet:	25/round			

History: Before the German occupation of Czechoslovakia in March 1939, CKD (later known as BMM) had sought export orders for their tanks. In 1938/39, Sweden placed an order for 90 TNH–SV tanks. In the spring of 1940, the Germans commanded that all tanks under construction for Sweden be delivered to the Wehrmacht. Early in 1941, Sweden received a licence to build the TNHPS tank, which she did, under the designation Strv m/41. Deliveries to the Swedish Army took place from February 1943. The Strv m/41 was basically similar to the Pz Kpfw 38(t) Ausf G. The 'Swedish' vehicles were to have been assembled from February 1941, but difficulties arose because of their obsolete configuration, and because of the modifications which had been incorporated specifically for the export order.
Specific features: Similar in appearance to Pz Kpfw 38(t) Ausf A, but without battle aerial. These tanks were fitted with turret-ring splash-protectors, as fitted to the contemporary Ausf E and F.
Combat service: Tanks of this type were exported to the Slovak Free State and served with their Fast Division in southern Russia in 1941 and 1942.

Panzerkampfwagen 38(t) Ausf G

Other designation: VII Serie TNHPS
Type: Light tank

Manufacturer: BMM
Chassis Nos.: 1101–1600
321 produced from October 1941 to June 1942

Crew: 4	Engine: Praga EPA
Weight (tons): 9.85	Gearbox: 5 forward, 1 reverse
Length (metres): 4.61	Speed (km/hr): 42
Width (metres): 2.14	Range (km): 250
Height (metres): 2.4	Radio: FuG5

Armament: One 3.7cm KwK38(t) L/47.8	One 7.92mm MG37(t)	One 7.92mm MG37(t)
Traverse: 360° (hand)	10° left 10° right	35° left 11° right
Elevation: −10° +25°	−14° +25°	=
Sight: TZF(t)	MGZF(t)	=

Armour (mm/angle):	Front	Side	Rear	Top/Bottom
Turret:	50/10°	30/10°	22/10°	15/90°
Superstructure:	50/17°	15+15/0°	10/	8/90°
Hull:	50/16°	15/0°	15/12°	8/90°
Gun mantlet:	25/round			

History: The final outgrowth of the demand for heavier armour resulted in the Pz Kpfw 38(t) Ausf G, which used basic 50mm armour plate for all frontal surfaces. More extensive use of welding was made in the construction of this model. The growing obsolescence of this tank led Hitler to order that its chassis be used as the basis of a self-propelled anti-tank gun. A proportion of the output for March 1942, and all output for April were used for this purpose. The final 47 tanks were manufactured in May and June 1942.
Specific features: Driver's plate located by only three rivets; no rivets on the engine covers.

Combat service: Served mainly in Russia. Various models of the Pz Kpfw 38(t) series were exported to the German allies, Hungary, Rumania, and Slovakia. In September 1944, the Pz Kpfw 38(t), despite being obsolete, was still in service mainly with armoured train units, two tanks being carried on the flat cars of each train. At this time, 229 Pz Kpfw 38(t) of all models were listed as available.

Plate 130. Pz Kpfw 38(t) Ausf G.

Panzerkampfwagen 38(t) neuer Art

Type: Light reconnaissance tank

Plate 131. Pz Kpfw 38(t) nA.

Manufacturer: BMM
15 claimed to have been produced in early 1942

Crew: 4	Engine: Praga V–8
Weight (tons): 14.8	Gearbox: 4 forward, 1 reverse
Length (metres): 5	Speed (km/hr): 62
Width (metres): 2.5	Range (km): 200
Height (metres): 2.14	

Armament: One 3.7cm KwK38(t)   One 7.92mm MG37(t)
    L/47.8

Traverse: 360° (hand)	=	
Elevation: −10° +25°	=	
Sight: TZF(t)	=	

Armour (mm):	Front	Side	Rear	Top
Turret:	35/7°		112°	8
Superstructure:	35/20°	10°		8
Hull:	35/25°			8
Gun mantlet:	35/round			

History: Offered as the BMM solution to the Waffenamt requirement for a reconnaissance tank which had originally been issued to MAN as early as September 1939. The Pz Kpfw 38(t) nA followed very closely the successful layout of the Pz Kpfw 38(t), but the latest techniques of welded armour were incorporated, and the vehicle was powered by a V–8 engine of 250PS. Despite successful performance and a very high speed achieved during tests in 1942, no production order was placed. The transmission and steering gear, however, were ordered to be fitted in the VK903, which, in turn, did not pass beyond the development phase.
Specific features: New welded construction for hull and turret. Road wheels more closely spaced, and new V–8 engine.
Combat service: None.

Panzerjäger 38(t) für 7.62cm PaK36(r) (Sd Kfz 139)

Other designations: Marder III, VII und VIII Serie TNHPS
Type: Self-propelled captured anti-tank gun on tank chassis

Manufacturer: BMM
Chassis Nos.: between 1351 & 1510, 1511–1768
344 produced from April to October 1942
19 converted from Pz Kpfw 38(t) in 1943

Crew: 4	Engine: Praga EPA & EPA/2
Weight (tons): 10.67	Gearbox: 5 forward, 1 reverse
Length (metres): 5.85	Speed (km/hr): 42
Width (metres): 2.16	Range (km): 185
Height (metres): 2.5	Radio: FuG Spr d

Armament: One 7.62cm PaK36(r)   One 7.92mm MG37(t)
    L/51.5

Traverse: 21° left 21° right (hand)	35° left 11° right (hand)	
Elevation: −8° +13½°	−14° +25°	
Sight: ZF3×8	MGZF(t)	
Ammunition: 30 Pzgr 39Rot,	1,200	
Pzgr 40 & Sprgr 39		

Armour (mm/angle):	Front	Side	Rear	Top/Bottom
Superstructure:	50/17°	16/11° + 14°	10/65°	10/90°
Hull:	50/16°	15/0°	15/16°	10 + 8/90°
Gun shield:	11/31°	11/12°	open	open

History: The problems faced by the German troops in Russia when they encountered superior Russian armour was to be solved in the short term by the production of self-propelled anti-tank guns. Since the Pz Kpfw 38(t) was obsolete as a battle tank and considered too slow as a reconnaissance tank, it was ordered that a number of the chassis under construction be converted to gun carriages. A prototype Sf (SP) mounting a Russian 7.62cm gun was built in December 1941, and an order dated 22 December 1941 called for production of 17 units per month from 24 March 1942, and for capacity for 30 per month from July. Several orders were issued so that eventually 344 were built. From July 1942, Hitler ordered that all Pz Kpfw 38(t) production be used as Sf. The 7.62cm PaK36(r) was the Russian FK296 rebuilt to German specifications and rechambered to take a PaK40 cartridge. Conversion was made from the large stocks of guns captured during the initial success in Russia.
Specific features: To cope with the greater weight of the self-propelled guns, the motor was increased in power to 150PS. This model was introduced in July 1942 as the Ausf H (chassis numbers from 1601).
Combat service: Served mainly with Panzerjäger detachments in Russia. A total of 66 were dispatched to North Africa where those that arrived from July to November 1942 served with the 33rd Panzerjägerabteilung of the 15th Panzer Division, and with the 39th Panzerjägerabteilung. The first six units, which arrived in North Africa in May 1942, remained with the HQ of the Tank Army.

Plates 132-133. Pz Jäg 38(t) für 7.62cm PaK36(r): above, on the Russian Front.

7.5cm PaK40/3 auf Panzerkampfwagen 38(t) Ausf H (Sd Kfz 138)

Other designation: VIII Serie TNHPS
Type: Self-propelled anti-tank gun on tank chassis

Manufacturer: BMM
Chassis Nos.: 1601–2100
242 produced from November 1942 to April 1943 plus 1 prototype
175 converted from Pz Kpfw 38(t) in 1943

Crew: 4	Engine: Praga EPA/2
Weight (tons): 10.8	Gearbox: 5 forward, 1 reverse
Length (metres): 5.77	Speed (km/hr): 35
Width (metres): 2.16	Range (km): 240
Height (metres): 2.51	Radio: FuG5

Armament: One 7.5cm PaK40/3 L/46	One 7.92mm MG37(t)	
Traverse: 30° left 30° right (hand)	35° left 11° right (hand)	
Elevation: −5° +22°	−14° +25°	
Sight: ZF3×8	MGZF(t)	
Ammunition: 38	600	

Armour (mm/angle):	Front	Side	Rear	Top/Bottom
Superstructure:	50/15°	15/0°	open	10/65° + 90°
Hull:	50/15°	15/0°	15/16°	8/90°
Gun shield:	15/25°	15/25°	open	8/90°

Plates 134-135. 7.5cm PaK40/3 auf Pz Kpfw 38(t) Ausf H.

History: In May 1942, discussions took place concerning the manufacture of a new self-propelled gun, based on the Pz Kpfw 38(t) chassis, but mounting the normal German 7.5cm PaK40 in place of the 7.62cm PaK36(r). The prototype was ready in June 1942, and incorporated a redesigned superstructure which was lower, lighter and provided superior protection.

Specific features: Both the 7.5cm PaK40 prototype and a 7.5cm StuK40 prototype were built on the Pz Kpfw 38(t) Ausf G chassis. By November 1942, however, the Ausf H chassis with the more powerful engine was available. The Ausf H hull was similar to the hull of the Ausf G, but the side armour was reduced by omitting the additional 15mm plate from the fighting compartment.

Combat service: The Sd Kfz 138 was issued to Panzerjäger detachments (SP) from late 1942. Luftwaffe and SS units as well as Wehrmacht units received these guns. From December 1942, they were in action with 'Leibstandarte Adolf Hitler', 1st SS Panzer Division in Russia, and served also in Tunisia and Italy in 1943.

15cm Schweres Infanteriegeschütz 33 (Sf) auf Panzerkampfwagen 38(t) Ausf H (Sd Kfz 138/1)

Other designations: VIII Serie TNHP, Gerät 805, Grille
Type: Self-propelled heavy infantry gun on tank chassis

Manufacturer: BMM
Chassis Nos.: between 1601 & 2100
90 produced from February to April 1943 plus 1 prototype

Crew: 5	Engine: Praga EPA/2
Weight (tons): 11.5	Gearbox: 5 forward, 1 reverse
Length (metres): 4.61	Speed (km/hr): 35
Width (metres): 2.16	Range (km): 185
Height (metres): 2.4	Radio: FuG16

Armament: One 15cm sIG33/1 L/12	One 7.92mm MG34	
Traverse: 5° left 5° right (hand)	loose	
Elevation: −3° +72°	loose	
Sight: Rblf36	direct	
Ammunition: 15		

Armour (mm/angle):	Front	Side	Rear	Top/Bottom
Superstructure:	25/12°	15/	15/10°	open
Hull:	50/15°	15/0°	15/16°	8/90°
Gun shield:	15/12°			

History: The Grille was originally ordered for construction on the new self-propelled gun chassis which BMM were developing as the Sf 38(t) Ausf K. Two hundred sIG33 were to be thus mounted. On 6 February 1943, however, Hitler agreed to a proposal to adapt the sIG33 for mounting in the rear-engined Ausf H in order to make the Grille available as soon as possible. An additional advantage would be that Pz Kpfw 38(t) returned from the front could be converted to Grille. As a result, Hitler ordered that from March 1943, all repaired vehicles were to be used for this purpose. It was agreed, however, that after the order for 200 had been fulfilled, any further Grille production was to be manufactured from the Pz Kpfw 38(t) returned to the factory for refit.

Specific features: The standard Ausf H chassis with a new fighting compartment superstructure which had to be extended over the engine compartment to accommodate the heavy gun and its ammunition.

Combat service: The Grille were issued to the schwere Infanteriegeschütz companies of the Panzergrenadier regiments, and served in Russia, Tunisia, Italy and France from early 1943. In June 1944 this version of Grille was still in service with the 38th Panzer schwere Infanteriegeschütz Abteilung of the 2nd Panzer Division in Normandy. Six vehicles were issued to each detachment.

Plate 136. 15cm sIG33(Sf) auf Pz Kpfw 38(t) Ausf H.

Panzerjäger 38(t) mit 7.5cm PaK40/3 Ausf M (Sd Kfz 138)

Other designations: Marder III, X Serie TNHP, 7.5cm Pak 40 auf Pz Jäg 38(t)
Type: Self-propelled anti-tank gun on tracked carriage

Manufacturer: BMM
Chassis Nos.: 2101-
975 produced between April 1943 and May 1944

Crew: 4	Engine: Praga AC
Weight (tons): 10.5	Gearbox: 5 forward, 1 reverse
Length (metres): 4.95	Speed (km/hr): 42
Width (metres): 2.15	Range (km): 190
Height (metres): 2.48	Radio: FuG Spr d

Armament: One 7.5cm PaK 40/3   One 7.92mm MG34
  L/46
Traverse: 21° left 21° right (hand) loose
Elevation: −5° +13°   loose
Sight: ZF3×8   direct
Ammunition: 27

Armour (mm/angle):	Front	Side	Rear	Top/Bottom
Superstructure:	10/30°	10/15°	10/0°	8/90°
Hull:	20/15°	15/0°	10/41°	10/90°
Gun shield:	6/28°	10/16°	10/17°	open

History: In July 1942, Hitler ordered that the total production capacity of the Pz Kpfw 38(t) be utilized for self-propelled gun chassis. It had been realised that in the existing make-shift self-propelled gun, many of the features of the tank chassis were wasteful. A new design was proposed in which the motor was moved to the middle, and this enabled the gun to be mounted more suitably at the rear of the vehicle. Frontal armour and, therefore, weight, was also reduced. On 6 February 1943, Hitler was informed that after test firing, the new self-propelled gun would be available in the shortest possible time, and BMM would be capable of producing 150 per month compared to their present output of 60 units. This level was not reached until October/November 1943, but not all were 7.5cm PaK40/3 Sf, although maximum monthly delivery of 141 was reached in October. In May 1944, production was terminated in favour of the Jagdpanzer 'Hetzer' (Tank-Hunter 'Baiter').

Specific features: Vehicles built during 1943 can be identified by the rounded, cast cover for the driving compartment at the front right-hand side of the vehicle. At the end of 1943, a simpler welded cover was introduced, and the front towing lugs were now formed from extensions of the side armour plate.

Combat service: Panzerjäger Detachments (SP) of both Panzer and infantry divisions were issued with these guns from May 1943. Because of the large number produced, they served on all fronts, with 350 still listed as available for action in the Wäffenamt inventory for 1 February 1945.

Plates 137-139. Pz Jäg 38(t) mit 7.5cm PaK40/3 Ausf M: below, a late production vehicle.

137

138

139

140

141

15cm Schweres Infanteriegeschütz 33/1 auf Selbstfahrlafette 38(t) (Sf) Ausf K (Sd Kfz 138/1)

Other designations: Grille, X Serie TNHP, Gerät 806, 15cm sIG33/1 (Sf), 15cm sIG33/ auf Sfl 38(t)
Type: Self-propelled heavy infantry gun on tracked carriage

Manufacturer: BMM
Chassis Nos.: 2101-
282 produced from April to June 1943 and from October 1943 to
    September 1944
Crew: 4
Weight (tons): 12
Length (metres): 4.95
Width (metres): 2.15
Height (metres): 2.47

Engine: Praga AC
Gearbox: 5 forward, 1 reverse
Speed (km/hr): 35
Range (km): 190
Radio: FuG16

Armament: One 15cm sIG33/2
Traverse: 5° left 5° right (hand)
Elevation: −0° +73°
Sight: Rblf36
Ammunition: 18

One 7.92mm MG34
loose
loose
direct

Armour (mm/angle):	Front	Side	Rear	Top/Bottom
Superstructure:	10/67°	10/15°	10/0°	8/90°
Hull:	20/15°	15/0°	10/41°	10/90°
Gun shield:	10/9°	10/16°	10/17°	open

History: The initial order for 200 Grille called for use of the old Ausf H chassis with a view to getting the Grille into service quickly. Ninety were built on the Ausf H, and the remaining 110 Grille were built on the new chassis. The contract was completed in June 1943, but a further order was placed, and regular production continued from October 1943 until September 1944. The Grille was the very last Selbstfahrlafette production. In fact, the ten units built in September 1944, were on chassis originally built for the Flakpanzer (Armoured AA SP).

Specific features: As for the Panzerjäger 38(t). In elevation, the gun was protected by a heavy spring flap which was a feature of all the sIG33 (Sf).

Combat service: Served on all fronts with the schwere Infanterie-geschütz companies (SP) of armoured infantry regiments. No distinction was made between Grille with Ausf H or Ausf K chassis. In February 1945, 173 Grille were still listed as available for service.

Plate 142. Munitionspanzer 38(t) (Sf) Ausf K.

Munitionspanzer 38(t) (Sf) Ausf K (Sd Kfz 138)

Other designation: X Serie TNHP
Type: Tracked armoured ammunition carrier

Manufacturer: BMM
Chassis Nos.: 2101-
102 produced from January to May 1944
Crew: 2
Weight (tons): 12
Length (metres): 4.95
Width (metres): 2.15
Height (metres): 2.47

Engine: Praga AC
Gearbox: 5 forward, 1 reverse
Speed (km/hr): 35
Range (km): 190
Radio: FuG16

Armament: One 7.92mm MG34
Traverse: loose
Elevation: loose
Sight: direct
Ammunition: 40 sIG· patr

Armour (mm/angle):	Front	Side	Rear	Top/Bottom
Superstructure:	10/67°	10/15°	10/0°	8/90°
Hull:	20/15°	15/0°	10/41°	10/90°
Gun shield:	10/28°	10/16°	10/17°	open

History: The second large order for Grille 15cm sIG33/1(Sf) allowed for the production of nearly forty per cent of the order as ammunition carriers. It had been recognized that the very limited ammunition capacity of the Grille was detrimental to its fighting capacity. It was planned to have two Munitionspanzer to every six Grille in an armoured heavy infantry gun detachment.

Specific features: In most respects, the Munitionspanzer 38(t) (Sf) was identical with the Grille. The 15cm sIG33/1 was replaced by ammunition racks, and the gun aperture was plated over. The conversion allowed the possibility of re-conversion to sIG vehicles.

Combat service: Issued to the schwere Infanteriegeschütz company (SP) of Panzergrenadier regiments and served on all fronts until 1945.

Flakpanzer 38(t) auf Selbstfahrlafette 38(t) Ausf L (Sd Kfz 140)

Other designation: X Serie TNHP
Type: Self-propelled anti-aircraft gun on tracked carriage

Manufacturer: BMM
Chassis Nos.: 2101-
140 produced from November 1943 to February 1944
1 converted in November 1943
Crew: 4
Weight (tons): 9.8
Length (metres): 4.61
Width (metres): 2.15
Height (metres): 2.25

Engine: Praga AC
Gearbox: 5 forward, 1 reverse
Speed (km/hr): 42
Range (km): 210
Radio: FuG5 or FuG2

Armament: One 2cm FlaK38 L/112.5
Traverse: 360° (hand)
Elevation: −5° +90°
Sight: Flakvisier 38
Ammunition: 360 2cm Br Sprgr L Spur, 360 2cm Br Sprgr, 320 2cm Pzgr L Spur Zerl

Armour (mm/angle):	Front	Side	Rear	Top/Bottom
Superstructure:	10/67°	10/25°	10/25°	8/90°
Hull:	20/15°	15/0°	10/41°	10/90°
Gun shield:	10/17°	10/25°	10/25°	open

History: During the autumn of 1943, Hitler approved the development of a 3.7cm Flakpanzer IV, but refused permission for the construction of the already available 2cm Vierlings FlaK auf Pz Kpfw IV (2cm Quadruple AA Mounting on AFV IV). On 15 October 1943, because of the urgent need for a Flakpanzer, Hitler agreed to a makeshift solution which could be produced immediately on the basis of the Selbstfahrlafette 38(t). 150 Flakpanzer 38(t) were ordered, and were to be produced until the heavier Flakpanzer IV became available early in 1944. This vehicle was demonstrated to Hitler on 16 December 1943. Lack of firepower was a major drawback. The last ten vehicles of the order were used for the production of 15cm sIG33/2 Sf.

Specific features: 2cm FlaK38 with all-round traverse was mounted in the rear fighting compartment. A new superstructure was provided, the upper part of which could be folded down to allow easier access to the weapon and permit traverse at low elevation.

Combat service: Issued in January and February 1944 to the AA Platoon of each tank regiment in the Panzer divisions. A considerable proportion of these guns were issued to divisions in the West and saw action in Normandy, for example, with the 12th SS Panzer Division 'Hitlerjugend' (Hitler Youth).

Plate 25 (Page 12). Flakpanzer 38(t) in action.
Plates 143-144. Flakpanzer 38(t) auf Sf 38(t) Ausf L.

Aufklärer auf Fahrgestell Panzerkampfwagen 38(t) mit 2cm KwK38 oder 7.5cm KwK38 L/24

Type: Tracked armoured reconnaissance vehicle on tank chassis.

Manufacturer: BMM
50 with 2cm Hängelafette 38 converted in February and March 1944; 2 with 7.5cm KwK L/24

Crew: 4
Weight (tons): 9.75
Length (metres): 4.51
Width (metres): 2.14
Height (metres): 2.17

Engine: Praga EPA/2
Gearbox: 5 forward, 1 reverse
Speed (km/hr): 42
Range (km): 210
Radio: FuG12

Armament: One 2cm KwK38 L/55   One 7.92mm MG42
Traverse: 360° (hand)   =
Elevation: −4° +70°   =
Sight: TZF3a   =

Armour (mm/angle):	Front	Side	Rear	Top/Bottom
Turret:	30/40°	8/40°	8/40°	open
Superstructure:	50/25°	15/30°	15/0°	8/90°
Hull:	50/15°	15/0°	15/12°	8/90°
Gun mantlet:	30/round			

History: Since production of the fully-tracked reconnaissance vehicle 'Luchs' (Lynx) was scheduled to end in January 1944 after only 100 had been built, plans were made to provide an alternative by using the chassis of Pz Kpfw 38(t) returned for repair. From December 1943, BMM were to convert 118 tanks by April 1944. After delays, however, only 70 chassis were prepared in February and March 1944. Only 15 of the units without the 2cm Hängelafette (2cm Swivel Mounting) were delivered, and 13 of these were held back by BMM until at least November 1944. BMM proposed two designs for the 7.5cm KwK version. Later, an Aufklärer auf Fgst Jagdpanzer 38(t) mit 7.5cm K51 L/24 was tested, because it was intended to have a reconnaissance vehicle using the 38(t) chassis built along-

side the Jagdpanzer 38(t) and Jagdpanzer 38(d) from mid 1945.
Specific features: A new superstructure was fitted to the old Pz Kpfw 38(t) chassis, and on that, was mounted the 2cm Hängelafette 38 turret, as used for the Sd Kfz 250/9, 251/23 and 234/1. The 7.5cm mounting was achieved by extending the sides of the new superstructure upwards.
Combat service: Issued to armoured reconnaissance companies from April 1944. Saw service on both Eastern and Western fronts.

Plate 145. Aufkl auf Fgst Pz Kpfw 38(t) mit 2cm KwK38.   (*Continued overleaf.*)

Munitionsschlepper auf Fahrgestell Panzerkampfwagen 38(t)

Type: Ammunition carrier

History: From 1942, these Munitionspanzer were created by removing the turrets from the older models of Pz Kpfw 38(t). The opening was then covered by rails to carry a canvas cover. These makeshift load-carriers served with many units, mainly in the East. Turrets from Pz Kpfw 38(t) converted to self-propelled guns, etc., were used in fixed fortification mountings. By May 1944, 351 turrets had been issued for such purposes, and a further 84 were available.

Schützenpanzerwagen auf Fahrgestell Panzerkampfwagen 38(t)

Type: Armoured personnel carrier

History: During 1944, a prototype of a personnel carrier based on the 38(t) chassis was built and tested. The engine was mounted in the front left-hand side, as in the Ausf M. The troop compartment was open-topped, and was based on the design of the Sd Kfz 251 Ausf D. Projects for troop carriers with 6 road wheels, as in the mittlerer Einheitswaffenträger (Medium Standard Weapons Carrier), were favoured in 1945.

Mörserträger auf Fahrgestell Panzerkampfwagen 38(t)

Type: Mortar carrier

History: Only a prototype of this vehicle was built. It was similar to the SPW (APC), but shorter.

148

Plate 148. Mun Schl auf Fgst Pz Kpfw 38(t).
Plate 149 (right). Mrs tr auf Fgst Pz Kpfw 38(t).
Plate 29 (Page 12). Bergepanzer 38)t).

Jagdpanzer 38(t) Hetzer (Panzerjäger 38(t)) für 7.5cm PaK39

Other designations: Gerät 555, Pz Jäg Wg 638/10, Pz Jäg 38(t) (Hetzer)
Type: Tank destroyer

Manufacturer: BMM	Chassis Nos.: 321001–323000
Skoda	323001–

2,584 produced from April 1944 to May 1945
Production plan for 1945 called for 1,000 units per month by mid-year

Crew: 4	Engine: Praga AC/2
Weight (tons): 15.75	Gearbox: 5 forward, 1 reverse
Length (metres): 6.38	Speed (km/hr): 42
Width (metres): 2.63	Range (km): 177
Height (metres): 2.17	Radio: FuG5 + FuG Spr f

Armament: One 7.5cm PaK39 L/48	One 7.92mm MG34 or 42
Traverse: 5° left 11° right (hand)	360° (hand)
Elevation: −6° +12°	
Sight: SflZF1a	Periskop 3 × 8°
Ammunition: 41	1,200

Armour (mm/angle):	Front	Side	Rear	Top/Bottom
Superstructure:	60/60°	20/40°	8/70°	8/90°
Hull:	60/40°	20/15°	20/15°	10/90°
Gun mantlet:	60/Saukopfblende			

150

History: As early as March 1943, Col. Gen. Heinz Guderian, the Inspector of Armoured Units, demanded a light tank destroyer, which would be adequately armoured, with overhead protection and low silhouette, to replace existing light self-propelled guns and towed anti-tank guns. Development was based on the chassis of the Pz Kpfw 38(t). Following tests in December 1943, it was ordered that the complete production facilities for the 38(t) be switched to production of the new Panzerjäger. Production commenced in April 1944 at BMM and was taken up by Skoda in September 1944. It had been intended to switch over to rigid mounted guns as soon as possible, but this was deferred at the beginning of 1944 and, again, in November 1944. May 1945 was the deadline for change over to rigid mounting of the PaK39/1 and 10.5cm StuH42 (10.5cm Assault Howitzer 42).

Specific features: The Hetzer was a completely new design using the well-proven components of the Pz Kpfw 38(t). A new wide hull with extensive use of angled armour was employed. Cramped fighting compartment and limited angle of fire presented problems in battle. A roof-mounted remote-controlled MG was provided for close defence.

Combat service: The first combat units to receive the Hetzer, in July 1944, were Panzerjägerabteilungen 731 and 743, and the 15th and 76th Infantry Divisions. It was subsequently issued to tank-hunter detachments attached to all types of formation. In 1946, the Swiss Army purchased 158 Hetzer from Czechoslovakia under the designation G13. The Hetzer also served with the post-war Czech Army.

151

Plates 150-152. Jgd Pz 38(t) Hetzer für 7.5cm PaK39.
Plate 150 shows an early production model, Plate 152 a late model.

Flammpanzer 38(t) Hetzer

Type: Flame-thrower on tank destroyer chassis

Manufacturer: BMM
20 converted from Hetzer in December 1944

Crew: 4	Engine: Praga AC/2
Weight (tons): 15.5	Gearbox: 5 forward, 1 reverse
Length (metres): 4.87	Speed (km/hr): 42
Width (metres): 2.63	Range (km): 177
Height (metres): 2.17	

Armament: One 14mm Flammenwerfer 41	One 7.92mm MG34 or MG42
Traverse: 5° left 11° right (hand)	360° (hand)
Elevation: −6° +12°	
Sight: SflZF1a	Periskop 3 × 8°
Ammunition: 24 bursts (154 gal)	1,200

Armour (mm/angle):	Front	Side	Rear	Top/Bottom
Superstructure:	60/60°	20/40°	8/70°	8/90°
Hull:	60/40°	20/15°	20/15°	10/90°

Plates 153-154. Flammpanzer 38(t) Hetzer: right, with the cover removed from the flame-projector.

History: During the planning of the Ardennes offensive, it was decided that some flame-thrower tanks would be required. Twenty Jagdpanzer 38(t) were converted for this task by the fitting of a projector in place of the normal 7.5cm PaK39. 700 litres (154 gal) of flame fuel were carried. Consumption allowed for 87.5 seconds fire, but the number of bursts was governed by the number of starter cartridges. Range was 50 to 60 metres.

Specific features: Identical with Jagdpanzer Hetzer, except for the small funnel-shaped cover for the flame-projector.

Combat service: Used by special units in the Ardennes, a number were captured and photographed, giving this vehicle more prominence than its small production deserves.

Bergepanzer 38(t) Hetzer

Other designations: Gerät 573, Bergepanzer 638/16
Type: Armoured recovery vehicle

Manufacturer: BMM
106 produced
64 converted from Hetzer

Crew: 4	Engine: Praga AC/2
Weight (tons): 14.5	Gearbox: 5 forward, 1 reverse
Length (metres): 4.87	Speed (km/hr): 42
Width (metres): 2.63	Range (km): 177
Height (metres): 1.71	Radio: FuG5

Armament: One 7.92mm MG34
Traverse: loose
Elevation: loose
Sight: direct

Armour (mm/angle):	Front	Side	Rear	Top/Bottom
Superstructure:	60/60°	20/40°	8/70°	open
Hull:	60/40°	20/15°	20/15°	10/90°

History: The Bergepanzer 38(t) was developed to accompany and recover Hetzer for the units operating these new Jagdpanzer. A note of August 1944 indicates that for every 14 Jagdpanzer, a Bergepanzer was to be manufactured, but by September, only 7 were available. In October, the deficit was made up by the completion of 64 Bergepanzer 38(t) which had been converted from Hetzer set aside in June and July. From December, regular production commenced.

The open-topped Bergepanzer was an ideal vehicle for conversion, and although the number of AFV types was supposed to have been drastically reduced, special demands continued to come from front-line troops. Official production commenced of the 15cm sIG33 Sf based on the Bergepanzer, while photographic evidence shows a 2cm FlaK38 mount. This was to be designated Gerät 563 Pz Aufklwg 638/11. In 1945, a 'Vollkettenaufklärer 38' designated Gerät 564 Pz Aufklwg 638/12 (Full-Tracked Scout (38) armed with the 7.5cm K51 L/24 mounted on a modified Bergepanzer chassis was under test.

Specific features: The Bergepanzer 38(t) was based on the Hetzer, but the superstructure was lower and was open topped. The front plate was unbroken. The fighting compartment contained a winch, and a tubular derrick was carried.

Combat service: From October 1944, served with those tank-hunter detachments operating Hetzer.

Plate 155. Bergepanzer 38(t) Hetzer.

15cm Schweres Infanteriegeschütz 33/2 (Sf) auf Jagdpanzer 38(t) Hetzer

Other designations: Gerät 588, GW 638/27
Type: Self-propelled heavy infantry gun on tank destroyer chassis

Plate 156. 15cm sIG33/2(Sf) auf Jgd Pz 38(t) Hetzer.

Manufacturer: BMM
5 converted and 24 produced from December 1944

Crew: 4	Engine: Praga AC/2
Weight (tons): 16.5	Gearbox: 5 forward, 1 reverse
Length (metres): 4.87	Speed (km/hr): 32
Width (metres): 2.63	Range (km): 130
Height (metres): 2.2	Radio: FuG16

Armament: One 15cm sIG33/2 (Sf)   One 7.92mm MG34 or 42
Traverse: 5° left 5° right (hand)   loose
Elevation: −0° +73°   loose
Sight: Rblf36   direct
Ammunition: 15

Armour (mm/angle):	Front	Side	Rear	Top/Bottom
Superstructure:	60/60° +40°	20/40°	8/70°	open
Hull:	60/40°	20/15°	20/15°	10/90°
Gun shield:	10/9°			

History: The last few 38(t) Ausf M chassis were completed as 15cm sIG33/2 Sf in August 1944, but the demand for a self-propelled 15cm sIG33 continued, and was the subject of discussions between Hitler and Speer in October 1944. By November, it had been decided to introduce a new design of Selbstfahrlafette (self-propelled mounting), based on the components of the Jagdpanzer 38(t) Hetzer, which would carry the 15cm sIG33.

Specific features: Based on the superstructure of the Bergepanzer 38(t), with an additional raised superstructure surrounding the sIG33 which used the same mounting and shield as an earlier self propelled version.

Combat service: Issued (as replacements) to the schwere Infanteriegeschütz company (SP) of armoured infantry regiments.

Jagdpanzer 38(t) Starr

Type: Tank destroyer with rigid mounted gun

Manufacturer: BMM
10 pre-production series; production was to have begun in May 1945

Crew: 4	Engine: Praga AC/2
Weight (tons): 14	Gearbox: 5 forward, 1 reverse
Length (metres): 6.38	Speed (km/hr): 42
Width (metres): 2.63	Range (km): 177
Height (metres): 2.17	Radio: FuG5 + FuG Spr f

Armament: One 7.5cm PaK39/1   One 7.92mm MG42
Starr L/48 or one 10.5cm StuH42 Starr
Traverse: 8° left 8° right (hand)   360° (hand)
Elevation: −8° +15°
Sight: WZF2/2   Periskop 3 × 8°
Ammunition: 1,200

Armour (mm/angle):	Front	Side	Rear	Top/Bottom
Superstructure:	60/60°	20/40°	8/70°	8/90°
Hull:	60/40°	20/15°	20/15°	10/90°
Gun mantlet:	60/Saukopfblende			

History: The initial decision to proceed with the production of the Jagdpanzer 38(t) Hetzer in December 1943 was on the basis that it would be built with a rigid, mounted gun. Early in 1943, Rheinmetall had proved the feasibility of the idea, by mounting a 12cm GrW (r) (Mortar (Russian)) on an old Pz Kpfw II chassis. Alkett took over the development with a rigid mount 7.5cm PaK39 in the Jagdpanzer IV, and a mounting for the 38(t). Ten 38(t) units were ordered and the first was delivered by mid-1944. Problems with seating of the sights and unmanageable handwheels, lead to postponement of production of the rigid mount Jagdpanzer 38(t), but interim production of this vehicle, with a recoiling 7.5cm PaK39, was continued. By November 1944, little progress had been achieved with the various solutions proposed, and the normal Hetzer was confirmed in production. Rheinmetall again took over development, with orders to achieve production as soon as possible. The final design of weapon mount and sight was sent to Prague at the beginning of April 1945, and a decision for full production was to have been taken on 20 April 1945. Success achieved by Rheinmetall lead to the commencement of a prototype 38(t) to mount the 10.5cm StuH42 which was to have been fitted in 10 per cent of all rigid mount production on the 38(t) chassis.

Specific features: Same features as for Hetzer, but the rigid mounted guns had to be moved nearer the centre-line of the vehicle. The smaller ball mount allowed this move, and made for a stronger front plate because of the small opening required. The new mount reduced nose heaviness and overall weight. Production vehicles were to be fitted with an elevation stabilizer, and the coaxial MG mount, being designed for the Jagdpanzer 38(d), was to be incorporated when available.

Leichte Einheitswaffenträger

Other designations: 10.5cm leFH18/40/5—GW 638/26, Gerät 587
Type: Light standardized weapons carriage

Prototypes only. Production was to have begun in Spring 1945 with output of 350 units per month by September 1945, based upon the 38(d) components
With 10.5cm leFH mounted:

Crew: 4	Engine: Praga AC/2
Weight (tons): 13.5	Gearbox: 5 forward, 1 reverse
Length (metres): 6.53	Speed (km/hr): 35
Width (metres): 3.16	Range (km):
Height (metres): 2.25	Radio: FuG16

Armament alternatives:
One 10.5cm leFH18/40/5 L/28 or   One 8.8cm PaK43 L/71
Traverse: 360° (hand)   =
Elevation: −5° +42°   −8° +20°
Sight: Rblf36   Rblf36
Ammunition: 96   34

Armour (mm):*	Front	Side	Rear	Top
Superstructure:	20	10	10	8
Hull:	15	10	10	8
Gun shield:	15	10	open	open

* Unarmed Munitionspanzer

History: The initial designs for Waffenträger based on the large and complicated Pz III/IV chassis, were built during 1943. The Wa Prüf 4 (Ordnance Proving Branch 4) decided that these were too heavy and too costly for the purposes of the Artillery. In February 1944, a new specification was issued for a Waffenträger to replace towed artillery weapons. Again, the weapon was to be dismountable, but from a low rear platform without special equipment. The traverse was to be 360°, fire height 1.8m and elevation −8° +45°. Krupp were given overall responsibility for the project, with Rheinmetall, Krupp and Ardelt and Steyr developing the different chassis. The Krupp light-vehicle project was managed by a Herr Woelfert. Initially, it was proposed to have a rear drive in keeping with current thinking, but the more conventional front drive was adopted as it allowed a lower gun platform. Steyr produced a prototype vehicle with running gear based on the RSO (Raupenschlepper Ost=Tracked Tractor, East), Rheinmetall's prototype was built with normal Pz Kpfw 38(t) wheels but the Ardelt design with Hetzer wheels was accepted for production. The engine and transmission were placed to the right of the driver, and the driver's compartment could be folded to give increased depression to the gun. Prototypes based on the 38(t) were built late in 1944. Production was to be on the basis of the 38(d) which featured a new transmission, the Tatra-103 220PS motor, and new idler/drive sprockets. A 38(d) mounting the 8.8cm PaK43 was tested successfully at Hillersleben on 27 April 1945, this probably was the later Ardelt prototype.

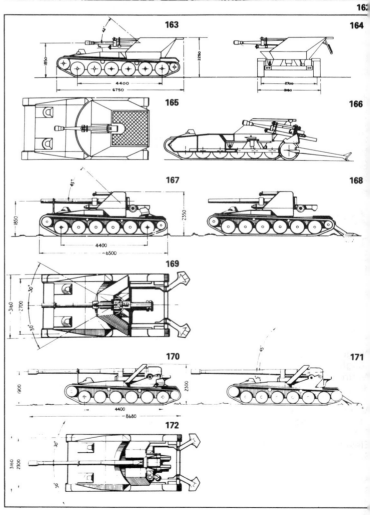

Plate 157. Rheinmetall-Borsig prototype for 8.8cm PaK43 on le Einheitswaffenträger.
Plates 158-159. Krupp-Steyr prototype for 8.8cm PaK43/3 L/71 Waffenträger.
Plates 160-162. Ardelt 8.8cm PaK43/3 Waffenträger vehicles. Plate 160 shows the prototype, using Krupp-Steyr trackwork; Plate 161 shows the second prototype, with new drive sprocket and rear idler wheel; Plate 162 shows the production machine. (Note that the gun stay has now been moved further back on the hull.)

Plates 163-166. Design for Mittlere Einheitswaffenträger mounting 10.5cm leFH18/40 L/28.
Plates 167-169. Design for Mittlere Einheitswaffenträger mounting 15cm sFH18/6 L/30.
Plates 170-172. Design for Mittlere Einheitswaffenträger mounting 12.8cm K18/3(Sf) L/55.

Mittlere Einheitswaffenträger

Other designations: 10.5cm leFH18/40/5 — Gerät 578 GW 638/21, 15cm sIg33/2 — Gerät 577 GW 638/20, 12.8cm K81/3 (Sf) — Gerät 579 GW 638/22, 15cm sFH18/6 — Gerät 580 GW 638/23

Type: Medium standardized weapons carriage

Prototypes only
With 10.5cm leFH mounted:

Crew: 4
Weight (tons): 13*
Length (metres): 6.75
Width (metres): 3.16
Height (metres): 2.25

Engine: Praga AC/2
Gearbox: 5 forward, 1 reverse
Speed (km/hr): 35
Radio: FuG16

Armament alternatives:

	Traverse:	Elevation:	Sight:	Ammu-nition:
10.5cm leFH18/40/5 L/28	360° (hand)	−5° +42°	Rblf36	40
15cm sIG33/2 L/11				
10.5cm sK18/1				
12.8cm K81/3 (Sf) L/55	30° left 30° right (hand)	−5° +45°		30
15cm sFH18/6 L/30	30° left 30° right (hand)	−0° +45°		20
8.8cm PaK43 L/71	360° (hand)	−8° +40°	Rblf32/ 36	34

Armour (mm):	Front	Side	Rear	Top
Superstructure:	20	10	10	8
Hull:	15	10	10	8
Gun shield:	15	10	open	open

* Weight with 12.8cm K81/3(Sf) mounted: 15.8 tons

History: At the same time as the leichter Einheitswaffenträger (Light Standard Weapons Carrier) was being built, a parallel project was being managed by a Mr Egen, also of Krupp. This was a larger vehicle, with 6 38(t) wheels per side, and was known as the Krupp I, while the four-wheel version became known as the Krupp II. It had been intended to develop this vehicle so as to have more possibilities in the types of gun mounted, but certain problems arose with the length/width ratio and the design had not been adopted when hostilities ceased. Like the 4-wheel design, production vehicles were to have been based on the 38(d), with its new drive train and Tatra 103 220PS air-cooled motor.

Plates 173-174. Mittlere Einheitswaffenträger mounting 10.5cm leFH18/40/5

Jagdpanzer 38(d)

Other designations: Gerät 548 — Jagdpanzer 638/29 für 7.5cm PaK42/1, Gerät 547 — Jagdpanzer 638/28 für 10.5cm StuH42/2, Gerät 543 — Jagdpanzer 38(d) für PWK 1000

Type: Tank destroyer

Prototypes only: production decision was to have been taken on 20 April 1945. From mid 1945, production plan called for 1,250 units per month from Alkett, Vomag, Krupp-Gruson, MIAG and Ni-werke. Alkett were to include 125 StuH42 in their batch.

Crew: 4
Weight (tons): 16
Length (metres): 5.27
Width (metres): 2.81
Height (metres): 1.75

Engine: Tatra 103
Gearbox: 5 forward, 1 reverse
Speed (km/hr): 42
Range (km): 220
Radio: FuG5 + FuG Spr f

Armament: One 7.5cm PaK42/1 L/70 or 10.5cm StuH42/2 L/28
Traverse: 8° left 8° right (hand)
Elevation: −8° +15°
Sight: WZF2/2

One 7.92mm MG42
=
=
=

Armour (mm/angle):	Front	Side	Rear	Top/Bottom
Superstructure:	80/60°	20/55°	8/78°	8/90°
Hull:	60/40°	20/0°	20/12°	8/90°
Gun mantlet:	60/Saukopfblende			

History: Long-term plans for AFV production indicated that the Pz Kpfw V chassis was to be replaced by the Pz III/IV chassis by mid 1945, and many changes had already been incorporated in the production of vehicles. However, in the autumn of 1944, production of the Pz III/IV was cancelled, and Hitler ordered that all production facilities thus freed were to be used for 38(t) and 38(d). The 38(t), the original Czech model, was to continue in production as the Hetzer, some with rigid mounted guns, and some in the existing variants. The 38(t) was also to be the basis for a reconnaissance vehicle. The 38(d) was a slightly larger, redesigned version, differing mainly in that it used the Tatra 220PS diesel air-cooled engine and a new drive train. This redesigned vehicle was capable of mounting the 7.5cm PaK42/1(L/70), either in a recoiling mount, or rigidly, and could thus replace the Pz IV/70. The 7.5cm PaK39(L/48) and 10.5cm StuH42/2 were alternative weapons, as the 38(d) was also to be a replacement for the StuG III. The 38(d) production was to be taken up by all the German manufacturers engaged in the Pz Kpfw IV and StuGIII programme, while BMM and Skoda continued for the time being with the 38(t). In addition to the Jagdpanzer vehicles, the 38(d) was intended to be the basis of a replacement Kugelblitz (ball-lightning: AA Tank) when the Pz Kpfw IV chassis was terminated. A wooden mock-up indicated that it was to use a smaller turret race than that on the Pz IV version. Development of the turret allowed two 2cm MG in addition to the two 3cm MK 103 to be controlled by one crew man. The hydraulic traverse and elevation control permitted movement of 45° per second. Traverse was 360° and elevation was −5° +70°. 1,200 3cm and 1,000 2cm rounds were to be carried. There were two versions, Ausf Protektorat and Ausf Reich. The difference between them was in the hull configuration.

Panzerkampfwagen III
and variants

Panzerkampfwagen III Ausf A (Sd Kfz 141)

Other designation: 1 Serie ZW, ZW38
Type: Medium tank

Manufacturer: Daimler-Benz
Chassis Nos.: 60101–60110
10 produced in 1937
Crew: 5
Weight (tons): 15.4
Length (metres): 5.69
Width (metres): 2.81
Height (metres): 2.34

Engine: Maybach HL108TR
Gearbox: 6 forward, 1 reverse
Speed (km/hr): 35
Range (km): 165
Radio: FuG5

Armament:	One 3.7cm KwK L/46.5	Two 7.92mm MG34	One 7.92mm MG34
Traverse:	360° (hand)	=	
Elevation:	−10° +20°	=	
Sight:	TZF5a	=	KgZF2
Ammunition:	150 Pzgr & Sprgr	4,500 Patr SmK	

Armour (mm/angle):	Front	Side	Rear	Top/Bottom
Turret:	15/15°	15/25°	15/0°–21°	10/82°–90°
Superstructure:	15/10°	15/0°	15/0°	10/70°–90°
Hull:	15/20°	15/0°	15/0°	5/90°
Gun mantlet:	15/round			

History: In 1935, development orders were issued for a full-tracked vehicle in the 15-ton class. Originally known as the 3.7cm Geschütz-Panzerwagen (Vs Kfz 619) (Armoured Gun-tank) (Trial Vehicle) No 619)), the Pz Kpfw III went into production on a development series in 1937. By early May 1937, five of this 1 Serie Zugführerwagen (1st Series Platoon Commander's Vehicle), the Ausf A had been produced.

Special features: The Ausf A had a 3.7cm gun mounted in the turret with two coaxial machine-guns. A third machine-gun, manned by the radio operator was mounted in the front of the superstructure. The Pz Kpfw III had a crew of five; commander, gunner, loader, driver and radio operator. Power was provided by a V–12 gasoline engine, transferred through a five-speed gearbox and controlled by an epicyclic clutch and brake steering system. The suspension consisted of five road wheels dampened by coil springs, and two return rollers. The

15mm armour was designed to withstand armour-piercing rounds from rifles or small calibre machine-guns only.

Combat service: The first Ausf A were issued to Panzer regiments in the spring of 1937. Having only 15mm armour and an unsatisfactory suspension, they were all withdrawn from combat units in February 1940.

Plates 175-176. Krupp's export tank similar to the ZW ('Zugführerwagen') specification, which they codenamed 'MKA'.
Plate 177. The turret of Pz Kpfw III Ausf A, showing the 3.7cm KwK L/46.5 in its internal gun mantlet, and the original cupola.
Plate 178. Pz Kpfw III Ausf A.
Plate 179 (opposite page, top). Pz Kpfw III Ausf A in Poland in 1939.

Panzerkampfwagen III Ausf B (Sd Kfz 141)

Other designation: 2 Serie ZW
Type: Medium tank

Manufacturer: Daimler-Benz
Chassis Nos.: 60201–60215
5 produced in 1937

Crew: 5	Engine: Maybach HL108TR
Weight (tons): 15.9	Gearbox: 5 forward, 1 reverse
Length (metres): 5.67	Speed (km/hr): 40
Width (metres): 2.81	Range (km): 165
Height (metres): 2.39	Radio: FuG5

Armament:	One 3.7cm KwK L/46.5	Two 7.92mm MG34	One 7.92mm MG34
Traverse:	360° (hand)	=	
Elevation:	−10° +20°	=	
Sight:	TZF5a	=	KgZF2
Ammunition:	121 Pzgr + Sprgr	4,500 Patr SmK	

Armour (mm/angle):	Front	Side	Rear	Top/Bottom
Turret:	15/15°	15/25°		10/83°–90°
Superstructure:	15/10°	15/0°	15/0°–21°	10/90°
Hull:	15/25°	15/0°	15/0°	5/90°
Gun mantlet:	15/round			

History: The Ausf B was the second attempt at a design solution for a tank in the 15-ton class. Only a small number of these design series vehicles were produced to provide a gun-armed Pz Kpfw for training.
Specific features: The design of the suspension of the Ausf B was completely different from that of the Ausf A. In place of the five road wheels with coil springs, the Ausf B had eight road wheels per side, divided into pairs, with long leaf springs supporting a pair of road wheels at each end. Further improvements were made by increasing the number of return rollers to three, redesigning the cupola, and altering the rear deck and engine air louvres.
Combat service: The Ausf B were issued to Panzer units in 1937. After action in Poland, they were all removed from combatant units in February 1940 because of their unsatisfactory suspension and

15mm armour. In October 1940, the five Ausf B Fgst, which had been used for the experimental (0–Serie) series of the Sturmgeschütz, were returned to the Armoured troops and used as training vehicles.

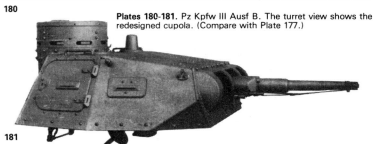

Plates 180-181. Pz Kpfw III Ausf B. The turret view shows the redesigned cupola. (Compare with Plate 177.)

Panzerkampfwagen III Ausf C (Sd Kfz 141)

Other designation: 3a Serie ZW
Type: Medium tank

Manufacturer: Daimler-Benz
Chassis Nos.: 60301–60315
15 produced from 1937 to January 1938

Crew: 5	Engine: Maybach HL108TR
Weight (tons): 16	Gearbox: 5 forward, 1 reverse
Length (metres): 5.85	Speed (km/hr): 40
Width (metres): 2.82	Range (km): 165
Height (metres): 2.42	Radio: FuG5

Armament: One 3.7cm   Two 7.92mm MG34   One 7.92mm MG34
KwK L/46.5

Traverse: 360° (hand)	=	hand
Elevation: −10° +20°	=	
Sight: TZF5a	=	KgZF2
Ammunition: 121 Pzgr	4,500 Patr SmK	
+ Sprgr		

Armour (mm/angle):	Front	Side	Rear	Top/Bottom
Turret:	15/15°	15/25°	15/0°–21°	10/83°–90°
Superstructure:	15/11°	15/0°	15/9°	10/73°–90°
Hull:	15/25°	15/0°	15/23°	5/90°
Gun mantlet:	15/round			

History: The third vehicle in the development series, the Ausf C, was yet another attempt to improve the design of the suspension.
Specific features: The Ausf C still had eight road wheels on each side with the first and last pairs on a short leaf spring, mounted parallel to the ground. The second and third pairs were supported by a longer leaf-spring assembly. Also featured were a servo-operated epicyclic clutch, brake steering and a new design for the drive sprocket and idler.
Combat service: By 20 January 1938, there were only twenty-three Pz Kpfw III in the total Army Inventory, but this number had increased to forty-two by the end of March 1938. The Ausf C saw action only in Poland. It was withdrawn from Panzer regiments in February 1940 before the start of the campaign in the West.

Panzerkampfwagen III Ausf D (Sd Kfz 141)

Other designation: 3b Serie ZW
Type: Medium tank

Manufacturer: Daimler-Benz
Chassis Nos.: 60221–60225, 60316–60340
30 produced from January to June 1938

Crew: 5	Engine: Maybach HL108TR
Weight (tons): 16	Gearbox: 6 forward, 1 reverse
Length (metres): 5.92	Speed (km/hr): 40
Width (metres): 2.82	Range (km): 165
Height (metres): 2.42	Radio: FuG5

Armament: One 3.7cm   Two 7.92mm MG34   One 7.92mm MG34
KwK L/46.5

Traverse: 360° (hand)	=	hand
Elevation: −10° +20°	=	
Sight: TZF5a	=	KgZF2
Ammunition: 121 Pzgr	4,500 Patr SmK	
& Sprgr		

Armour (mm/angle):	Front	Side	Rear	Top/Bottom
Turret:	15/15°	15/25°	15/0°–21°	10/83°–90°
Superstructure:	15/10°	15/0°	15/10°	10/75°–90°
Hull:	15/20°	15/0°	15/33°	5/90°
Gun mantlet:	15/round			

History: The Ausf D was the fourth of the development series for an armoured vehicle in the 15 ton class. Again, emphasis was placed on improving the suspension.
Specific features: The suspension was again improved over previous vehicles by inclining the leaf-spring assemblies supporting the first and last pairs of road wheels, in order to increase support. The Ausf D had a newly-designed sprocket, idler and transmission. This was the last model in the series with 15mm basic armour, although a new style cupola had been introduced, with 30mm armour and five vision slits.
The design of the rear deck and hull rear was changed to improve armour protection. The louvres on top were replaced by hatches which could be braced open.
Combat service. During 1938, the official organization called for three Pz Kpfw III in a Zug (platoon) in the light tank company (a) of each armoured detachment. Thus, each Panzer regiment was to have only six Pz Kpfw III, and each Panzer division, twelve. After action in Poland, the Ausf D was also withdrawn from the Panzer regiments in February 1940. Its front-line service was lengthened by several months, however, when Ausf D were issued to Pz Abt z b V40 (Tank Detachment for Special Employment 40), which fought in Norway in April 1940.

Plate 182. Pz Kpfw III Ausf D chassis.
Plate 183. Close-up of the new cupola design used on Pz Kpfw III Ausf D, E, F, G and on Pz Kpfw IV Ausf B, C and D.
Plate 184. Pz Kpfw III Ausf D.

182

183

Panzerkampfwagen III Ausf E (Sd Kfz 141)

Other designation: 4 Serie ZW
Type: Medium tank

Manufacturer: Daimler-Benz, Henschel, MAN
Chassis Nos.: 60401–60496
96 produced from December 1938 to October 1939

Crew: 5	Engine: Maybach HL120TR
Weight (tons): 19.5	Gearbox: 10 forward, 4 reverse
Length (metres): 5.38	Speed (km/hr): 40
Width (metres): 2.91	Range (km): 165
Height (metres): 2.44	Radio: FuG5

Armament: One 3.7cm Two 7.92mm MG34   One 7.92mm MG34
KwK L/46.5

Traverse: 360° (hand) =   15° left 20° right
(hand)

Elevation: −10° +20° =   −10° +10°

Sight: TZF5a =   KgZF2

Ammunition: 131 Pzgr 4,500 Patr SmK
& Spgr

Armour (mm/angle):	Front	Side	Rear	Top/Bottom
Turret:	30/15°	30/25°	30/0°–21°	12/83°–90°
Superstructure:	30/9°	30/0°	21/29°	17/77°–90°
Hull:	30/21°	30/0°	21/10°	16/90°
Gun mantlet:	30/round			

185

History: The Ausf E was the first in the series to go into extended production. Its basic design remained unchanged throughout the rest of the series, as a result of the adaptation of a successful suspension system supported by torsion bars.

Specific features: The increase in armour protection, with a resultant increase in weight, was allowed by the new suspension design, consisting of six road wheels, individually supported by torsion bars. The hull side was made of single plate instead of the previous segmented plates. Escape hatches were introduced on both sides of the hull, and during the production run, a vision port for the radio operator was added to the superstructure side. A larger engine and a new gearbox were introduced, and trouble with the latter caused problems for mass-production. All Ausf E came off the production-line mounting the 3.7cm KwK. From August 1940 until 1942, many were converted to carry the 5cm KwK L/42 with an external mantlet. Orders were also issued to increase the armour protection by adding 30mm plates to the hull front and rear and superstructure front, at the same time as the upgunning took place.

Combat service: On 1 September 1939 there were only 98 Pz Kpfw III in the entire Army inventory, at the start of the campaign in Poland. The production of the Ausf E had allowed a slight increase in the official organization of from three to five Pz Kpfw III in the 1 Zug (1st Platoon) of the light tank companies. However, production delays and the formation of special organizations such as the Panzer Lehr Armoured Training Detachment, meant that some Panzer divisions in Poland were without a single Pz Kpfw III. The service life of the Ausf E was extended by rearming them with the 5cm KwK L/42 and, from 1943, converting several of them to Pz Beob Wg (Armoured Observation Vehicles).

186

187

188

189

Plates 185-186. Pz Kpfw III Ausf E.
Plates 187-188. Pz Kpfw III Ausf E or F upgunned with the 5cm KwK L/42 in an external mantlet (in contrast to the internal mantlet used for the original 3.7cm KwK L/46.5 shown in Plate 186). Plate 188 also shows the additional armour that was added to the hull front.
Plate 189. Kugelblende 30, the hull machine-gun housing used on Pz Kpfw III Ausf E, F, G and H, and on Pz Kpfw IV Ausf A, D and E.

Panzerkampfwagen III Ausf F (Sd Kfz 141)

Other designation: 5 Serie ZW
Type: Medium tank

Manufacturer: Daimler-Benz, Henschel, MAN, Alkett, FAMO
Chassis Nos.: 61001–61650
435 produced from September 1939 to July 1940

Crew: 5	Engine: Maybach HL120TRM
Weight (tons): 19.8	Gearbox: 10 forward, 4 reverse
Length (metres): 5.38	Speed (km/hr): 40
Width (metres): 2.91	Range (km): 165
Height (metres): 2.44	Radio: FuG5

Armament: One 3.7cm KwK L/46.5	Two 7.92mm MG34	One 7.92mm MG34
Traverse: 360° (hand)	=	15° left 20° right (hand)
Elevation: −10° +20°	=	−10° +10°
Sight: TZF5a	=	KgZF2
Ammunition: 131 Pzgr & Sprgr	4,500 Patr SmK	

Armour (mm/angle):	Front	Side	Rear	Top/Bottom
Turret:	30/15°	30/25°	30/0°–21°	12/83°–90°
Superstructure:	30/9°	30/0°	21/29°	17/77°–90°
Hull:	30/21°	30/0°	21/10°	16/90°
Gun mantlet:	30/round			

History: Basically, the Ausf F was the same vehicle as the Ausf E. In fact, it was the result of an order to mass-produce an effective battle tank. In January 1939, the order was reduced by 250, after production orders had been placed for the improved models, Ausf G and H.
Specific features: The basic change was to the ignition system. Early in the production run, cast air-intakes were added to the upper hull plate to allow air circulation for brakes and final-drive cooling. The majority were produced mounting the 3.7cm KwK, but approximately 100 were equipped with the 5cm KwK L/42 and external mantlet as original equipment. From August 1940 until 1942, many of the remainder were converted from the 3.7cm KwK to the 5cm KwK L/42 and external gun mantlet. Orders were also issued to up-armour the hull and superstructure, by adding 30mm plates, at the same time as the upgunning took place.

Combat service: In late 1939 and early 1940, the Ausf F were issued to the Panzer regiments as quickly as they could be produced. On 10 May 1940, 348 Pz Kpfw III, mostly Ausf E and F, but with a few Ausf G, were with seven Panzer divisions on the Western Front. At this time, there were two light tank companies with each tank detachment, but the actual strength varied greatly between the seven Panzer divisions, ranging from five to seventeen Pz Kpfw III in each light tank company. The last Ausf F known to have been in action were with the 116th Panzer Division in June 1944. They are now on display at the Patton Museum at Fort Knox, Kentucky.

Plates 190-191. Pz Kpfw III Ausf F. The vehicle shown above carries the 5cm KwK L/42 gun in an external mantlet.

Panzerkampfwagen III Ausf G (Sd Kfz 141)

Other designation: 6 Serie ZW
Type: Medium tank

Manufacturer: Daimler-Benz, MAN, Alkett, Henschel, Wegmann, FAMO, MNH
Chassis Nos.: 65001–65950
600 produced from April 1940 to February 1941
Crew: 5

Weight (tons): 20.3	Engine: Maybach HL120TRM
Length (metres): 5.41	Gearbox: 10 forward, 4 reverse
Width (metres): 2.95	Speed (km/hr): 40
Height (metres): 2.44	Range (km): 165
	Radio: FuG5

Armament: One 5cm KwK L/42   One 7.92mm MG34   One 7.92mm MG34

Traverse: 360° (hand)	=	15° left 20° right (hand)	
Elevation: −10° +20°	=	−10° +10°	
Sight: TZF5d	=	KgZF2	
Ammunition: 99 Pzgr & Sprgr	2,700 Patr SmK		

Armour (mm/angle):

	Front	Side	Rear	Top/Bottom
Turret:	30/15°	30/25°	30/0°–21°	12/83°–90°
Superstructure:	30/9°	30/0°	30/30°	17/77°–90°
Hull:	30/21°	30/0°	30/10°	16/90°
Gun mantlet:	37/0°–45°			

History: An initial order for 1,250, placed in January 1939, had been reduced to 800 by May 1939, when the Pz Kpfw 38(t) production became available from Czechoslovakia. The entire series was to have had the 3.7cm KwK, but the lessons learned in Poland and France accelerated the introduction of the 5cm KwK L/42, so that the great majority of the Ausf G received this armament.

Specific features: The main differences from previous models were the increase from 21mm to 30mm in the armour thickness of the hull rear, and the introduction of a new pivoting visor for the driver. The turret was modified to include an exhaust fan mounted on the roof, and one signal port was eliminated. In mid-production, a newly-designed cupola was introduced, and, late in the series, wider (40cm) tracks. Approximately fifty Ausf G were equipped with the 3.7cm KwK L/46.5 with internal mantlet. The remainder had the 5cm KwK L/42 with external mantlet. From August 1940 until 1942, many of those mounting the 3.7cm KwK were up-armoured and up-gunned to the 5cm KwK L/42. The sight for the 3.7cm KwK was the TZF5a.

Combat service: Early Ausf G produced from April to June 1940, were issued as replacements to the Panzer regiments at the front in France. Contrary to popular belief, all Pz Kpfw III in service in France had the 3.7cm KwK. Pz Kpfw III with the 5cm KwK L/42 were first produced in July 1940. Pz Kpfw III with the 3.7cm KwK had been phased out of service in Russia by the end of 1941. Most survivors mounting the 3.7cm KwK were converted to mount the 5cm KwK L/42, but fifty-four remained on the Army inventory as late as September 1944.

92

Plates 192-193. Pz Kpfw III Ausf G. The vehicles in the top photograph have the redesigned cupola and driver's visor (and the third vehicle along mounts the 5cm KwK L/42). The vehicle shown in North Africa (left) has the 5cm KwK L/42, but retains the old type of cupola.
Plate 194. The cupola used on Pz Kpfw III Ausf G, H, J, L, M and N, and on Pz Kpfw IV Ausf E, F and G.

93

Panzerkampfwagen III Ausf H (Sd Kfz 141)

Other designation: 7 Serie ZW
Type: Medium tank

Manufacturer: MAN, Alkett, Henschel, Wegmann, MNH, MIAG
Chassis Nos.: 66001–66650
308 produced from October 1940 to April 1941

Crew: 5	Engine: Maybach HL120TRM
Weight (tons): 21.8	Gearbox: 6 forward, 1 reverse
Length (metres): 5.41	Speed (km/hr): 40
Width (metres): 2.95	Range (km): 165
Height (metres): 2.44	Radio: FuG5

Armament: One 5cm KwK L/42	One 7.92mm MG34	One 7.92mm MG34
Traverse: 360° (hand)	=	15° left 20° right (hand)
Elevation: −10° +20°	=	−10° +10°
Sight: TZF5d	=	KgZF2
Ammunition: 99 Pzgr & Sprgr	2,700 Patr SmK	

Armour (mm/angle):	Front	Side	Rear	Top/Bottom
Turret:	30/13°	30/25°	30/13°	10/85°–90°
Superstructure:	30+30/90°	30/0°	30/30°	17/77°–90°
Hull:	30+30/23°	30/0°	30+30/8°	16/90°
Gun mantlet:	37/0°–45°			

History: An initial order for 759 Ausf H was placed in January 1939. This was to be the first model to mount the 5cm KwK, and the turret was redesigned to accommodate it. The campaigns in France and Poland had shown a need for increased protection and although it was too late to increase the basic armour, additional plates were bolted to it. The order for the Ausf H was reduced by 450 when the new model of the Pz Kpfw III with heavier basic armour (Ausf J) was planned.

Specific features: The Ausf H had a newly designed turret, the rear of which was formed from a single plate. The basic 30mm armour was increased by the addition of 30mm plates to the hull rear, hull front and superstructure front. A new transmission, sprocket and idler design were also introduced with this model. To protect the smoke

Plates 951-952, 954 (Page 247) the interior of the Pz Kpfw III Ausf H.

candles, an armoured cover was fitted. The Ausf H was the firs model to have a turret basket, and this was subsequently retro-fitted to the Ausf E, F and G. The 30mm + 30mm armour on the front of the hull and superstructure of the Ausf H was impenetrable at comba ranges by the main enemy tank and anti-tank guns in use in 1941, the British 2-pounder, the American 37mm M5 and the Russian 45mm Model 1937.

Combat service: On 20 June 1941, there were seventeen Panzer divisions on the border of the territory held by the Russians. Of these six had been issued with Pz Kpfw 38(t) and eleven had Pz Kpfw III Each and every light armoured company had its full complement o seventeen Pz Kpfw III, which gave a total of 960 Pz Kpfw III Ausf E to J, if those at detachment and regimental headquarters were included.

Plates 195-196. Pz Kpfw III Ausf H. A new type of drive sprocket, with six D-shaped hole and open eight-spoked rear idler, was introduced with this model. Note the 30mm armou plates bolted on to the upper and lower nose plates. Above: in Sofia, 1941; below, at speed in North Africa.

Panzerkampfwagen III Ausf J (Sd Kfz 141)

Other designation: 8 Serie ZW
Type: Medium tank

Manufacturer: Daimler-Benz, MAN, Alkett, Henschel, Wegmann, MIAG, MNH
Chassis Nos.: 68001–69000, 72001–74100
1,549 produced from March 1941 to July 1942

Crew: 5	Engine: Maybach HL120TRM
Weight (tons): 21.5	Gearbox: 6 forward, 1 reverse
Length (metres): 5.52	Speed (km/hr): 40
Width (metres): 2.95	Range (km): 155
Height (metres): 2.50	Radio: FuG5

Armament: One 5cm KwK L/42   One 7.92mm MG34   One 7.92mm MG34

Traverse: 360° (hand)	=		hand
Elevation: −10° +20°	=		
Sight: TZF5d	=		KgZF2
Ammunition: 99 Pzgr & Sprgr	2,700 Patr SmK		

Armour (mm/angle):	Front	Side	Rear	Top/Bottom
Turret:	30/15°	30/25°	30/12°	10/83°–90°
Superstructure:	50/9°	30/0°	50/15°	17/75°–90°
Hull:	50/21°	30/0°	50/10°	16/90°
Gun mantlet:	50/0°–45°			

History: The Ausf J was the first model of the series to have the armour protection increased to a basic 50mm. An initial order for 900 was later increased to 2,700 and assigned a second chassis number series.

Specific features: The increase to 50mm of the main front and rear surface armour, necessitated newly-designed fittings. An improved visor for the driver was fitted, together with a new ball-shaped hull machine-gun mount. Single-piece access hatches in the glacis, hinged at the front, were fitted in place of the double-hatch. Newly-designed air-intakes for brake and final-drive cooling were mounted on the upper hull front. The smoke-cradle rack was re-positioned and mounted inside the redesigned upper tail plate, for additional armour protection. From April 1942, 20mm spaced armour was added to the gun mantlet and/or superstructure front.

Combat service: The Ausf J with the 5cm KwK L/42 were used to equip the 2nd and 5th Panzer Divisions, and an independent Panzer regiment, which were sent as reinforcements to Russia in September 1941. The remainder were used to replace the loss of approximately 1,400 Pz Kpfw III during the first year of fighting in Russia and North Africa. At the start of the summer campaign on the Eastern front in June 1942, approximately 500 Pz Kpfw III (5cm KwK L/42) were with the Panzer divisions at the front. A year later, at the start of the offensive at Kursk, there were still 141 with Army Groups Centre and South.

197

198

199

Plate 197. Pz Kpfw III Ausf J.
Plate 198. Kugelblende 50, which was fitted to Pz Kpfw III Ausf J, L, M and N, and to Pz Kpfw IV Ausf F, G, H and J.
Plates 199-200. Pz Kpfw III Ausf J. Plate 199 shows the addition of spaced armour on the gun mantlet and hull front.
Plate 1028 (Page 260) Pz Kpfw III Ausf J.

Panzerkampfwagen III Ausf J (Sd Kfz 141/1)

Other designation: 8 Serie ZW
Type: Medium tank

Manufacturer: Daimler-Benz, Alkett, Henschel, Wegmann, MNH, MIAG, MAN
Chassis Nos.: 72001–74100, 68001–69000
1,067 produced from December 1941 to July 1942

Crew: 5	Engine: Maybach HL120TRM
Weight (tons): 21.5	Gearbox: 6 forward, 1 reverse
Length (metres): 6.28	Speed (km/hr): 40
Width (metres): 2.95	Range (km): 155
Height (metres): 2.5	Radio: FuG5

Armament: One 5cm KwK39 L/60	One 7.92mm MG34	One 7.92mm MG34
Traverse: 360° (hand)	=	hand
Elevation: −10° +20°	=	
Sight: TZF5e	=	KgZF2
Ammunition: 84 Pzgr & Sprgr	2,700 Patr SmK	

Armour (mm/angle):	Front	Side	Rear	Top/Bottom
Turret:	30/15°	30/25°	30/12°	10/83°–90°
Superstructure:	50/9°	30/0°	50/15°	17/75°–90°
Hull:	50/21°	30/0°	50/10°	16/90°
Gun mantlet:	50/0°–45°			

History: Orders were given to get the 5cm KwK39 L/60 gun into a production series as quickly as possible which resulted in the Ausf J series being split between this gun and the 5cm KwK L/42. Originally,

Plates 201-202. Pz Kpfw III Ausf J armed with the 5cm KwK39 L/60 (right, in Russia).

in August 1940, Hitler had ordered the L/60 gun, but the Ordnance Department did not implement the decision as the L/42 had recently been introduced and had proved successful. At his birthday demonstration in April 1941, Hitler saw the Pz Kpfw III Ausf J still without the long gun and insisted on its fitting as soon as possible. Events in Russia two months later proved the need for a more powerful armament.

Specific features: The only differences between the Ausf J with the 5cm KwK L/42 and those with the 5cm KwK39 L/60, were the gun itself and the ammunition stowage which was reduced because of the increase in the shell length.

Combat service: The Ausf J with the long-barrelled 5cm KwK39 L/60 were issued to the five tank detachments formed in early 1942 for the 3rd, 16th, 29th and 60th Motorized Infantry Divisions, and the 5th SS Motorized Infantry Division 'Wiking'. The remainder were used as replacements for the extremely high losses which had been sustained in Russia and North Africa. The long 5cm KwK was very useful in North Africa when engaging the Grant and Valentine tanks, but was of little value in a frontal engagement against a Russian T-34 or KV-

Plate 203. Pz Kpfw III Ausf J or L; note that the gunner's vision port on the side of the turret has been eliminated.

Panzerkampfwagen III Ausf L (Sd Kfz 141/1)

Type: Medium tank

Manufacturer: Henschel, Wegmann, Alkett, MNH, MIAG, MAN, Daimler-Benz
Chassis Nos.: 74101–75500
653 produced from June to December 1942

Crew: 5	Engine: Maybach HL120TRM
Weight (tons): 22.7	Gearbox: 6 forward, 1 reverse
Length (metres): 6.28	Speed (km/hr): 40
Width (metres): 2.95	Range (km): 155
Height (metres): 2.5	Radio: FuG5

Armament: One 5cm KwK39 L/60	One 7.92mm MG34	One 7.92mm MG34
Traverse: 360° (hand)	=	hand
Elevation: −10° +20°	=	
Sight: TZF5e	=	KgZF2
Ammunition: 92 Pzgr & Spgr	4,950 Patr SmK	

Armour (mm/angle):	Front	Side	Rear	Top/Bottom
Turret:	57/15°	30/25°	30/12°	10/83°–90°
Superstructure:	50+20/9°	30/0°	50/17°	18/79°–90°
Hull:	50/21°	30/0°	50/9°	16/90°
Gun mantlet:	50+20/0°–45°			

History: In March 1942, a study was undertaken to determine whether the Pz Kpfw IV turret would fit on the Pz Kpfw III superstructure. Analysis revealed that the resultant weight was excessive, and numerous modifications would be necessary. The idea was dropped, and production of the Pz Kpfw III with the 5cm KwK39 L/60 continued. The original order for 1,100 Ausf L was reduced by an order, early in June 1942, to mount 450 7.5cm KwK L/24 in the Pz

Kpfw III. 447 Ausf L were used to mount the short 7.5cm gun and thus became Ausf N. One Ausf L was completed with an experimental, tapered-bore KwK0725.

Specific features: Improvements to the Ausf L included increasing the armour on the turret front from 30mm to 57mm, installing torsion-bar counter-balance instead of a coil spring for the main gun, and altering the air-instake louvres and hatches on the rear deck. A

Ausf L had 20mm spaced armour on the superstructure front, and most had 20mm spaced armour on the gun mantlet. Early in the production run, the hull escape hatches on the hull side, the loader's vision port on the gun mantlet and the turret side ports were deleted. A system designed to transfer heated engine coolant from one vehicle to another was also introduced with the Ausf L.

Combat service: Late in June 1942, at the start of the summer offensive, there were approximately 600 Pz Kpfw III mounting the 5cm KwK L/60 with units at the front in Russia. Apart from replacing

losses, Ausf L were issued to the newly-formed Panzer regiments of the 1st (Leibstandarte Adolf Hitler), 2nd (Das Reich) and 3rd (Tötenkopf) SS Panzergrenadier Divisions, and the Panzergrenadier Division Grossdeutschland.

Plates 204-205. Pz Kpfw III Ausf L, showing the spaced armour on the gun mantlet and hull front. (Note also the elimination of the loader's vision port on the side of the turret.)

Panzerkampfwagen III Ausf M (Sd Kfz 141/1)

Type: Medium tank

Manufacturer: Wegmann, MAN, MIAG, MNH
Chassis Nos.: 76101–77800
250 produced from October 1942 to February 1943

Crew: 5	Engine: Maybach HL120TRM
Weight (tons): 22.7	Gearbox: 6 forward, 1 reverse
Length (metres): 6.41	Speed (km/hr): 40
Width (metres): 2.95	Range (km): 155
Height (metres): 2.5	Radio: FuG5

Armament: One 5cm KwK39 L/60	One 7.92mm MG34	One 7.92mm MG34
Traverse: 360° (hand)	=	hand
Elevation: −10° +20°	=	
Sight: TZF5e		KgZF2
Ammunition: 92 Pzgr & Sprgr	3,750 Patr SmK	

Armour (mm/angle):	Front	Side	Rear	Top/Bottom
Turret:	57/15°	30/25°	30/12°	10/83°−90°
Superstructure:	50+20/9°	30/0°	50/17°	18/79°−90°
Hull:	50/21°	30/0°	50/9°	16/90°
Gun mantlet:	50+20/0°−45°			

History: As early as March 1942, the OKH was considering replacing as soon as possible the Pz Kpfw III by the Panther. In July 1942, the order for 1,000 of the final Pz Kpfw III series, the Ausf M, was cut back to 775. Shortly afterwards, it was decided to use Pz Kpfw III chassis to build StuG, and 165 Ausf M chassis were set aside for this purpose. Reaction to the Ausf N, with its short 7.5cm KwK L/24, had been very positive and resulted in an order issued early in November 1942 to complete the Ausf M series as Ausf N with the 7.5cm KwK L/24. Also in November 1942, was conceived the idea to mount a flame-

thrower in the turret of the Pz Kpfw III, and 100 Ausf M were earmarked for this purpose. A further 47 Pz Kpfw III were never completed, with the result that, of the initial order for 1,000 Ausf M, only 250 were completed.

Specific features: The basic difference between the Ausf L and the Ausf M was the fording equipment on the Ausf M. This was achieved by sealing devices around all hull air-inlets and discharge-louvres and by a modified muffler with a closure-valve mounted high on the hull rear. In addition, the smoke-laying device was changed from the 5 smoke-candle rear-mounted rack to 3 dischargers mounted forward on each turret side. When fitted with the wide Ostkette, the width increased to 3.27m, and for this reason, vehicles with Schürzen (apron armour) were 3.41m wide.

Combat service: The Ausf M were mainly used to replace front-line losses. Although it had lost its effectiveness in frontal tank-versus-tank actions, there were still 432 Pz Kpfw III (5cm KwK L/60) with the armoured and armoured infantry divisions of Army Groups Centre and South, at the start of the offensive at Kursk in July 1943. At the same time, the Panzer Division Hermann Göring and the 15th Panzergrenadier Division had 49 Pz Kpfw III (5cm KwK L/60) for the defence of Sicily.

Plates 206-207. Pz Kpfw III Ausf M. Note the modified exhaust valve for deep wading and the absence of both the hull escape hatch and the loader's vision port in the turret side. Right: vehicles equipped with Schürzen (armour skirts) on the Russian Front.

Plate 1020 (Page 258) Pz Kpfw Ausf M.

Panzerkampfwagen III Ausf N (Sd Kfz 141/2)

Type: Medium support tank

Manufacturer: Henschel, Wegmann, MNH, MIAG, MAN
Chassis Nos.: 73851–77800
663 produced from June 1942 to August 1943 plus 37 converted from rebuilt Pz Kpfw III

Crew: 5
Weight (tons): 23
Length (metres): 5.52 (Ausf L)
5.65 (Ausf M)
Width (metres): 2.95
Height (metres): 2.5

Engine: Maybach HL120TRM
Gearbox: 6 forward, 1 reverse
Speed (km/hr): 40
Range (km): 155
Radio: FuG5

Armament: One 7.5cm KwK L/24   One 7.92mm MG34   One 7.92mm MG34

Traverse: 360° (hand)	=		hand
Elevation: −8° +20°	=		
Sight: TZF5b	=		KgZF2

Ammunition: Ausf L:
56 Pzgr, Sprgr & Nebel 3,450 Patr SmK
Ausf M;
64 Pzgr, Sprgr & Nebel 3,750 Patr SmK

Armour (mm/angle):	Front	Side	Rear	Top/Bottom
Turret:	57/15°	30/25°	30/12°	10/83°–90°
Superstructure:	50+20/9°	30/0°	50/17°	18/79°–90°
Hull:	50/21°	30/0°	50/9°	16/90°
Gun mantlet:	50/0°–45°			

History: In June 1942, because of the decreased effectiveness of the Pz Kpfw III against enemy armour, it was decided to mount the 7.5cm KwK L/24 in the Pz Kpfw III. This gun not only fired a more effective high-explosive (Spgr) round, but also fired a shaped-charged (Hohlladung) round with better armour penetrating ability than the long-barrelled 5cm KwK39 L/60 which it replaced. The initial order for 450 was produced, using 3 from the Ausf J series and 447 from the Ausf L series. Since the troops liked the Ausf N, an order was issued in November to complete the Ausf M series with the short 7.5cm KwK. 213 Ausf M were so converted, and an additional 37 Pz Kpfw III, returned from the front for major overhaul, were also converted to Ausf N to complete the series of 700.

Specific features: The basic features were the same as the Ausf J, L and M series. The only differences were that the Ausf N had the 7.5cm KwK L/24 instead of the 5cm KwK, and did not have spaced armour on the gun mantlet because the additional weight of the 7.5cm KwK. Many of the late model Ausf N were fitted with a new cupola with thicker armour and a single hatch in place of the earlier design with a split hatch. From March 1943, the Ausf N were fitted with skirting armour during production.

Combat service: From September 1942 to May 1943, the heavy tank companies' organisation called for 10 Pz Kpfw Ausf N to render close-support for the nine Tigers. In addition, the Ausf N were issued to the Panzer regiments of the Panzer divisions and used in the same combat role as the Pz Kpfw IV with the short 7.5cm KwK. At the start of the Kursk offensive in July 1943, there were 155 Ausf N with the Panzer troops in Army Groups Centre and South.

208

Plate 208. Pz Kpfw III Ausf N. This particular vehicle is based on the Ausf L chassis. Note the jerrycan rack on the hull rear and the track link rack on the turret roof.
Plate 209. Pz Kpf III Ausf N tanks being surrendered to Allied forces in Norway. These are late production types, with single hatch covers and Schürzen.
Plate 210 (opposite page). An Ausf N in T

Panzerkampfwagen III (FI) (Sd Kfz 141/3)

Type: Medium flame-thrower tank

Manufacturer: Wegmann
Chassis Nos.: 77609–77708
100 produced from February to April 1943

Crew: 3	Engine: Maybach HL120TRM
Weight (tons): 23	Gearbox: 6 forward, 1 reverse
Length (metres): 6.41	Speed (km/hr): 40
Width (metres): 2.95	Range (km): 155
Height (metres): 2.50	Radio: FuG5 (+FuG2 for Commanders)

Armament: One 14mm   One 7.92mm MG34   One 7.92mm MG34
 Flammenwerfer
Traverse: 360° (hand) =   hand
Elevation: −8° +20° =
Sight: KgZF2
Ammunition: 1,000 litres 3,750 Patr SmK
 Flammöl

Armour (mm/angle):	Front	Side	Rear	Top/Bottom
Turret:	57/15°	30/25°	30/12°	10/83°−90°
Superstructure:	50+20/9°	30/0°	50/17°	18/17°−90°
Hull:	50+30/21°	30/0°	50/9°	16/90°
Gun mantlet:	50+20/0°−45°			

History: In November 1942, the idea arose to mount a flame-thrower in the turret of the Pz Kpfw III for use in close-range combat such as had been experienced at Stalingrad. Production was to have begun in January, but was set back a month because of problems with the 'Flammenwerfer' production. One hundred Pz Kpfw III of the Ausf M series were built by MIAG, and were turned over to Wegmann for completion as the Pz Kpfw III (FI).

Specific features: The Pz Kpfw III (FI) had the same basic features as the Ausf M since this was the model used to furnish the chassis. A flame-thrower was mounted in the turret in place of the 5cm KwK L/60. Additional protection was afforded by welding 30mm plates to the hull front. Range of the flame-projector was 55m to 60m.

Combat service: The Pz Kpfw III(FI) never reached the troops at Stalingrad, but were issued to Panzer regiments at the rate of seven tanks to each Flame-thrower Platoon. In July 1943, forty-one were available in the 6th Panzer Division, 11th Panzer Division and Panzer Division Grossdeutschland, for the attack on Kursk.

Plates 211-212. Pz Kpfw III (FI).

Panzerkampfwagen III als Tauchpanzer

Other designation: Tauchpanzer III
Type: Submersible battle tank

168 converted from July to October 1940.
Data as for Pz Kpfw III Ausf F (3.7cm) and (5cm), Pz Kpfw III Ausf G and Ausf H, and gr Pz Bef Wg.

History: The Tauchpanzer was developed in mid-1940 for the proposed invasion of England (Sea Lion). The Pz Kpfw III were modified and provided with a submersion kit. Air-intakes were fitted with locking covers, and the exhaust was fitted with non-return valves. The cupola, gun mantlet and hull MG were sealed with waterproof fabric covers. An inflatable rubber tube surrounded the turret ring. While submerged, the tank drew air through a pipe from a float carrying a snorkel device and radio antenna which remained on the surface. A gyro-compass was used for underwater navigation. The Tauchpanzer could operate in depths of up to 15 metres. A vessel with a hinged ramp was used to disembark the Tauchpanzer at a suitable distance from the shore. With the cancellation of 'Sea Lion', the Tauchpanzer were no longer required in quite the same form. At Milowitz near Prague, in the spring of 1941, most of the tanks were modified to make them suitable for river crossing, with a fixed snorkel pipe attached through the commander's cupola.

Combat service: From July 1940, four sections of volunteers from existing Panzer regiments were trained on the Island of Sylt, and the Tauchpanzer were to be ready for operations at Putlos by 10 August. In mid October, three of these sections were attached to the 18th Panzer Division, and the remainder went to the 6th Panzer Regiment of the 3rd Panzer Division. On 22 June 1941, the Tauchpanzer of the 18th Panzer Division crossed the River Bug at Patulin.

214

215

Plates 213-218. Pz Kpfw III als Tauchpanzer. In Plate 214, which shows the submersible tank being lowered into the sea, the air pipe has been connected at the rear of the tank, over the engine compartment; in Plate 215 the air pipe has been connected to the turret roof. With the tank submerged, in Plate 216, a towed float keeps the schnorkel device and radio antenna above water. Plate 217 shows trials being conducted from a beach; here, the tanks are using a different form of schnorkel, which was carried on the rear of the vehicles and detached upon entering the water. Plate 218: a river-crossing modification, consisting of a fixed schnorkel attached to the commander's cupola.

218

Panzerbefehlswagen Ausf D¹ (Sd Kfz 267, 268)

Other designation: 3c Serie ZW
Type: Medium tracked command vehicle

Manufacturer: Daimler-Benz
Chassis Nos.: 60341–60370
30 produced from June 1938 to March 1939

Crew: 5	Engine: Maybach HL108TR
Weight (tons): 18.2	Gearbox: 6 forward, 1 reverse
Length (metres): 5.98	Speed (km/hr): 40
Width (metres): 2.87	Range (km): 165
Height (metres): 2.42	Radio: FuG6 + FuG8 (Sd Kfz 267)
	FuG6 + FuG7 (Sd Kfz 268)

Armament: One 7.92mm MG34
Traverse: 60° (hand)
Elevation: −15° +35°
Sight: Kg ZF2
Ammunition: 1,500 Patr SmK

Armour (mm/angle):	Front	Side	Rear	Top/Bottom
Turret:	30/15°	30/21°	30/0°−21	12/83°−90°
Superstructure:	30/11°	30/0°	30/9°	17/78°−90°
Hull:	30/21°	30/0°	30/37°	16/90°
Gun mantlet:	30/round			

History: The need of command vehicles for tactical control of the Panzer regiments was realized from the inception of the armoured troops in 1935. More space was required than was provided by the kleine Panzerbefehlswagen, resulting in the adaptation of the Pz Kpfw III design for the grosse Panzerbefehlswagen (Large Armoured Command Vehicle). The external appearance was maintained as closely as possible to that of the Pz Kpfw III, so that the command vehicle would not unduly attract enemy fire. The initial order for 32 was not completed because of production delays and the introduction of a better suspension design.

Specific features: The Ausf D¹ had the same basic design and suspension as the Pz Kpfw III Ausf D. The differences were: thicker armour, dummy main armament, turret bolted in place, additional vision and pistol ports on the superstructure sides, and a pistol port in place of the machine-gun on the superstructure front. The large frame antenna on the rear deck readily distinguished this vehicle from a Pz Kpfw III.

Combat service: From 1938 to 1939, the Stab (Headquarters) of each Panzer detachment, Panzer regiment and Panzer brigade, were to have one grosse Panzerbefehlswagen. With only 38 Pz Bef Wg Ausf D¹ and E available on 1 September 1939, most units were short of the required number, and several units did not receive any. The Ausf D¹ remained in service during the Western campaign in 1940, but had been retired by early 1941 because of their inadequate suspension.

Plates 219-220. Pz Bef Wg III Ausf D¹, showing the large frame antenna and the dummy 3.7cm gun.

Panzerbefehlswagen Ausf E (Sd Kfz 266-268)

Other designation: 2 Serie gr Pz Bef Wg
Type: Medium tracked command vehicle

Manufacturer: Daimler-Benz
Chassis Nos.: 60501–60545
45 produced from July 1939 to February 1940

Crew: 5	Engine: Maybach HL120TR
Weight (tons): 19.5	Gearbox: 10 forward, 1 reverse
Length (metres): 5.38	Speed (km/hr): 40
Width (metres): 2.91	Range (km): 165
Height (metres): 2.44	Radio: FuG6 + FuG2 (Sd Kfz 266)
	FuG6 + FuG8 (Sd Kfz 267)
	FuG6 + FuG7 (Sd Kfz 268

Armament: One 7.92mm MG34
Traverse: 60° (hand)
Elevation: −15° +35°
Sight: KgZF2
Ammunition: 1.500 Patr SmK

Armour (mm/angle):	Front	Side	Rear	Top/Bottom
Turret:	30/15°	30/25°	30/0°−21°	12/83°−90°
Superstructure:	30/9°	30/0°	21/29°	17/77°−90°
Hull:	30/21°	30/0°	21/10°	16/90°
Gun mantlet:	30/round			

History: The second order for the gr Pz Bef Wg was for 45 based on the same design and suspension as the Pz Kpfw III Ausf E. The series was not completed as quickly as originally planned because of material shortages early in the war.

Specific features: The Ausf E had the same hull and suspension as the Pz Kpfw III Ausf E. The differences were: dummy main armament, turret bolted in place, additional vision and pistol ports on the superstructure sides, and a pistol port in place of the machine-gun on the superstructure front. The large frame antenna on the rear deck readily distinguished this vehicle from a Pz Kpfw III.

Combat service: Sixty-four Pz Bef Wg Ausf D[1] and E were available with Panzer divisions at the start of the Western campaign in 1940, with 8 sent in as replacements during the fighting. The Ausf E remained in service until the end of the war, being gradually phased out by attrition.

221

222

Plates 221-222. Pz Bef Wg III Ausf E.

Panzerbefehlswagen Ausf H (Sd Kfz 266-268)

Other designation: 3 Serie gr Pz Bef Wg
Type: Medium tracked command vehicle

Plates 223 and 224 (opposite page, top). Pz Bef Wg III Ausf H, with additional armour on nose and front vertical plate.

Manufacturer: Daimler-Benz
Chassis Nos.: 70001–70145, 70146–70175
145 produced from November 1940 to September 1941 and 30 from December 1941 to January 1942

Crew: 5	Engine: Maybach HL120TRM
Weight (tons): 21.8	Gearbox: 6 forward, 1 reverse
Length (metres): 5.4	Speed (km/hr): 40
Width (metres): 2.95	Range (km): 165
Height (metres): 2.44	Radio: FuG6 + FuG2 (Sd Kfz 266)
	FuG6 + FuG8 (Sd Kfz 267)
	FuG6 + FuG7 (Sd Kfz 268)

Armament: One 7.92mm MG34
Traverse: 60° (hand)
Elevation: −10° +35°
Sight: KgZF2
Ammunition: 2,550

Armour (mm/angle):	Front	Side	Rear	Top/Bottom
Turret:	30/15°	30/25°	30/13°	10/85°−90°
Superstructure:	30+30/9°	30/0°	30/30°	17/77°−90°
Hull:	30+30/23°	30/0°	30+30/8°	16/90°
Gun mantlet:	30/round			

History: In January 1939, the order was placed for the third series amounting to 145 grosse Panzerbefehlswagen. As a result of lessons learned in Poland and France, the original design, specifying only 30mm armour, was changed to require an additional 30mm armour plate to be bolted to the front of the hull and superstructure and hull rear. Directly after completion of the first Ausf H series, a second series of 30 'alter Typ' (old type) was ordered in October 1941. Most of these indeed had the old style Ausf H hull, but a few of the last produced used the chassis of the Pz Kpfw III Ausf J.

Specific features: The Ausf H had the same hull and suspension as the Pz Kpfw III Ausf H. The differences were in the main armament, turret bolted in place, additional vision and pistol ports on the super-structure sides, and a pistol port in place of the machine-gun on the superstructure front. The dummy gun on the early models resembled the 3.7cm KwK L/45. This was changed on later models to a dummy gun resembling the 5cm KwK L/42. A TSF1 periscope was mounted in the turret roof.

Combat service: With increased production, the number of Pz Bef Wg at Panzerabteilung and Tank Regiments headquarters was increased to two. In addition, the revised organization of the Pz Nachrichten (Signals) Abteilung in the Panzer divisions called for seven Pz Bef Wg, Sd Kfz 267 and 268. At the start of the summer offensive in 1941 120 gr Pz Bef Wg Ausf E and H were with the 17 Panzer divisions The second series of Pz Bef Wg Ausf H were mainly used to equip new units such as the 25th Panzer Division, 2nd SS Panzergrenadier Division 'Das Reich' and the Armoured Infantry Division 'Grossdeutschland'. At the start of the summer offensive in late June 1942 there were approximately 75 grosse Pz Bef Wg at the front.

Panzerbefehlswagen mit 5cm KwK L/42 (Sd Kfz 141)

Other designation: Pz Kpfw III (Sd Kfz 141) (als Pz Bef Wg)
Type: Medium command tank

Plate 225. Pz Bef Wg III mit 5cm KwK L/42.

Manufacturer: Daimler-Benz
Chassis Nos.: 72001–74100
81 produced from August to November 1942
104 converted from Pz Kpfw III from March to September 1943

Crew: 5	Engine: Maybach HL120TRM
Weight (tons): 21.5	Gearbox: 6 forward, 1 reverse
Length (metres): 6.28	Speed (km/hr): 40
Width (metres): 2.95	Range (km): 155
Height (metres): 2.50	Radio: FuG5 + FuG7
	FuG5 + FuG8

Ammunition: 75 Pzgr	One 7.92mm MG34
Traverse: 360° (hand)	=
Elevation: −10° +20°	=
Sight: TZF5d	=
Ammunition: 75 Pzgr & Spgr	1,500 Patr SmK

Armour (mm/angle):	Front	Side	Rear	Top/Bottom
Turret:	30/15°	30/25°	30/12°	10/83°−90°
Superstructure:	20+50/9°	30/0°	50/15°	17/75°−90°
Hull:	50/21°	30/0°	50/10°	16/90°
Gun mantlet:	20+50/0°−45°			

History: Ever since the campaign in Poland, the troops had been asking for a command vehicle with more effective armament than a few machine-pistols and the single machine-gun. They finally got their wish three years later when Daimler-Benz was given an order to convert Pz Kpfw III to Pz Bef Wg by the addition of a long-range radio. In January 1943, the WaA issued an order that there would be no further production of specially-designed Pz Bef Wg. All Command vehicles would be produced by conversion of standard production Pz Kpfw. From March to September 1943, an additional 104 Pz Kpfw III (5cm KwK L/42) were converted to Pz Bef Wg by removing an ammunition rack and adding the long-range radio.

Specific features: Virtually the same vehicle as the Pz Kpfw III Ausf J. The only differences were the elimination of the hull machine-gun,

and reduction in the number of rounds carried in order to make room for the additional radio sets. A TSF1 periscope was mounted in the turret roof of these command vehicles.

Combat service: Issued to the newly-formed SS Panzer Divisions, 'Leibstandarte Adolf Hitler', 'Das Reich', 'Tötenkopf' and 'Wiking', and as replacements in many other units. In addition to their normal role with Panzer regiments and Panzer Nachrichten Abteilung, from 1943 the Pz Bef Wg L/42 were to be issued as command vehicles for Sturmpanzer detachments, assault gun detachments and armoured radio-control detachments.

Panzerbefehlswagen mit 5cm KwK39 L/60

Other designation: 4 Serie Pz Bef Wg Ausf K
Type: Medium command tank

Manufacturer: Daimler-Benz
Chassis Nos.: 70201–70250
50 produced from December 1942 to February 1943

Crew: 5	Engine: Maybach HL120TRM
Weight (tons): 23	Gearbox: 6 forward, 1 reverse
Length (metres): 6.41	Speed (km/hr): 40
Width (metres): 2.95	Range (km): 155
Height (metres): 2.51	Radio: FuG5 + FuG8 (Sd Kfz 267)
	FuG5 + FuG7 (Sd Kfz 268)

226

Armament:	One 5cm KwK39 L/60	One 7.92mm MG34
Traverse:	360° (hand)	=
Elevation:	−10° +20°	=
Sight:	TZF5e	=
Ammunition: 65 Pzgr & Sprgr		1,500 Patr SmK

Armour (mm/angle):	Front	Side	Rear	Top/Bottom
Turret:	57/15°	30/25°	30/12°	10/83°−90°
Superstructure:	50 + 20/9°	30/0°	50/12°	18/79°−90°
Hull:	50/21°	30/0°	50/9°	16/90°
Gun mantlet:	50/0°−45°			

History: The original order for 200 Pz Bef Wg 4 Serie was issued in October 1941. The main feature was the retention of a proper main armament, the 5cm KwK L/60. This order was postponed, first as a result of the building of 30 additional Pz Bef Wg Ausf H, and then because of the order for 80 Pz Bef Wg mit 5cm KwK to be converted from the Pz Kpfw III Ausf J production. Finally, the 4 Serie Pz Bef Wg mit 5cm KwK L/60 Schmal (small gun mantlet) was to be produced alongside the Pz Kpfw III Ausf M from October 1942, but the order was reduced to 50 because Pz Kpfw III production was being terminated and it had been decided to convert Pz Kpfw III to Bef Wg from early 1943.

Specific features: The Ausf K had the same hull and superstructure as the Ausf M with the exception of additional vision and pistol ports on the superstructure sides. The turret was modified: the difference being a shortened gun mantlet, deletion of the coaxial machine-gun and the addition of a visor to the turret front, quite similar in design to the driver's visor. The large-frame antenna on previous command tank models was replaced by a star antenna.

Combat service: The Ausf K were issued as replacements for the heavy losses sustained during the winter of 1942/43. The Ausf K were maintained as command vehicles until mid 1944 in armoured detachments which, otherwise, were completely equipped with the Pz Kpfw IV.

Plates 226-227. Pz Bef Wg III Ausf K. Plate 226: a vehicle disabled during fighting on the Ukrainian Front. Plate 227: in Russia, with supplementary armour plate on the front superstructure.
Plate 228. A command tank based on the Ausf L.

228

Artillerie-Panzerbeobachtungswagen (Panzerkampfwagen III) (Sd Kfz 143)

Type: Armoured observation post based on obsolete tank chassis

Chassis Nos.: 60401–78000
262 produced by converting Pz Kpfw III from February 1943 to April 1944

Crew: 5
Weight (tons): 19.5–23
Length (metres): 5.52
Width (metres): 2.92
Height (metres): 2.50

Engine: Maybach HL120TRM or TR
Gearbox: 10 forward, 4 reverse or 6 forward, 1 reverse
Speed (km/hr): 40
Range (km): 165
Radio: FuG8 & FuG4

Armament: One 7.92mm MG34
Traverse: hand
Sight: TBF2
Ammunition: 1,500 Patr SmK

Armour (mm/angle):	Front	Side	Rear	Top/Bottom
Turret:	30/15°	30/25°	30/12°	10/83°–90°
Superstructure:	30+30/9°	30/0°	30/30°	17/77°–90°
Hull:	30+30/21°	30/0°	30+30/10°	16/90°
Gun mantlet:	50/0°–45°			

History: With the development of fully-tracked, self-propelled artillery, came the need of a fully-tracked armoured observation-vehicle. Since the older Pz Kpfw III Ausf E to H had lost most of their combat effectiveness, it was decided, as an interim solution, to modify them. Plans were made to replace them with a Pz Beob Wg specifically designed for that purpose, but this never materialized.

Specific features: The hull, superstructure and turret remained the same as the Pz Kpfw III Ausf E to Ausf M, upon which the Pz Beob Wg was based, with the following exceptions: (1) 30mm armour plate was added to the hull front and rear, and superstructure rear of all converted Ausf E to G. (2) The machine-gun mounted in the superstructure front was removed and the hole plugged. (3) The original gun mantlet was removed and replaced by a thicker mantlet, with a dummy gun and a machine-gun mounted in the centre of the mantlet.

Combat service: Introduced with the first Hummel and Wespe Batteries (Hummel=bumble-bee; Wespe=wasp) early in 1943, they remained in service until the end of the war. The organization of each Wespe and Hummel Battery included two Pz Beob Wg.

230

229

231

Plate 229. Pz Beob Wg based on the Pz Kpfw III Ausf F.
Plate 230. Pz Beob Wg based on the Pz Kpfw III Ausf G.
Plate 231. Pz Beob Wg based on the Pz Kpfw III Ausf H carrying Russian prisoners.

Bergepanzer III

Type: Armoured recovery vehicle on tank chassis

Approx. 150 converted from March to December 1944

Crew: 3	Engine: Maybach HL120TRM
Weight (tons): 19	Gearbox: 6 forward, 1 reverse
Length (metres): 6.28	Speed (km/hr): 40
Width (metres): 2.95	Range (km): 200
Height (metres): 2.45	Radio: FuG5

Armament: Two 7.92mm MG34
Traverse: hand
Sight: KggZF2

Armour (mm/angle):	Front	Side	Rear	Top/Bottom
Superstructure:	50/9°	30/0°	50/17°	18/79°–90°
Hull:	50/21°	30/0°	50/9°	16/90°

232

233

Plate 24 (Page 12). Instandsetzungskraftwagen based on Pz Kpfw III Ausf J or L.
Plate 232. Instandsetzungskraftwagen (maintenance vehicle) based on Pz Kpfw III Ausf J or L.
Plates 233-236. Bergepanzer III, showing the use of the recovery anchor. (Note, in Plate 236, the wide Ostkette tracks.)

History: In January 1944, it was ordered that all Pz Kpfw III returned for overhaul be converted to Bergepanzer. The production plan called for fifteen to be converted in March, thirty in April and thirty in May. These vehicles were to be used with the Panzerbergeanker (1 achs) (=armoured recovery anchor; 1-axle) (Sd Ah 40). This large anchor was placed at an appropriate location, and the Bergepanzer pulled the vehicle to be recovered, via a reduction tackle attached by cable to the anchor.

Specific features: A large wooden box body was mounted on top of the former fighting compartment. A derrick crane, like that on the Bergepanther, was provided with mounting locations on the rear engine covers. The wide Ostkette (=East track; for Russia) tracks were generally used.

Combat service: Issued to the Workshop Company of the Panzer detachments equipped with the Pz Kpfw IV or Sturmgeschütz III or IV. In February 1945, 130 Bergepanzer III were listed as available.

234

Panzerkampfwagen III mit Schachtellaufwerk

Type: Battle tank with experimental suspension

History: Prototype development of large interleaving road wheels, using a Pz Kpfw III Ausf H (7 ZW) turret and Ausf G (6 ZW) hull as the basis of the conversion. The one prototype built late in 1940 was used for training purposes after testing had been completed.

237

Plates 237-238. Pz Kpfw III mit Schachtellaufwerk (interleaved running gear).

238

Minenräumpanzer III

Type: Mine destroyer

History: Prototype development of a mine-destroyer vehicle. The turretless hull of a Pz Kpfw III was fitted with an extended and raised suspension system. It was designed to have a boom, extended to the front, carrying the mine-detonation equipment.

Plates 239-40. Minenräumpanzer III. Right: a close-up of the raised and reinforced suspension.

239

240

241

242

243

Panzerkampfwagen III Ausf N als Schienen-Ketten Fahrzeug SK1

Type: Battle tank with railway suspension

History: Two or three prototypes of these SK1 were converted from Pz Kpfw III Ausf N (7.5cm L/24) during late 1942 and early 1943. The suspension was re-configured so as to allow the railway bogie wheels to be retracted into the belly for normal cross-country performance.

The drive train was modified so that the rail bogies were driven by the tank engine. The speed on rails could reach 100km/hr. Saurer in Vienna carried out the development work on this project. The prototype was demonstrated on 20 October 1943.

Pionierpanzerwagen auf Fahrgestell Panzerkampfwagen III

Other designation: Pionierpanzer III
Type: Tracked carrier

History: From 1943, a number of Pz Kpfw III from the later series were converted to Engineers' vehicles by removing the turret and fitting racks for carrying equipment and small assault bridges.

Munitionspanzer auf Fahrgestell Panzerkampfwagen III

Other designations: Munitionspanzer III, Schlepper III
Type: Ammunition carrier

History: From May 1943, some old Pz Kpfw III returned for rebuilding, were converted to Bef Wg and Beob Wg. Others were converted to Munitionspanzer between May 1943 and May 1944. After that date, Pz Kpfw III were converted to Bergepanzer III, for use with tank detachments. Turrets from converted tanks were issued for use in fixed emplacements. In May 1944, 110 turrets armed with 5cm KwK L/42 and L/60 were available for such use.

Gepanzerter Selbstfahrlafette für Sturmgeschütz 7.5cm Kanone Ausf A (Sd Kfz 142)

Other designations: StuG Ausf A, 1 Serie
Type: Assault gun

Manufacturer: Alkett
Chassis Nos.: 90001–90100
5 prototypes of the 0-series built in 1937
30 produced from January to May 1940

Crew: 4	Engine: Maybach HL120TR
Weight (tons): 19.6	Gearbox: 10 forward, 4 reverse
Length (metres): 5.38	Speed (km/hr): 40
Width (metres): 2.92	Range (km): 160
Height (metres): 1.95	Radio: FuG15 or FuG16

Armament: One 7.5cm StuK37 L/24
Traverse: 12° left 12° right
Elevation: −10° +20°
Sight: Rblf32
Ammunition: 44

Armour (mm/angle):	Front	Side	Rear	Top/Bottom
Superstructure:	50/10°	30/0° + 9/30°	30/30°	11/78°−90° & 17/85°
Hull:	50/21°	30/0°	30/30° + 10°	16/90°

History: On 15 June 1936, the order was given to develop an armoured vehicle for infantry support, mounting a gun of at least 7.5cm calibre. The gun was required to have a minimum of 25° traverse, and to be mounted in the hull, eliminating the requirement for a turret, which could result in a vehicle not exceeding the height of an average man. The experimental (0-serie) series consisted of five Pz Kpfw III Ausf B chassis (Chassis Nos 90216–90220), upon which were mounted the soft steel superstructures containing the fixed 7.5cm StuK. After the successful testing of these prototypes, the 1 Serie Ausf A went into production in January 1940.

Specific features: The StuG Ausf A had the same suspension, drive-train components and basic hull shape as the 5 ZW (Pz Kpfw III Ausf F), but the similarity stopped there. The StuG front and rear armour was thicker, there were no escape hatches on the hull sides, and the brake access hatches on the glacis were hinged at the sides instead of fore and aft. The 7.5cm StuK37 was mounted offset to the right in the squat superstructure. Vision for the driver was provided by a pivoting visor and a twin periscope device in the superstructure front, and a vision port in the left superstructure. The gunner's artillery-type periscope sight was provided with a direct vision port in the left upper superstructure, and the commander had a scissors periscope which could be raised by opening the front half of his access hatch. Additional armour protection was provided for the crew, by attaching 9mm plates at an angle to the superstructure sides.

Combat service: The first StuG was issued to the troops in February 1940, with an additional 24 by the end of May. These were used to equip Sturmartillerie Batteries 640, 659, 660 and 665, which went into action in France.

244

245

246

Plates 244-245. StuG III Ausf A (having suspension similar to the Pz Kpfw III Ausf F suspension).
Plate 246. One of the pre-production (0-serie) vehicles.

Gepanzerter Selbstfahrlafette für Sturmgeschütz 7.5cm Kanone Ausf B (Sd Kfz 142)

Other designations: StuG III Ausf B, 2 und 3 Serie, 7.5cm StuG (L/24), Gep Sfl für 7.5cm StuG
Type: Assault gun

Manufacturer: Alkett
Chassis Nos.: 90101–90420
320 produced from June 1940 to May 1941

Crew: 4	Engine: Maybach HL120TRM
Weight (tons): 20.2	Gearbox: 6 forward, 1 reverse
Length (metres): 5.4	Speed (km/hr): 40
Width (metres): 2.93	Range (km): 160
Height (metres): 1.98	Radio: FuG15 or FuG16

Armament: One 7.5cm StuK37 L/24
Traverse: 12° left 12° right (hand)
Elevation: −10° +20°
Sight: Rblf32
Ammunition: 44

Armour (mm/angle):	Front	Side	Rear	Top/Bottom
Superstructure:	50/10°	30/0° + 9/30°	30/30°	11/78°–90° & 17/85°
Hull:	50/21°	30/0°	30/30° + 10°	16/90°
Gun mantlet:	50/15°			

History: The Ausf B was the 2nd and 3rd Series of the StuG, differing from the previous model by improvements to the drive train.
Specific features: Improvements were made to the ignition system, and a synchromesh transmission replaced the pre-selective type used in the Ausf A. Some of the 2nd Series of the Ausf B production had a new six-spoke drive sprocket, and an eight-spoke idler, designed for the wide 40cm track. The remainder of the vehicle was unchanged.
Combat service: By the end of 1940, the number of Sturmartillerie batteries had been raised to seven, and four assault-artillery detachments, each with three batteries had been formed. Additional assault-artillery detachments equipped with Ausf B were formed early in 1941. Two Sturmartillerie Abteilung were present during the Balkans campaign and six Abteilung advanced into Russian territory in June 1941.

Plate 2 (Title Page).
StuG Ausf B or C.

Plates 247-248. StuG Ausf B

Gepanzerter Selbstfahrlafette für Sturmgeschütz 7.5cm Kanone Ausf C und D (Sd Kfz 142)

Other designations: StuG Ausf C und D, 4 und 5 Serie
Type: Assault gun

Manufacturer: Alkett
Chassis Nos.: 90551–90750
50 Ausf C and 150 Ausf D produced from May to September 1941

Crew: 4	Engine: Maybach HL120TRM
Weight (tons): 20.2	Gearbox: 6 forward, 1 reverse
Length (metres): 5.4	Speed (km/hr): 40
Width (metres): 2.93	Range (km): 160
Height (metres): 1.98	Radio: FuG15 or FuG16

Armament: One 7.5cm StuK37 L/24
Traverse: 12° left 12° right (hand)
Elevation: −10° +20°
Sight: Rblf32
Ammunition: 44

Armour (mm/angle):	Front	Side	Rear	Top/Bottom
Superstructure:	50/10°	30/0° + 9/30°	30/30°	11/89°–90° & 17/85°
Hull:	50/21°	30/0°	30/30° + 10°	16/90°
Gun mantlet:	50/15°			

History: The 4th Series of production was the Ausf C, and the 5th Series, the Ausf D. Both models featured an improved superstructure design.
Specific features: A new superstructure design was introduced with the Ausf C. The main changes were the elimination of the direct vision port for the gunner's sight, the redesigning of the roof hatch above the gunner to allow the gun sight to be raised beside the closed hatch, and a different armour layout for the front of the superstructure.

With the Ausf D, a percentage of the production were built as commander's vehicles by adding an armoured pannier to the right side of the superstructure, of a similar design to the pannier on the left superstructure side of all Ausf A–D.

Combat service: The Ausf C and D were used to replace the front-line losses of 105 assault guns which had occurred in 1941, and to equip additional Sturmartillerie detachments. Three Ausf D found their way to North Africa with the Sonderverband (Detachment for Special Employment 288) early in 1942, seeing action in the enveloping attack around the Gazala position, and the capture of Tobruk.

Plates 249-250. Comparative top views of StuG Ausf C or D (left) and StuG Ausf E. (Note the shape of the two armoured side panniers on the Ausf E.)

Gepanzerter Selbstfahrlafette für Sturmgeschütz 7.5cm Kanone Ausf E (Sd Kfz 142)

Other designations: StuG Ausf E, 6 Serie
Type: Assault gun

Manufacturer: Alkett
Chassis Nos.: 90751–91036
272 produced from September 1941 to March 1942

Crew: 4	Engine: Maybach HL120TRM
Weight (tons): 20.8	Gearbox: 6 forward, 1 reverse
Length (metres): 5.4	Speed (km/hr): 40
Width (metres): 2.93	Range (km): 160
Height (metres): 1.98	Radio: FuG15 or FuG16

Plate 251. StuG Ausf E.

Armament: One 7.5cm StuK37 L/24		One 7.92mm MG34
Traverse: 12° left 12° right (hand)		loose
Elevation: −10° +20°		loose
Sight: Rblf32		direct
Ammunition: 44 (50)		600

Armour (mm/angle):	Front	Side	Rear	Top/Bottom
Superstructure:	50/10°	30/0°	30/30°	17/78°–90° & 17/85°
Hull:	50/21°	30/0°	30/30° + 10°	16/90°
Gun mantlet:	50/15°			

History: The Ausf E was part of the 6th Series of StuG production. Original plans were for 500 StuG in this series, but the Ausf E production was cut back with the introduction of the long StuK40 in 1942. One Ausf E was used as a prototype for this long gun, while a second Ausf E was used for the StuH prototype. Twelve further Ausf E chassis were used for the StuIG33B.

Specific features: The major improvement in the Ausf E was the addition of an armoured pannier on the right side of the superstructure to all StuG in this Series. Both the right and left panniers were longer than those on previous models. The 9mm slanted armour plates on the superstructure sides of previous Ausf were discontinued. Another distinguishing feature of the Ausf E were the small hinges for the glacis hatches, replacing the bulky hinges used on previous Ausf. The fire power of the StuG was increased by the addition of an MG34, which was stowed internally. The StuG was not provided with a mount or gun shield for the MG34. To bring the automatic weapon into action, the crew member was exposed above the hatch.

Combat service: A few new production Ausf E went to additional Sturmgeschütz detachments, but most were used to replace front-line losses. In early July 1942, there were 619 StuG Ausf A–E listed as combat ready. By early July 1943, this total had been reduced to 142 Ausf A–E of which, only 37 were with units at the front.

Gepanzerter Selbstfahrlafette für Sturmgeschütz 7.5cm Sturmkanone 40 Ausf F (Sd Kfz 142/1)

Other designations: StuG Ausf F, 6 und 7 Serie, 7.5cm StuK 40 auf StuG III
Type: Assault gun / tank destroyer

Manufacturer: Alkett
Chassis Nos.: 91037–91400
359 produced from March to September 1942 plus 1 prototype

Crew: 4	Engine: Maybach HL120TRM
Weight (tons): 21.6	Gearbox: 6 forward, 1 reverse
Length (metres): 6.31	Speed (km/hr): 40
Width (metres): 2.92	Range (km): 140
Height (metres): 2.15	Radio: FuG15 or FuG16

Armament: One 7.5cm StuK40   One 7.92mm MG34
  L/43 or L/48

Traverse: 10° left 10° right (hand)	loose		
Elevation: −6° +20°	loose		
Sight: SflZF1a	direct		
Ammunition: 44	600		

Armour (mm/angle):	Front	Side	Rear	Top/Bottom
Superstructure:	50 or 50+ 30/10°	30/10°	30/30°	11/78°−90° & 17/85°
Hull:	50 or 50+ 30/21°	30/0°	30/30° 10°	+16/90°
Gun mantlet:	50/0°	30/17°		30/90°

History: On 28 September 1941, a letter from the OKW (Oberkommando der Wehrmacht=Wehrmacht High Command) to the OKH (Oberkommando des Heeres=Army High Command) stated that Hitler requested that the armour of the StuG be increased, and that a larger 7.5cm Kanone be mounted. These improvements were to be made as quickly as possible in order to regain superiority over the new types of enemy tanks (specifically KV–1 and T–34). This request resulted in the Ausf F, with the long StuK40, finishing the 6th Series from March to July 1942, and the 7th Series from July to September 1942. Additional armour fitting started in June 1942, and continued for the rest of the Ausf F production, so that 182 had the Zusatz Panzerung (additional armour). Thirty-one Ausf F were fitted with the L/48 gun.

Specific features: The Ausf F retained the same hull and superstructure as the Ausf E with the exception of a new modification to the superstructure roof by the addition of an exhaust fan to remove gun fumes. Early in the production series, the upper front of the superstructure was modified to improve protection. The 7.5cm StuK40 was mounted in the same position as the StuK37, but the gun mantlet had been redesigned to contain the larger recoil mechanism of the larger gun.

Combat service: The Ausf F were issued mainly to Sturmgeschütz detachments, already at the front. Their appearance gave the front-line troops an effective anti-tank weapon which could easily defeat the Russian KV–1 and T–34. The Ausf F were also issued to the newly-formed F Skl Kp 312, 313 and 314 (Remote-Controlled Demolition Units) and to the Sturmgeschütz detachments of the Hermann Göring Division.

252

253

Plates 252-254. StuG Ausf F prototype.
Plate 253. StuG Ausf F in action.

254

Gerpanzerter Selbstfahrlafette für Sturmgeschütz 7.5cm Sturmkanone 40 Ausf F/8 (Sd Kfz 142/1)

Other designations: StuG Ausf F/8, 8 Serie
Type: Assault gun / tank destroyer

Manufacturer: Alkett
Chassis Nos.: 91401–91750
334 produced from September to December 1942

Crew: 4	Engine: Maybach HL120TRM
Weight (tons): 23.2	Gearbox: 6 forward, 1 reverse
Length (metres): 6.77	Speed (km/hr): 40
Width (metres): 2.92	Range (km): 140
Height (metres): 2.15	Radio: FuG15 or FuG16

Armament: One 7.5cm StuK40 L/48		One 7.92mm MG34
Traverse: 10° left 10° right (hand)		loose
Elevation: −6° +20°		loose
Sight: SflZF1a		direct
Ammunition: 44		600

Armour (mm/angle):

	Front	Side	Rear	Top/Bottom
Superstructure:	50+30/10°	30/0°	30/30°	11/78°−90° & 17/85°
Hull:	50+30/21°	30/0°	50/90°	16/90°
Gun mantlet:	50/0°	30/17°		30/90°

History: The Ausf F/8 was the 8th Series of the StuG production. The basic design change was the improvement of the hull. Four Ausf F/8 were converted to StuH42, and twelve chassis were used for the StuIG33B.

Specific features: The same hull design had been maintained from the Ausf A to F. This was changed in the Ausf F/8 by the introduction of an improved hull design similar to that used for the Pz Kpfw III Ausf J and L. The side plates were extended past the front plate, with holes drilled to provide towing brackets. The rear deck was extended farther to the rear, and the air-louvre design was altered to improve ventilation. The rear hull armour thickness was increased from 30mm to 50mm, and all Ausf F/8 had the additional 30mm armour bolted to the front of the hull and superstructure. During 1942, with increased demand for the StuG in preference to the Pz Kpfw III, Alkett ceased production of the latter and concentrated on the StuG. As a result, a proportion of the Ausf F/8 were built on Pz Kpfw III type hulls, which can be identified by the single-piece forward-opening hatch over the final drive.

Combat service: Some expansion of new Sturmgeschütz detachments continued in the autumn and winter of 1942. But again, most Ausf F/8 were used to replace losses in existing units. In addition to the independent units under Army control, the Leibstandarte Adolf Hitler, Das Reich, Tötenkopf and Grossdeutschland Divisions each received a Sturmgeschütz detachment, or had their Sturmgeschütz company expanded to detachment strength and equipped with Ausf F and Ausf F/8 in 1942.

255

Plates 255-256. StuG Ausf F/8. Note the additional armour on the skirt armour, which was fitted at a later date.

256

7.5cm Sturmgeschütz 40 Ausf G (Sd Kfz 142/1)

Other designation: StuG III Ausf G
Type: Assault gun / tank destroyer

Manufacturer: Alkett, MIAG
Chassis Nos.: 76101–77550, 91751–94250, 95001– , 105001–
7,720 produced from December 1942 to March 1945 plus 173 converted
from Pz Kpfw III in 1944

Crew: 4	Engine: Maybach HL120TRM
Weight (tons): 23.9	Gearbox: 6 forward, 1 reverse
Length (metres): 6.77	Speed (km/hr): 40
Width (metres): 2.95	Range (km): 155
Height (metres): 2.16	Radio: FuG15 & FuG16

Armament: One 7.5cm StuK40 L/48	One MG34*	7.92mm	One 7.92mm MG34 or MG42
Traverse: 10° left 10° right (hand)	=		loose
Elevation: −6° +20°	=		loose
Sight: SflZF1a	=		direct
Ammunition: 54	600		

Armour (mm/angle):	Front	Side	Rear	Top/Bottom
Superstructure:	50+30 or 80/10°	30/11°	30/0°	11–17/75°–90°
Hull:	50+30 or 80/21°	30/0°	50/10°	16/90°
Gun mantlet:	50 or 50 +30/0° Saukopfblende	30/17°		30/90°

*Late production only (coaxial mount)

History: The Ausf G was the last production series of the StuG. Rolling off the assembly-line in December 1942, the Ausf G was produced until the end of the war, with no major design changes. In 1942, the decision was made to use Pz Kpfw III Fgst for StuG production, since the Pz Kpfw III was being phased out and replaced by the Panther. In response to this request, 165 Pz Kpfw III Ausf M Fgst were used as chassis for StuG Ausf G, with production from February to November 1943. In 1944, 173 Pz Kpfw III, returned to the factory for overhaul, were converted to StuG Ausf G.

Specific features: The hull of the Ausf G remained unaltered from the design used for the Ausf F/8. The main design changes were to the superstructure. The roof was altered, and a cupola with periscopes was added for the commander, and a shield for the machine-gun was installed in front of the loader's hatch. The superstructure sides were now slanted, and slanted plates were added to protect the front of both panniers. Various improvements were instituted during the production run, including introduction of the Saukopf (sow's head) gun mantlet in February 1944, the coaxial machine-gun early in 1944, and the Nahverteidigungswaffe (close-in defence weapon) and remote-control machine-gun to the superstructure roof late in spring 1944. Vehicles issued to Funklenk Kompanien (Remote-Control Companies) were fitted with an additional radio aerial on the left front of the fighting compartment roof.

Combat service: Twenty-eight independent Sturmgeschütz detachments, four divisional Sturmgeschütz detachments, two 2nd Funklenk companies and twelve Sturmgeschütz platoons (with Luftwaffe Field Divisions) were at the front in Russia at the start of the Kursk offensive. From the start of the war, the use of the assault-gun spread from Sturmgeschütz detachments to the other types of formations, including Panzer detachments, Panzerjäger detachments and Funklenk companies and detachments.

257

Jacket Illustration: StuG III Ausf G.

258

Plates 257-259. StuG III Ausf G. (Note, in Plate 259, the additional armour bolted to the front of the vehicle.)
Plate 260 (opposite page, top). StuG III Ausf G with Saukopf gun mantlets which were introduced on some vehicles from February 1944.
Plate 1013 (Page 257) A StuG III Ausf G.
Plate 1014 (Page 257) A StuG III Ausf G converted from a Pz Kpfw III Ausf M chassis.

259

10.5cm Sturmhaubitze 42 (Sd Kfz 142/2)

Other designation: StuH42
Type: Assault howitzer

Manufacturer: Alkett
Chassis Nos.: 91251–94250, 105001–
1,211 produced from October 1942 to February 1945 plus 1 prototype

Crew: 4	Engine: Maybach HL120TRM	
Weight (tons): 24	Gearbox: 6 forward, 1 reverse	
Length (metres): 6.14	Speed (km/hr): 40	
Width (metres): 2.95	Range (km): 155	
Height (metres): 2.16	Radio: FuG15 or FuG16	

Armament: One 10.5cm   One 7.92mm MG34*   One 7.92mm MG34
 StuH42 L/28

Traverse: 10° left	=		loose
10° right (hand)			
Elevation: −6° +20°	=		loose
Sight: SflZF1	=		direct
Ammunition: 36	600		

Armour (mm/angle):	Front	Side	Rear	Top/Bottom
Superstructure:	50+30 or 80/10°	30/11°	30/0°	11–17/75°–90°
Hull:	50+30 or 80/21°	30/0°	50/10°	16/90°
Gun mantlet:	50 or 50+ 30/0°	30/17°		30/90°
	Saukopfblende			

*Late production only (co-axial mount).

History: From the lessons of combat, the Sturmgeschütz units realized the need of a heavier weapon to supplement the 7.5cm StuK of their StuG. This resulted in an order, in 1941, to mount the leFH18 in a trial series of 12 StuG to be produced from January to March 1942. Because of various delays, only a single prototype was finished in March 1942, with 5 StuH on StuG Ausf F, and 4 on StuG Ausf F/8 chassis completed in October 1942. Delivery of the first production series of StuH42 started in March 1943, with peak production hitting 119 in September 1944.

Plates 261-262. StuH 42 based on the StuG Aust F (top) and the Ausf G (below).
Plate 1015 (Page 257). Additional armour and wide track fitted to StuH 42 Ausf F.

Specific features: The StuH42 had the same hull and superstructure as the StuG Ausf F, F/8 and G, upon which it was based. During the production series, as improvements were made in the StuG Ausf G, these same improvements were made on the StuH42. The basic difference between the StuH and StuG, was the altered gun mount to take the 10.5cm StuH, and altered internal storage for the larger rounds.

Combat service: From 1943, StuH were issued to many of the Sturmgeschütz detachments later renamed Sturmgeschütz brigades. Each detachment equipped with these vehicles received nine StuH42 which they used to support the StuG40, to provide heavier destructive firepower and to supplement anti-tank defence. At the start of the Kursk offensive, sixty-eight StuH42 were with Army Groups Centre and South, at the front in Russia.

Plate 263. A late model of StuH42 without muzzle-brake, and fitted with the remote-controlled machine-gun.
Plate 264 (right). StuH42 based on the StuG III Ausf G, with Saukopf gun mantlet.

263

Sturmgeschütz (Fl)

Other designation: StuG (Fl)
Type: Flame-thrower on assault gun chassis

10 converted in May and June 1943

Crew: 4	Engine: Maybach HL120TRM
Weight (tons): 23	Gearbox: 6 forward, 1 reverse
Length (metres): 5.52	Speed (km/hr): 40
Width (metres): 2.95	Range (km): 155
Height (metres): 2.16	Radio: FuG5

Armament: One 14mm Flammenwerfer	One 7.92mm MG34
Traverse: 10° left 10° right (hand)	loose
Elevation: −6° +20°	loose
Sight:	direct
Ammunition:	600

History: In December 1942, plans were made to increase Sturmgeschütz III production by utilizing the chassis already on order for the Pz Kpfw III. With the ending of the Pz Kpfw III production, only 100 tanks would be available for manufacture as Flammpanzer (flame-throwing vehicle), and it was decided that of the 220 Sturmgeschütz to be delivered in June 1943, ten would be armed with the Flammenwerfer (flame-thrower). Only these ten were eventually converted.

Specific features: The Sturmkanone (assault-gun) was replaced by the Flammenwerfer, and flame fuel tanks were fitted, but otherwise, as for Sturmgeschütz III, from which they were converted. The only photographic evidence of these Flammenwerfer shows a unit converted from a StuG III Ausf F/8.

Armour (mm/angle):	Front	Side	Rear	Top/Bottom
Superstructure:	50+30/10°	30/11°	30/0°	11–17/75°−90°
Hull:	50+30/21°	30/0°	50/10°	16/90°

Sturminfanteriegeschütz 33B

Type: Assault infantry gun

Manufacturer: Alkett
Chassis Nos.: 90751–91036, 91401–91750
24 produced from December 1941 to October 1942

Crew: 5	Engine: Maybach HL120TRM
Weight (tons): 21	Gearbox: 6 forward, 1 reverse
Length (metres): 5.4	Speed (km/hr): 20
Width (metres): 2.9	Range (km): 110
Height (metres): 2.3	Radio: FuG Spr d

Armament: One 15cm Stu I G L/11	One 7.92mm MG34
Traverse: 3° left 3° right (hand)	15° left 20° right (hand)
Elevation: −3° +25°	−10° +20°
Sight: Rblf36 + SflZF1	KgZF2
Ammunition: 30	600

Plate 7 (Page 4). StuG 33B
Plate 265. StuIG33B

Armour (mm/angle):	Front	Side	Rear	Top/Bottom
Superstructure:	80/10°	50/25°	15/0°	10/90° + 17/11°−90°
Hull:	30+50 or 50/21°	30/0°	30 or	16/90°
Gun mantlet:	30/10°		50/10°	

History: The StuIG33B was the third attempt at mounting the 15cm sIG33 on a Pz Kpfw chassis. Unlike those mounted on the Pz Kpfw I and II chassis, the sIG33B was to have a fully-enclosed fighting compartment. In July 1941, Alkett was ordered to furnish twelve chassis which were to be completed by the middle of September. This initial version was completed in December 1941 and January 1942. On 20 September 1942, twelve assault-vehicles mounting a heavy weapon capable of demolishing houses with two or three rounds, were ordered to be completed within 14 days. The original twelve sIG33B were rebuilt, and an additional twelve new sIG33B were built in October 1942.

Specific features: The sIG33B had the same hull as the StuG, Ausf E and F/8. The superstructure was completely redesigned. The front, sides and rear were extended, and a roof added to form a completely enclosed fighting compartment. The sIG33 was mounted in a sliding gun mantlet, offset to the right of the vehicle's centre-line. Secondary armament was provided by an MG34 in a hull mount in the right superstructure front.

Combat service: A Sturmgeschütz company was sent to Stalingrad in November 1942, to support the Panzer and Panzergrenadier divisions. A second Sturm schwere Infanteriegeschütz company was formed as the 9th Company, 201st Panzer Regiment, 23rd Panzer Division. This division was sent to try to break the Russian encirclement of Stalingrad, and to delay the Russian advance during the winter of 1942/43.

Plate 266. StuIG33B.

Munitionspanzer auf Fahrgestell Sturmgeschütz III Ausf G

Type: Ammunition carrier

History: In 1944 and 1945, a number of Sturmgeschütz were field converted to ammunition carriers by the removal of the Sturmkanone 40. A flat armour plate covered the front of the gun aperture.

Plate 267. Munitionspanzer auf Fgst StuG III Ausf G.

267

Plate 268 (below). One of a number of StuG Ausf E III tanks that were captured by the Russians and re-armed with their 7.62cm anti-tank gun. (Touched up photo.)
Plate 269 (below right). A design project to mount the 8.8cm gun on the StuG III.

269   PANZERKAMPFWAGEN III AND VARIANTS   87

Panzerkampfwagen IV
and variants

BW (Rh-B)

Type: Battle tank prototype

History: Ordered in 1930 by the OKH. Rheinmetall-Borsig built one prototype in competition with Krupp. The 18 ton vehicle was powered by a 300PS motor which gave a speed of 35km/hr. Steering was of the Wilson type. Many of the features of the Rheinmetall BW were later used in the development of the Krupp BW which was mass produced as the Pz Kpfw IV.

270

271

272

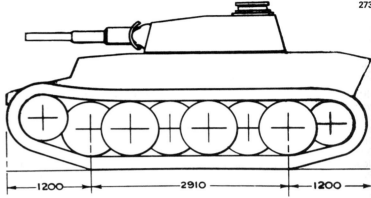

273

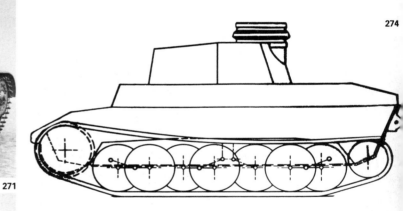

274

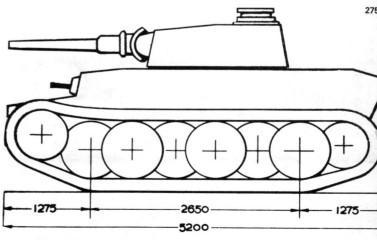

275

Plates 270-275 (this page). Pilot designs for the Panzerkampfwagen IV project.
Plates 270-271. The Rheinmetall-Borsig pilot model, VK2001 (Rh).
Plate 272. Modified version of the VK2001 (Rh).
Plate 273. Design drawing for the VK2002 (MAN).
Plate 274. Design drawing for the VK2001(D)—the Daimler version.
Plate 275. Krupp's design drawing, the VK2001(K).

Plates 276-280 (opposite page).
Plates 276-277. Pilot model for Pz Kpfw IV, originally coded 'BW' ('Bataillonsführerwagen' or 'battalion commander's vehicle). Note that the cupola was of the same type as that used on Pz Kpfw III Ausf A.
Plates 278-280. Pz Kpfw IV Ausf A. Note that the cupola on the production model was of the same type as that used on Pz Kpfw III Ausf B.

Panzerkampfwagen IV Ausf A (Sd Kfz 161)

Other designation: 1 Serie BW
Type: Medium support tank

Manufacturer: Krupp-Gruson
Chassis Nos.: 80101–80135
35 produced from October 1937 to March 1938

Crew: 5	Engine: Maybach HL108TR
Weight (tons): 18.4	Gearbox: 5 forward, 1 reverse
Length (metres): 5.6	Speed (km/hr): 31
Width (metres): 2.9	Range (km): 150
Height (metres): 2.65	Radio: FuG5

Armament:	One 7.5cm KwK37 L/24	One 7.92mm MG34	One 7.92mm MG34
Traverse:	360° (electric)	=	hand
Elevation:	−10° +30°	=	
Sight:	TZF5b	=	KgZF2
Ammunition:	122 Pzgr, Sprgr+Nebel	3,000 Patr SmK	

Armour (mm/angle):	Front	Side	Rear	Top/Bottom
Turret:	15/10°	15/25°	15/0°−25°	10/83°−90°
Superstructure:	15/7°	15/0°	15/10°	12/85°−90°
Hull:	15/12°	15/0°	15/10°	5/90°
Gun mantlet:	15/round			

History: The development contract for a Pz Kpfw in the 20 ton class was issued to Krupp in 1935. Known originally as the 7.5cm Geschütz-Panzerwagen (Vs Kfz 618) (7.5cm gun armoured vehicle; experimental vehicle No. 618), the Pz Kpfw IV started production in the autumn of 1937. In April 1936, the name was changed from Geschütz-Panzerwagen to Panzerkampfwagen IV, and received the designation Vs Kfz 622, which had previously been assigned to the Pz Kpfw II. All of the original order of thirty-five Pz Kpfw IV Ausf A were completed, and accepted for issue.

Specific features: The suspension of the Pz Kpfw IV consisted of a forward-drive sprocket, four pairs of road-wheels with leaf springs, a rear idler and four return rollers. Power was provided by a 12 cylinder gasoline engine, through a five-speed transmission to the final drives, and an epicyclic clutch and brake steering system. An auxiliary engine was provided to drive a generator which provided power for the electric turret traverse. The 7.5cm KwK and a coaxial MG34 were mounted in an inner moving mantlet in the turret, and a second MG34 was mounted in the front of the superstructure. The 15mm armour was designed to prevent penetration by armour-piercing rounds from smallarms, and by shell fragments. Numerous vision slits and pistol ports were provided for the crew, with observation provided for the commander by a drum cupola with 8 vision slits. The driver's front plate was forward of the rest of the superstructure front, allowing the driver to see to his right front, and providing more room for internal ammunition storage.

Combat service: By January 1938, three Pz Kpfw IV had been issued to the troops, and this number had increased to thirty by 1 April 1938. Seeing action in Poland, Norway and France, the Ausf A were withdrawn from the Panzer regiments before the spring campaigns of 1941.

278

276

279

277

280

Panzerkampfwagen IV Ausf B (Sd Kfz 161)

Other designation: 2 Serie BW
Type: Medium support tank

Manufacturer: Krupp-Gruson
Chassis Nos.: 80201–80245
42 produced from April to September 1938

Crew: 5
Weight (tons): 18.8
Length (metres): 5.92
Width (metres): 2.83
Height (metres): 2.68

Engine: Maybach HL120TR
Gearbox: 6 forward, 1 reverse
Speed (km/hr): 40
Range (km): 200
Radio: FuG5

Armament: One 7.5cm KwK37 L/24   One 7.92mm MG34
Traverse: 360° (electric)   =
Elevation: −10° +20°   =
Sight: TZF5b   =
Ammunition: 80 Pzgr, Sprgr+Nebel 2,400 Patr SmK

Armour (mm/angle):	Front	Side	Rear	Top/Bottom
Turret:	30/10°	15/25°	15/0°−24°	10/83°−90°
Superstructure:	30/7°	15/0°	15/10°	12/85°−90°
Hull:	30/12°	15/0°	15/10°	5/90°
Gun mantlet:	30/round			

History: Krupp-Gruson had been given an order to produce 45 of the 2nd Series BW, but three were not completed because of shortage of parts.

Specific features: Improvements incorporated in the Ausf B included a larger engine and six-speed transmission, an increase in the frontal armour thickness to 30mm, and a new type of cupola. Other modifications included a conical-shaped hood over the right signal port in the turret roof, to shield signal lamps, and single-piece hatches over the driver and radio-operator. The superstructure front on the Ausf B was in one straight piece, without the hull machine-gun which had been replaced by a visor and a pistol port. In order to prolong their combat life, from late 1940, additional armour plates were bolted to the hull and superstructure sides of some Ausf Bs.

Combat service: During the period in which the Ausf B was produced in 1938, only three Pz Kpfw IV were issued to a Zug (platoon) in the Le Pz Kp (a) of each Panzer detachment, which resulted in Panzer regiments with only six Pz Kpfw IV. The Ausf B saw service in Poland, France, the Balkans and Russia, and had been gradually phased out through attrition by late 1943.

Plate 281. Pz Kpfw IV Ausf B.
Plate 282. The turret for Pz Kpfw IV Ausf B and C, showing the 7.5cm gun mounted in an internal mantlet.

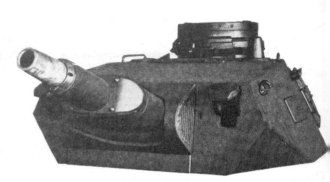

Panzerkampfwagen IV Ausf C (Sd Kfz 161)

Other designation: 3 Serie BW
Type: Medium support tank

Plate 283. Pz Kpfw IV Ausf C in Poland.

Manufacturer: Krupp-Gruson
Chassis Nos.: 80301–80440
134 produced from September 1938 to August 1939

Crew: 5
Weight (tons): 19
Length (metres): 5.92
Width (metres): 2.83
Height (metres): 2.68

Engine: Maybach HL120TR & TRM
Gearbox: 6 forward, 1 reverse
Speed (km/hr): 40
Range (km): 200
Radio: FuG5

Armament: One 7.5cm KwK37 L/24   One 7.92mm MG34
Traverse: 360° (electric)   =
Elevation: −10° +20°   =
Sight: TZF5b   =
Ammunition: 80 Pzgr, Sprgr+Nebel 2,400 Patr SmK

Armour (mm/angle):	Front	Side	Rear	Top/Bottom
Turret:	30/10°	15/25°	15/0°−24°	10/83°−90°
Superstructure:	30/7°	15/0°	15/10°	12/85°−90°
Hull:	30/12°	15/0°	15/10°	5/90°
Gun mantlet:	30/round			

History: Of the initial order for 300 Ausf C, only 134 were completed as Pz Kpfw IV. In August 1939, six chassis had been handed over to the Inspectorate for Engineers, for use as the basic chassis for bridge-laying tanks. The remainder of the order, amounting to 160, were dropped in March 1938, before production had started.

Specific features: The Ausf C included a series of minor changes to the design of the Ausf B, including an altered motor mount, improved turret race, redesigned gun-mantlet housing, and an armour sleeve to protect the coaxial machine-gun. From Chassis No. 80341, the

Ausf Cs were equipped with an engine, modified to improve carburation. From late 1940, to prolong combat life, additional armour plates were bolted to the hull and superstructure sides of some Ausf C.

Combat service: With increased production of the Ausf C, the organization of the light tank company (a) was altered early in 1939, so that the 2 Zug (2nd platoon) was to have four to six Pz Kpfw IV. By the start of the Polish campaign, the medium company had been introduced in the 1st Panzer Division and the 1st Light Division. The former had fourteen Pz Kpfw IV in each medium company, the latter had eight. On 1 September 1939, the remainder of the Panzer divisions still had the light tank company (a) with four to six Pz Kpfw IV, during the Polish Campaign. The Ausf C remained in active service until 1943, but its numbers had been gradually reduced by attrition.

Plates 284-285. Pz Kpfw IV Ausf C during manoeuvres in the West in early 1940.

Panzerkampfwagen IV Ausf D (Sd Kfz 161)

Other designation: 4 und 5 Serie BW
Type: Medium support tank

Manufacturer: Krupp-Gruson
Chassis Nos.: 80501–80748
229 produced from October 1939 to May 1941

Crew: 5	Engine: Maybach HL120TRM
Weight (tons): 20	Gearbox: 6 forward, 1 reverse
Length (metres): 5.92	Speed (km/hr): 40
Width (metres): 2.84	Range (km): 200
Height (metres): 2.68	Radio: FuG5

Armament: One 7.5cm KwK37 L/24	One 7.92mm MG34	One 7.92mm MG34
Traverse: 360° (electric)	=	20° left 20° right (hand)
Elevation: $-8° +20°$	=	$-10° +15°$
Sight: TZF5b	=	KgZF2
Ammunition: 80	2,700	

Armour (mm/angle):	Front	Side	Rear	Top/Bottom
Turret:	30/10°	20/25°	20/0°–24°	10/83°–90°
Superstructure:	30/7°	20/0°	20/9°	12/84°–90°
Hull:	30/12°	20/0°	20/10°	10/90°
Gun mantlet:	35/0°–29°			

History: In January 1938, Krupp-Gruson received an order to produce 200 in the 4th Series BW and 48 in the 5th Series. Of this total, only 229 were completed as gun-armed Pz Kpfw. The other 19 chassis were utilized to produce 16 bridge-laying tanks, 2 self-propelled guns and a Munitionsschlepper for Karl. Later in 1941, in an endeavour to seek a more powerful armament, an Ausf D was rebuilt with a 5cm KwK39 L/60.

Specific features: The main improvements incorporated in the Ausf D were the increase in the side and rear armour from 15 to 20mm, and the provision of an external mantlet for the 7.5cm KwK. The superstructure front was stepped so that the plate in front of the radio-operator was farther back than that in front of the driver. The driver had a pistol port to the right front, and the hull MG was reintroduced

Plate 1 (Half title page) Pz Kpfw IV Ausf D in action.
Plate 286. Pz Kpfw IV Ausf D. Note that the hull machine-gun position has been re-introduced within the Kugelblende 30.
Plates 955-956 (Page 248) Pz Kpfw IV Ausf D gun mount.
Plate 974 (Page 251) Experimental 5cm KwK mounting for Pz Kpfw IV Ausf D.

in front of the radio-operator. Ausf D, produced late in the series, had additional 30mm plates bolted and welded to the superstructure and hull front, and 20mm plates bolted to the hull and superstructure sides. Later, in 1943, several Ausf D were refitted with 7.5cm KwK L/48 for use with training and replacement units.

Combat service: By May 1940, Pz Kpfw production had been sufficient for every tank detachment to have a medium tank company of from six to eleven Pz Kpfw IV. On 10 May 1940, at the start of the campaign in France, there were 280 Ausf A, B, C and D in the Panzer divisions. The Ausf D saw service in France, the Balkans, Africa and Russia. The last few were phased out by attrition early in 1944.

287

Plate 287. The turret for Pz Kpfw IV Ausf D, showing the 7.5cm gun in an external mantlet.
Plate 288. Rear view of the turret for Pz Kpfw IV Ausf B and C.

288

289

292

Plate 289. Pz Kpfw IV Ausf D, in service at a tank driver school, exhibiting the later types of drive sprocket. (The machines in the background are Fahrschulwanne IV tank training vehicles.)
Plate 290. Pz Kpfw IV Ausf D, followed by a column of Pz Kpfw IV Ausf C, moving through a French town.
Plate 291. Pz Kpfw IV Ausf D with snow-plough attachment.
Plate 292. Pz Kpfw IV Ausf D upgunned with a 7.5cm KwK L/48 and with additional armour plates bolted to the front superstructure. This vehicle, like that shown in Plate 289, is in service at a tank driver school.

Panzerkampfwagen IV Ausf E (Sd Kfz 161)

Other designation: 6 Serie BW
Type: Medium support tank

Manufacturer: Krupp-Gruson
Chassis Nos.: 80801–81023
223 produced from September 1940 to April 1941

Crew: 5	Engine: Maybach HL120TRM	
Weight (tons): 21	Gearbox: 6 forward, 1 reverse	
Length (metres): 5.92	Speed (km/hr): 42	
Width (metres): 2.84	Range (km): 200	
Height (metres): 2.68	Radio: FuG5	

Armament: One 7.5cm KwK37 L/24	One 7.92mm MG34	One 7.92mm MG34
Traverse: 360° (electric)	=	20° left 20° right (hand)
Elevation: −8° +20°	=	−10° +15°
Sight: TZF5b	=	KgZF2
Ammunition: 80 Pzgr, Sprgr+Nebel	2,700 Patr SmK	

Armour (mm/angle):	Front	Side	Rear	Top/Bottom
Turret:	30/10°	20/24°	20/14°	10/83°-90°
Superstructure:	30+30/7°	20+20/0°	20/15°	12/84°-90°
Hull:	50/15°	20+20/0°	20/10°	10/90°
Gun mantlet:	35/0°-29°			

History: In January 1938, the order for 223 6th Series BW was issued to Krupp-Gruson, and this total was completed.

Specific features: The main improvements introduced with the Ausf E were a new cupola design, modifications to the turret, and increased armour protection. The turret now had a single bent plate for the turret rear, and an exhaust fan to extract gun fumes. While all Ausf E had a 50mm hull front and 20mm plate bolted to the hull and superstructure sides, several of the early Ausf E were minus the extra 30mm plate on the superstructure front. Minor modifications included a simplified sprocket design, glacis hatches countersunk level with surface of glacis, new design of driver's visor (pivoting), single signal post on turret roof and an armoured cover for the smoke-candle rack.

Combat service: With the continued production of the Ausf D, and the completion of the Ausf E, sufficient Pz Kpfw IV became available to furnish each medium tank company with ten Pz Kpfw IV for the campaigns in the Balkans, North Africa and Russia. Forty Ausf D and E were taken to North Africa with the 5th and 8th Panzer Regiments, and 438 Ausf B–F were with the seventeen Panzer divisions which attacked the Russians in June 1941. The last Ausf E were phased out by attrition early in 1944.

294

Plates 293-295. Pz Kpfw IV Ausf E. Above right, a factory photograph that shows the new driving sprocket, new driver's visor (Fahrersehklappe 30) and the extractor fan in the turret roof; above, in North Africa.
Plate 1011 (Page 257) Pz Kpfw IV Ausf E.
Plate 1030 (Page 260) Pz Kpfw IV Ausf E.

Panzerkampfwagen IV Ausf F (Sd Kfz 161)

Other designation: 7 Serie BW
Type: Medium support tank

Manufacturer: Krupp-Gruson, Vomag, Nibelungenwerke
Chassis Nos.: 82001–82614
462 produced from April 1941 to March 1942, of which 25 converted
  to Ausf F_2

Crew: 5	Engine: Maybach HL120TRM
Weight (tons): 22.3	Gearbox: 6 forward, 1 reverse
Length (metres): 5.92	Speed (km/hr): 42
Width (metres): 2.84	Range (km): 200
Height (metres): 2.68	Radio: FuG5

Armament: One 7.5cm   One 7.92mm MG34   One 7.92mm MG34
  KwK37 L/24
Traverse: 360° (electric) =   hand
Elevation: −8° +20°   =
Sight: TZF5b   =   KgZF2
Ammunition: 80 Pzgr,   3,000 Patr SmK
  Sprgr+Nebel

296

Armour (mm/angle):	Front	Side	Rear	Top/Bottom
Turret:	50/11°	30/26°	30/16°	10/83°−90°
Superstructure:	50/10°	30/0°	20/12°	12/85°−90°
Hull:	50/12°	30/0°	20/9°	10/90°
Gun mantlet:	50/0°−30°			

History: The initial Ausf F order was given to Krupp-Gruson for 500 in the 7th Series BW. This was later increased when Vomag received an order to produce 100 and Nibelungenwerke, 25. Before these series were completed the OKH issued an order to mount the 7.5cm KwK40 L/43 as quickly as possible, resulting in each series being completed as Ausf F_2. Twenty-five of the Ausf F_1, which had been fitted originally with the short 7.5cm KwK37, were converted to Ausf F_2 by mounting the 7.5cm KwK40 L/43, before being issued to the troops.

Specific features: The major improvement with the Ausf F was the increase of the armour thickness on most surfaces. Minor improvements included 40cm wide tracks with the accompanying dished sprocket and tubular idler, air-intake cowl on the glacis hatches to cool the steering brakes, and new muffler designs for the main and auxiliary engines. The vision ports, pistol ports, driver's visor, hull machine-gun mount and turret doors were all changed from previous models because of the increased armour thicknesses.

Combat service: The Ausf F_1, which equipped several new units and refitted the 2nd and 5th Panzer Divisions, was mainly issued piecemeal to units at the front, to replace losses. About 208 Ausf B to F_1 were available with units in Russia when the summer offensive started in June 1942. This was reduced to 60 available on the entire Eastern front at the time of the offensive at Kursk in July 1943.

297

Plate 14 (Page 7)
Pz Kpfw IV Ausf F_1

Plate 976 (Page 251)
Waffe 0725 mock up mounted in Pz Kpfw IV Ausf F_1

Plate 1029 (Page 260)
Pz Kpfw IV Ausf F_1

Plates 296-298. Pz Kpfw IV Aust F_1. Plate 296 shows the double doors in the sides of the turret, the new driving sprocket and rear idler wheel. In Plate 297, note that the front of the superstructure is now a single 50mm plate. A new machine-gun mounting (the Kugelblende 50) and an improved visor for the driver (the Fahrersehklappe 50) have also been installed. Plate 298 shows the Ausf F_1 on trials.

298

Panzerkampfwagen IV Ausf F₂ (Sd Kfz 161/1)

Other designation: 7 Serie BW
Type: Medium tank

Manufacturer: Krupp-Gruson, Vomag, Nibelungenwerke
Chassis Nos.: 82370–82650
175 produced from March to July 1942, plus 25 converted from Ausf F₁

Crew: 5	Engine: Maybach HL120TRM
Weight (tons): 23	Gearbox: 6 forward, 1 reverse
Length (metres): 5.62	Speed (km/hr): 40
Width (metres): 2.84	Range (km): 200
Height (metres): 2.68	Radio: FuG5

Armament: One 7.5cm   One 7.92mm MG34   One 7.92mm MG34
  KwK40 L/43

Traverse: 360° (electric)	=		hand
Elevation: −8° +20°	=		
Sight: TZF5f	=		KgZF2
Ammunition: 87?	3,000		

Armour (mm/angle):	Front	Side	Rear	Top/Bottom
Turret:	50/11°	30/26°	30/16°	10/83°–90°
Superstructure:	50/10°	30/0°	20/12°	12/85°–90°
Hull:	50/12°	30/0°	20/0°	10/90°
Gun mantlet:	50/0°–30°			

History: In November 1941, plans were made to improve the armament of the Pz Kpfw IV by installing a long-barrelled 7.5cm KwK. This change was to have taken place with the Ausf G. Because of the superiority of the Russian KV–1 and T–34, an order was issued to mount the 7.5cm KwK40 as quickly as possible. This resulted in the loss of a month's production in March 1942, and the Ausf F series was completed with 7.5cm KwK40 L/43, and was designated Ausf F₂.

Specific features: The differences between the Ausf F₁ and F₂ related largely but not entirely to the introduction of the new gun. Ammunition storage was modified to stow the larger rounds, the amount of ammunition carried was increased and the gunner's and commander's seats were changed to allow more room. The elevation mechanism was modified and an auxiliary hand traverse was installed for the loader. Because of the long barrel, a coil-spring counter-balance was installed for the 7.5cm KwK40.

Combat service: While some Ausf F₂ were issued to several newly-formed tank detachments and were given to the motorized infantry divisions, the majority went to front-line units to replace losses. This provided a Pz Kpfw which was superior to the Russian, British and American armour used at the fronts in the summer of 1942.

299

300

301

Plates 972-973 (Page 250). Experimental mock up of 7.5cm KwK L/70 in Pz Kpfw IV Ausf F₂.

Plates 299-301. Pz Kpfw IV Ausf F₂. The tank in Plate 300 has been captured in the Western Desert (where the model was known to the British as the 'Mk IV Special'). Fitted to the gun barrel is an aerial deflector similar to that used on the short 7.5cm gun. In Plates 299 to 301, the KwK40 gun has been fitted with the early single-baffle, globular muzzle-brake.

Plate 4 (Page 4). Early production Pz Kpfw IV Ausf G.
Plate 29 (Page 12). Pz Kpfw IV Ausf G under repair.

Plates 302-303. Pz Kpfw IV Ausf G. Top, early production model; note that the gun has been fitted with the new muzzle-brake. Below, middle production model with vision ports in the front and sides of the turret.

Plate 957 (Page 248). Interior of Pz Kpfw IV Ausf G turret.
Plate 958 (Page 248). Pz Kpfw IV Ausf G (7.5cm KwK40 L/43).
Plate 1027 (Page 259). Late production Pz Kpfw IV Ausf G (7.5cm KwK L/48) and additional welded hull armour.

302

303

Panzerkampfwagen IV Ausf G (Sd Kfz 161/1 und 161/2)

Other designation: 7 und 8 Serie BW
Type: Medium tank

Manufacturer: Krupp-Gruson, Vomag, Nibelungenwerke
Chassis Nos.: 82651–84400
1,687 produced from May 1942 to June 1943

Crew: 5
Weight (tons): 23.5
Length (metres): 6.62
Width (metres): 2.88
Height (metres): 2.68

Engine: Maybach HL120TRM
Gearbox: 6 forward, 1 reverse
Speed (km/hr): 40
Range (km): 210
Radio: FuG5

Armament: One 7.5cm KwK40 L/43 or L/48 — One 7.92mm MG34 — One 7.92mm MG34
Traverse: 360° (electric) = hand
Elevation: −8° +20° =
Sight: TZF5f/1 = KgZF2
Ammunition: 87 Pzgr, Sprgr+Nebel — 3,000 Patr SmK

Armour (mm/angle):	Front	Side	Rear	Top/Bottom
Turret:	50/11°	30/26°	30/10°	10/83°–90°
Superstructure:	50 or 50+30/10°	30/0°	20/12°	12/85°–90°
Hull:	50 or 50+30/12°	30/0°	20/9°	10/90°
Gun mantlet:	50/0°–30°			

History: The 1,750 Ausf G were acquired by ten separate orders, issued to Krupp-Gruson, Vomag and Nibelungenwerke. Of this number, only 1,687 were completed as Pz Kpfw. The remainder were used as prototypes for the Hummel (Bumble Bee) 10 chassis and the Brummbär (Grizzly Bear) 53 chassis. From late March 1943, the 7.5cm KwK40 L/48 was installed instead of the L/43, with a total of 1,275 Ausf G receiting the L/43. Delivery of Ausf G, with additional armour bolted or welded to the front of the hull and superstructure began on 20 June 1942. Starting at 16 per month from July to November 1942, half of the Ausf G production were to be fitted with additional armour, from December 1942, resulting in approximately 700 Ausf G having the extra protection.

Specific features: The first change entailed vision ports being eliminated from the turret sides and in the loader's side of the turret front. Other changes, in the summer of 1942, included a new style muzzle brake, installing a system which allowed the transfer of coolant to another Pz Kpfw to aid cold-weather starting, and smoke-dischargers mounted on the turret side instead of the hull rear. In January 1943, the drivers episcope (KFF2) was eliminated. Schürzen, which were thin steel plates attached to the sides of the hull and which surrounded the turret sides and rear, were introduced in 1943. The very late models of the Ausf G received a new type of drive sprocket and rear. The very late models of the Ausf G received a new type of drive sprocket, and the radio antenna was moved to the left hull rear, making it almost impossible to distinguish a late Ausf G from an early Ausf H.

Combat service: At the start of the summer offensive in Russia, late in June 1942, approximately 170 Ausf F₂ and G were with units at the front. This number had increased to 841 Pz Kpfw IV (lang) with Army Groups Centre and South, at the start of the Kursk offensive. In 1943, the Pz Kpfw IV were extended from medium companies to every company in each detachment of Panzer regiments, each company was supposed to have twenty-two Pz Kpfw IV.

Plate 304. A late production Pz Kpfw IV Ausf G, with Schürzen (armour skirts) and additional bolted armour on the hull front.

Panzerkampfwagen IV Ausf H (Sd Kfz 161/2)

Other designation: 9 Serie BW
Type: Medium tank

Manufacturer: Krupp-Gruson, Vomag, Nibelungenwerke
Chassis Nos.: 84401–91500
3,774 produced from April 1943 to July 1944

Crew: 5	Engine: Maybach HL120TRM
Weight (tons): 25	Gearbox: 6 forward, 1 reverse
Length (metres): 7.02	Speed (km/hr): 38
Width (metres): 2.88	Range (km): 210
Height (metres): 2.68	Radio: FuG5

Armament: One 7.5cm KwK40 L/48	One 7.92mm MG34	One 7.92mm MG34
Traverse: 360° (electric)	=	hand
Elevation: −8° +20°	=	
Sight: TZF5f/1	=	KgZF2
Ammunition: 87 Pzgr, Sprgr+Nebel	3,150 Patr SmK	

Armour (mm/angle):	Front	Side	Rear	Top/Bottom
Turret:	50/10°	30/26°	30/15°	15/84°–90°
Superstructure:	80/10°	30/0°	20/11°	12/85°–90°
Hull:	80/14°	30/0°	20/8°	10/90°
Gun mantlet:	50/0°–30°			

History: Of the 3,935 Ausf H chassis produced, 3,774 were completed as Pz Kpfw IV, with 30 used for the first StuG IV and 130 for Brummbär. In November 1943, an attempt was made to alter the suspension to gain ground clearance. The experiment failed and the Pz Kpfw IV retained the same basic suspension from 1937 until the end of the war.

Specific features: The basic change from the Ausf G was the SSG77 transmission fitted to the Ausf H. The frontal armour on the Ausf H evolved from 50mm basic with 30mm additional, to 80mm basic, to 80mm basic interlocked with the hull sides. Minor modifications, introduced during the production run of the Ausf H, included external air-filters, all-steel return rollers, a cupola mount for an anti-aircraft machine gun, a new style idler, the deletion of the side vision ports for the driver and radio operator and a new cupola with thicker armour and a single piece cupola hatch.

Combat service: From 1943, Panzer regiments in the Panzer divisions were to have one detachment equipped with Pz Kpfw IV and one detachment with Panthers. As a result of problems with the Panther, some Panzer divisions had a second detachment equipped with Pz Kpfw IV, while many had but a single detachment of four companies, each equipped with twenty-two Pz Kpfw IV, plus eight with the HQ Company. On 6 June 1944, most of the 748 Pz Kpfw IV with the nine Panzer divisions in France were Ausf H.

Plates 305-307. Pz Kpfw IV Ausf H. The vehicle in Plate 305 has the new type of drive sprocket but the old type of idler wheel; Plate 306 shows a late production model, with both new drive sprocket and idler wheel. Plate 307 (below): on manoeuvres in France in 1944.

305

Plate 1012 (Page 257). Pz Kpfw IV Ausf H with bolted 30mm armour added to 50mm hull front.

Panzerkampfwagen IV Ausf J (Sd Kfz 161/2)

Other designation: Gerät 550
Type: Medium tank

Manufacturer: Nibelungenwerke
Chassis Nos.: 91501–
1,758 produced from June 1944 to March 1945

Crew: 5	Engine: Maybach HL120TRM112
Weight (tons): 25	Gearbox: 6 forward, 1 reverse
Length (metres): 7.02	Speed (km/hr): 38
Width (metres): 2.88	Range (km): 320
Height (metres): 2.68	Radio: FuG5

Armament: One 7.5cm One 7.92mm MG34   One 7.92mm MG34
KwK40 L/48

Traverse: 360° (hand)	=		hand
Elevation: −8° +20°	=		
Sight: TZF5f/2	=		KgZF2

Ammunition: 87 Pzgr, 3,150 Patr SmK
Spgr + Nebel

Armour (mm/angle):	Front	Side	Rear	Top/Bottom
Turret:	50/10°	30/25°	30/15°	18/86° & 26/90°
Superstructure:	80/8°	30/0°	20/10°	12/85°–90°
Hull:	80/15°	30/0°	20/10°	10/90°
Gun mantlet:	50/0°–30°			

History: The Ausf J was the last series of the Pz Kpfw IV and was produced solely by Nibelungenwerke after Krupp had been switched to the StuG IV, and Vomag to the Jgd Pz IV. In addition to the 1,758 Pz Kpfw IV, 278 Ausf J chassis were used for Panzer IV/70(A) and 142 chassis were built for conversion to Brummbär.

Specific features: The main change introduced with the Ausf J was the elimination of the electric traverse and its associated auxiliary engine. A dual gear-ratio hand-traverse was fitted in its place, and the space previously occupied by the auxiliary engine was used to increase the fuel capacity. The armour thickness of the turret roof was increased and a 'Nähverteidigungswaffe' added as a smoke-projector and for close defence. Minor improvements introduced during the Ausf J production run included the deletion of pistol ports and vision ports from the turret rear and side doors, wire-mesh skirting on the hull sides, 3 instead of 4 return rollers, steel-tyred road wheels, vertical exhaust mufflers, and the hull sides extended beyond the front hull plate, and drilled to provide holes for towing shackles.

Combat service: As a result of combat attrition and loss of production through bombing, the number of Pz Kpfw IV per Company by official organization was cut back to 17, 14 or 10 in November 1944. Thus the Panzer divisions taking part in the Ardennes offensive had only 26 to 42 Pz Kpfw IV. A total of only 259 were on hand with eight Panzer divisions taking part in the offensive. During the war, Pz Kpfw IV had been furnished to Bulgaria, Croatia, Finland, Italy, Spain, Rumania, Turkey and Hungary.

Ausf H

Ausf H

Plates 308-312. Pz Kpfw IV Ausf J: Plate 309, with wire mesh side-skirts; Plate 311, with three track-return rollers; Plate 312, a rear view showing the new exhaust system.

Plate 1024 (Page 259). Pz Kpfw IV Ausf J.
Plate 1027 (Page 259). Pz Kpfw IV Ausf J with wire mesh Schürzen.

310

311

308

309

312

Panzerkampfwagen IV als Tauchpanzer

Other designation: Tauchpanzer IV
Type: Submersible medium support tank

42 converted from July 1940

Crew: 5	Engine: Maybach HL120TRM	
Weight (tons): 20	Gearbox: 6 forward, 1 reverse	
Length (metres): 5.92	Speed (km/hr): 40	
Width (metres): 2.84	Range (km): 200	
Height (metres): 2.68	Radio: FuG5	

Armament: One 7.5cm KwK37 L/24	One 7.92mm MG34	One 7.92mm MG34
Traverse: 360° (electric)	=	20° left 20° right (hand)
Elevation: −8° +20°	=	−10° +15°
Sight: TZF56b	=	KgZF2
Ammunition: 80?	2,700	

Plate 313. Tauchpanzer IV towing a fuel trailer, somewhere on the Russian Front in 1941

Armour (mm/angle):	Front	Side	Rear	Top/Bottom
Turret:	30/10°	20/25°	20/0°–24°	10/83°–90°
Superstructure:	30/7°	20/0°	20/9°	12/84°–90°
Hull:	30/12°	20/0°	20/10°	10/90°
Gun mantlet:	35/0°–29°			

History: The Tauchpanzer IV were converted in the same way as for the underwater version of the Pz Kpfw III. Additional sealing was provided for the engine air-intakes, and the exhaust was fitted with non-return valves in place of the normal mufflers. The cupola, mantlet and MG mountings were all covered with a waterproof fabric. The driver's visor was made watertight by a special metal cover with a vision block. An inflatable rubber tube was also used to seal the turret ring. The air was drawn from the usual surface float.
Combat service: After the abandonment of 'Sea Lion'—the Invasion of England—in late 1940, the Tauchpanzer were issued to ordinary Panzer units. The bulk of them went to the 18th Panzer Division, while the remainder were issued to the 6th Panzer Regiment of the 3rd Panzer Division. The 18th Panzer Division crossed the River Bug (Russia) underwater on 22 June 1941.

Panzerbefehlswagen mit 7.5cm KwK L/48 / Panzerbeobachtungswagen IV

Type: Medium command tank / observation post tank

Manufacturer: Nibelungenwerke
97 converted to Pz Bef Wg from March to September 1944
90 converted to Pz Beob Wg from July 1944 to March 1945

Crew: 5	Engine: Maybach HL120TRM & TRM112
Weight (tons): 25	Gearbox: 6 forward, 1 reverse
Length (metres): 7.02	Speed (km/hr): 40
Width (metres): 2.88	Range (km): 210
Height (metres): 2.68	Radio: FuG5 + FuG7 or FuG8
	FuG4 + FuG8 (Pz Beob Wg)

Armament: One 7.5cm KwK40 L/48	One 7.92mm MG34	One 7.92mm MG34
Traverse: 360° (hand)	=	hand
Elevation: −8° +20°	=	
Sight: TZF5f/1 or /2	=	KgZF2

Armour (mm/angle):	Front	Side	Rear	Top/Bottom
Turret:	50/10°	30/26°	30/15°	15/84°–90°
Superstructure:	80/10°	30/0°	20/11°	12/85°–90°
Hull:	80/14°	30/0°	20/8°	10/90°
Gun mantlet:	50/0°–30°			

Plate 314. Pz Beob Wg IV.

History: By 1944, the number of Pz Bef Wg based on Pz Kpfw III was insufficient, and a more suitable command vehicle which would be inconspicuous alongside Pz Kpfw IV was required. The aerial for the FuG5 was mounted on top of the turret roof, and a star antenna for the additional radio was fitted to the right-hand side of the tail plate of the hull. A TSF 1 periscope was fitted in the turret roof. The Beobachtungswagen was a similar vehicle, carrying different radio equipment. It was introduced shortly after conversion of old Pz Kpfw III to Beob Wg had been halted because of unavailability of Pz Kpfw III.
Specific features: Additional radio mast on the rear hull plate, and relocation of the aerial to the turret roof. A rotating mount for the periscope was fitted on the left side of the turret.
Combat service: Pz Bef Wg served with tank detachments equipped with Pz Kpfw IV, while the Beob Wg were issued as replacements to the Hummel (Bumble Bee) batteries.

Sturmpanzer IV (Sd Kfz 166)

Other designations: Brummbär, StuG IV mit 15cm StuH43
Type: Assault infantry gun on tank chassis

Manufacturer: Deutsche Eisenwerke
Chassis Nos.: 80801–84400, 86601–87100, 89101–
298 produced at Duisburg from April 1943 to March 1945 plus 8
converted from Pz Kpfw IV

Crew: 5
Weight (tons): 28.2
Length (metres): 5.93
Width (metres): 2.88
Height (metres): 2.52

Engine: Maybach HL120TRM & TRM112
Gearbox: 6 forward, 1 reverse
Speed (km/hr): 40
Range (km): 210
Radio: FuG5 + FuG2

Armament: One15cm StuH43 L/12   One 7.92 mm MG34*   One 7.92 mm MG34
Traverse: 10° left 10° right (hand)   15° left 15° right (hand) loose
Elevation: −5° +30°   −7° +20°   loose
Sight: SflZF   Kg ZF2   direct
Ammunition: 38?   600

Armour (mm/angle):

	Front	Side	Rear	Top/Bottom
Superstructure:	100/40°	50/15°	30/25° +0°	20/83° +10/90°
Hull:	80/12°	30/0°	20/10°	10/90°

*Late production only

315

History: The Sturmpanzer was developed by Alkett, who designed the superstructure, and Krupp, who altered the design of their Pz Kpfw IV chassis. On 20 October 1942, after seeing Alkett's plans, Hitler demanded that forty to sixty Brummbär be built as soon as possible. On 7 February 1943, it was decided that the forty must be completed by 12 May 1943, with a following production run of twenty. After this initial run from April to May 1943, the production of a long-term series went ahead in November 1943 and continued until the end of the war.

Specific features: The Brummbär had a box-like superstructure, housing the 15cm StuH43, mounted on a normal Pz Kpfw IV chassis. The first series was mounted on fifty-two new Pz Kpfw IV Ausf G chassis plus eight rebuilt Ausf E and F chassis, instead of the 80mm armour on the hull front, the first sixty had a 50mm armour plate bolted to the basic 50mm hull front. This first series had a sliding-shutter visor for the driver, similar to that mounted on the Tiger I. In the later series, the driver was provided with a periscope and a StuH43/1 was fitted. The final series, produced from April 1944, had a redesigned superstructure with a ball-mounted machine-gun in the top left-hand corner of the front plate, and a cupola for the commander.

316

Combat services: Sturmpanzerabteilung 216 was issued with the first Brummbär, and was rushed off to the Eastern front for the summer offensive at Kursk. This unit was also active in defensive battles near Zaparozhye up to October 1943. Three additional Sturmpanzer detachments (217, 218 and 219) were formed during the war, and fought on the major eastern and western fronts, and also in Italy.

Plates 315-317. Sturmpanzer IV: top, first series; centre, middle production model; bottom, late production model.

317

Sturmgeschütz IV (7.5cm StuK40 L/48) (Sd Kfz 167)

Other designation: Gerät 820
Type: Assault gun / tank destroyer on tank chassis

Plates 318-320. StuG IV: Plates 319 and 320 show the late production version, with remote-controlled machine-gun; Plate 320 shows the vertical exhaust mufflers.
Plate 1032 (Page 260). StuG IV with additional concrete protection.

Manufacturer: Krupp-Gruson
Chassis Nos.: 89301–89400, 100001–101108
First 31 on converted Pz Kpfw IV chassis, plus 1,108 produced from December 1943 to March 1945

Crew: 4	Engine: Maybach HL120TRM & TRM112
Weight (tons): 23	
Length (metres): 6.7	Gearbox: 6 forward, 1 reverse
Width (metres): 2.95	Speed (km/hr): 38
Height (metres): 2.2	Range (km): 210
	Radio: FuG15+FuG16

Armament: One 7.5cm StuK40 L/48		One 7.92mm MG34
Traverse: 20° (hand)		loose; later, 360° (hand)
Elevation: −6° +20°		loose, later, N/A
Sight: SflZf1a		direct, later, Periskop 3×8°
Ammunition: 63?		600

Armour (mm/angle):	Front	Side	Rear	Top/Bottom
Superstructure:	80/10°	30/11°	30/0°	11/75°−90°
Hull:	80/14°	30/0°	20/10°	10/90°
Gun mantlet:		Saukopfblende		

History: In 1943, a trials vehicle was built to determine whether the StuG III superstructure could be fitted to the Pz Kpfw IV chassis. This proved to be worthwhile when on 6 December 1943, Hitler demanded that the superstructure of the StuG III be fitted to the Pz Kpfw IV chassis, to replace the production of the StuG III which had been lost when Alkett was heavily bombed. The first 30 had chassis provided by Nibelungenwerke from their normal Pz Kpfw production. Krupp halted Pz Kpfw IV production in December 1943, switching totally to the production of the StuG IV in January 1944.

Specific features: The StuG IV had a normal Pz Kpfw IV chassis with a StuG III superstructure mounting the 7.5cm StuK40. The driver's position was moved from the normal superstructure to an armoured cab for the driver with two periscopes and an access hatch in the roof. Some StuG IV had additional protection provided by 6in thick concrete slabs in the front of the superstructure and driver's cab. The cast Saukopfblende mantlet was introduced in February 1944. In the summer of 1944 the external machine-gun shield for the loader was replaced by a remote-controlled machine-gun mount, and a 'Nähverteidigungsgerät' (close-defence weapon) was mounted in the superstructure roof.

Combat service: The StuG IV was issued to independent StuG brigades of the artillery and to assault gun detachments, Panzerjäger detachments and tank detachments of infantry and Panzer divisions. Acting as both an assault gun for support of the infantry, and as a tank-destroyer, the StuG IV was employed in the same manner and in the same type of units as the StuG III.

Sturmgeschütz neuer Art mit 7.5cm PaK L/48 auf Fahrgestell Panzerkampfwagen IV (Sd Kfz 162)

Other designations: Jagdpanzer IV, Gerät 821, Pz Jäg IV
Type: Tank destroyer

Manufacturer: Vomag
Chassis Nos.: 320001–321725
769 produced from January to November 1944, plus 26 chassis

Crew: 4	Engine: Maybach HL120TRM
Weight (tons): 24–25	Gearbox: 6 forward, 1 reverse
Length (metres): 6.85	Speed (km/hr): 40
Width (metres): 3.17	Range (km): 210
Height (metres): 1.85	Radio: FuG Spr f

Armament: One 7.5cm PaK39 L/48	Two, later one, 7.92mm MG42
Traverse: 20° (hand)	hand
Elevation: −5° +15°	
Sight: SflZF1a	
Ammunition: 79?	600

Armour (mm/angle):	Front	Side	Rear	Top/Bottom
Superstructure:	60/50°	30/30°	20/35°	20/90°
Hull (upper):	60/45°	30/0°	20/11°	10/90°
(lower):	50/55°	30/0°	20/9°	12+10−10/90°
Gun mantlet:	80/Saukopfblende			

History: The Jagdpanzer IV was developed as an improved version of the StuG III and eventually, was to take its place. A soft steel model was presented to Hitler in October 1943, and a final prototype in December 1943. Vomag produced the Jagdpanzer IV alongside their Pz Kpfw IV until May 1944 when the Pz Kpfw IV was completely replaced by Jagdpanzer IV production. Twenty-six chassis were issued as Bergegerät.

Specific features: The Jagdpanzer chassis had the same basic hull, suspension and drive train as the Pz Kpfw chassis from which it was designed. However, the front hull had been altered by replacing the vertical front plate with a sharp-nosed front consisting of two plates. The superstructure was built up from sloping plates. The gun was mounted in the superstructure front accompanied by two machine gun ports and the driver's periscope. In May 1944, the armour thickness of the upper hull front and superstructure front was increased to 80mm and the side superstructure armour was increased from 30mm to 40mm. The 0-Serie had utilized a front superstructure plate with rounded sides, but this was dropped for production and ballistic reasons.

Combat service: The Jagdpanzer IV were issued to tank-hunter

321

322

323

achments of Panzer divisions from March 1944. They first engaged enemy armour in Italy with the Hermann Göring Division, then in Russia with the 4th and 5th Panzer Divisions, and finally in France in June 1944, with the Panzerlehr Division, the 9th Panzer Division and the 12th SS Panzer Division, when 62 AFV's awaited the Allied thrust from the beaches of Normandy.

Plates 321-323. Jgd Pz IV: Plate 321 shows a pre-production model with 7.5cm PaK39 (L/43). Note the curved front corners on the superstructure.

Panzer IV/70(V) (Sd Kfz 162/1)

Other designations: Panzerwagen 604/10, Gerät 559, Pz Jäg IV mit 7.5cm PaK 42 (L/70)
Type: Tank destroyer

Manufacturer: Vomag
Chassis Nos.: 320001–321725
930 produced from August 1944 to March 1945

Crew: 4	Engine: Maybach HL120TRM
Weight (tons): 25.8	Gearbox: 6 forward, 1 reverse
Length (metres): 8.5	Speed (km/hr): 35
Width (metres): 3.17	Range (km): 210
Height (metres): 1.85	Radio: FuG Spr f

Armament: One 7.5cm PaK42 L/70   One 7.92mm MG42
Traverse: $10°$ left $10°$ right (hand)   hand
Elevation: $-5°$ $+15°$
Sight: SflZF
Ammunition: 55?   600

Armour (mm/angle):	Front	Side	Rear	Top/Bottom
Superstructure:	80/50°	40/30°	20/35°	20/90°
Hull (upper):	80/45°	30/0°	20/11°	10/90°
(lower):	50/55°	30/0°	20/9°	12+10−10/90°
Gun mantlet:	Saukopfblende			

History: The Panzer IV/70(V) was an improved version of the Jagdpanzer IV with the PaK42 L/70 mounted in place of the shorter PaK39 L/48. It went into production along-with the Jagdpanzer IV which it replaced completely in December 1944.

Specific features: As for the Jagdpanzer IV. The 7.5cm PaK was held at $+13°$ elevation by a travel lock when moving in non-combat areas. Late models were to have the Vorsatz P mount (additional machine-pistol mount) in the roof over the gunner. This was a mount for the 7.92mm MP44 with a curved barrel attachment. The long gun and 80mm superstructure front made the Pz IV/70(V)

nose heavy with resultant failures of the rubber-tyred wheels. Later models, therefore, were fitted with steel-rimmed wheels at the first two wheel stations. Late models also had only three return rollers (Ausf J Chassis)

Combat service: In August 1944, the Panzer IV/70(V) was issued to the 105th and 106th Independent Panzer Brigades. Other tank brigades received these vehicles together with the independent Panzerjäger detachments, and the tank-hunter detachments of the Panzer divisions. The Panzer IV/70(V) was first used in numbers during the Ardennes offensive in December 1944, when approximately 137 were available.

Plates 324-326. Pz IV/70(V); that in Plate 325 has Schürzen (armour side-skirts); Plate 326 shows the late production model, with three return rollers (Ausf J Chassis)
Plate 1031 (Page 260) Pz IV/70(V)

324

325

326

Panzer IV/70(A)

Other designations: Panzerwagen 604/9, Gerät 558
Type: Tank destroyer on tank chassis

Manufacturer: Nibelungenwerke
Chassis Nos.: 91501–
278 produced from August 1944 to March 1945

Crew: 4
Weight (tons): 28
Length (metres): 8.44
Width (metres): 2.88
Height (metres): 2.35

Engine: Maybach HL120TRM & TRM 112
Gearbox: 6 forward, 1 reverse
Speed (km/hr): 38
Range (km): 320
Radio: FuG5

Armament: One 7.5cm PaK42 L/70   One 7.92mm MG42
Traverse: 10° left 10° right (hand)   hand
Elevation: −5° +15°
Sight: SflZF

Armour (mm/angle):

	Front	Side	Rear	Top/Bottom
Superstructure (upper):	80/50°	40/30°	20/35°	20/90°
(lower):	80/10°	40/30°	20/10°	10/90°
Hull:	80/14°	30/0°	20/10°	10/90°
Gun mantlet:	Saukopfblende			

History: The Panzer IV/70(A) was the Alkett version of a tank-destroyer mounting the long-barrelled 75mm PaK42. It was mounted on the normal chassis of the Pz Kpfw IV from the same production-line producing normal Pz Kpfw IV Ausf J at Nibelungenwerke. The Panzer IV/70(V) and (A) were produced simultaneously from August 1944 to March 1945.

Specific features: The Panzer IV/70(A) had a chassis unaltered from the Pz Kpfw IV series. The superstructure was of similar design to that on the Panzer IV/70(V) and differed only in that the lower superstructure was vertical, extending out over the tracks, and a visor was provided for the driver. The gun was mounted in the front of the sloped, upper superstructure, in the same type of mount used for the Panzer IV/70(V). The Panzer IV/70(A) was nose-heavy and was, therefore, fitted with steel-rimmed wheels on the first four bogie stations.

Combat service: The Panzer IV/70(A) was employed in the same manner as the normal Pz Kpfw IV in tank detachments, or as an assault gun in place of the tank-hunter in independent assault gun brigades. Most of them were issued to or were replacements for units fighting in the East.

327

Plates 327-329. Pz IV/70(A): top, the prototype vehicle; the other two photographs show a vehicle captured by the French. (Note, in Plate 329, the hit it has received on the front superstructure.)

328

329

10.5cm K18 auf Panzer Selbstfahrlafette IVa

Type: Self-propelled gun on tank chassis

Manufacturer: Krupp-Gruson
Chassis Nos.:
2 produced in 1941
Crew: 5

Weight (tons): 25
Length (metres): 7.52
Width (metres): 2.84
Height (metres): 3.25

Engine: Maybach HL120TRM
Gearbox: 6 forward, 1 reverse
Speed (km/hr): 40
Range (km): 200
Radio: FuG5

Armament: One 10.5cm K18 L/52
Traverse: 8° left 8° right (hand)
Elevation: −15° +10°
Ammunition: 25?

One 7.92mm MG34
loose
loose
loose

Armour (mm/angle):	Front	Side	Rear	Top/Bottom
Turret:	30/14°	20/14°	20/20°	open
Superstructure:	50/10°	20/0°	20/10°	12/90°
Hull:	50/12°	20/0°	20/10°	10/90°
Gun mantlet:	50/10°			

History: This self-propelled gun was ordered from Krupp for the purpose of destroying heavily fortified bunkers. Two prototypes were built, and these were presented to Hitler on 31 March 1941. At a discussion with Hitler on 26 May 1941, it was decided that this type of vehicle be developed as a heavy Panzerjäger (alongside a proposed 12.8cm Panzerjäger) so as to be able to engage super-heavy tanks anticipated from Britain and elsewhere. Production of the 10.5cm K18 was to start in the spring of 1942. By this time, however, requirements had changed and manufacture did not take place.

Specific features: The 10.5cm K18, fitted with a muzzle-brake, was capable of penetrating 111mm of 30° sloped armour at 2,000 metres, or 132mm of vertical armour. The high, open-topped superstructure was moderately armoured and gave an indication of forthcoming lightly armoured Panzerjäger vehicles.

Combat service: The two 10.5cm K18 auf Pz Sfl IVa, were issued to the 521st Panzerjäger Detachment for the proposed attack on Gibraltar. Later, they were used in Russia with the 3rd Panzer Division. One vehicle was destroyed and the second was returned to Germany in October 1941, after considerable success against enemy armour.

330

Plates 330-332. 10.5cm K18 auf Pz Sf IVa. Plate 330 shows the vehicle on operations in Russia.

331

332

8.8cm PaK43/1 (L/71) auf Geschützwagen III und IV (Sf) (SdKfz 164)

Other designations: Hornisse, Nashorn
Type: Self-propelled heavy anti-tank gun on tracked carriage

Manufacturer: Deutsche-Eisenwerke
Chassis Nos.: 310001–310494
494 produced from February 1943 to March 1945
Crew: 4
Weight (tons): 24
Length (metres): 8.44
Width (metres): 2.86
Height (metres): 2.65

Engine: Maybach HL120TRM
Gearbox: 6 forward, 1 reverse
Speed (km/hr): 42
Range (km): 215
Radio: FuG Spr d

Armament: One 8.8cm PaK43/1 L/71
Traverse: 30° (hand)
Elevation: −5° +20°
Sight: SflZF1a, Rblf36

One 7.92mm MG34
loose
loose
direct
600

Armour (mm/angle):	Front	Side	Rear	Top/Bottom
Superstructure:	10/37°	10/16°	10/10°	open
Hull:	30/20°	20/0°	20/10°	15/90°
Gun shield:	10/37°			

History: The Nashorn (Rhinoceros), later known as Hornisse (Hornet), was designed in 1942, to provide an adequate self-propelled mount for the 8.8cm PaK43. In October 1942, it was decided to have 100 Hornisse built by 12 May 1943, in time for the summer offensive. The initial order was for a series of 500, of which 494 were completed.

Specific features: The 8.8cm PaK43/1 was mounted on the same Pz Kpfw III/IV chassis as the Hummel. Refer to the Hummel (overleaf) for details of the superstructure and chassis.

Combat service: Hornissen were issued to schwere Panzerjäger detachments which were independent units attached to a Korps or Armee, to provide a mobile, highly effective tank-killing force. Their first service was with the 655th schwere Panzerjägerabteilung on the Eastern Front in the summer of 1943. Five other heavy tank-hunter detachments were formed, and saw action in Italy and in the West, as well as in the East.

333

334

Plates 333-334.
Hornisse; left, in action on the Russian Front.

Plate 984 (Page 252)
Interior of Hornisse

15cm Schwere Panzerhaubitze auf Geschützwagen III/IV (Sf) (Sd Kfz 165)

Other designations: Hummel, Gerät 807
Type: Self-propelled heavy howitzer on tracked carriage

Manufacturer: Alkett, Deutsche-Eisenwerke
Chassis Nos.: 320001– , 325001–
Crew: 6
Weight (tons): 24
Length (metres): 7.17
Width (metres): 2.97
Height (metres): 2.81

Engine: HL120TRM
Gearbox: 6 forward, 1 reverse
Speed (km/hr): 42
Range (km): 215
Radio: FuG Spr f

Armament:	One 15cm sFH18/1 L/30	One 7.92mm MG34
Traverse:	15° left 15° right (hand)	loose
Elevation:	−3° +42°	loose
Sight:	Rblf36	direct
Ammunition:	18	600

Armour (mm/angle):	Front	Side	Rear	Top/Bottom
Superstructure:	10/37°	10/16°	10/10°	open
Hull:	30/20°	20/0°	20/10°	15/90°
Gun shield:	10/37°			

History: To provide armoured units with artillery support on an armoured fully-tracked chassis, the WaA (Waffenamt=Ordnance Department) had proposed that the 10.5cm leFH be mounted on the Pz Kpfw III and IV chassis. On 25 July 1942, it was decided to mount the 15cm sFH on the Pz Kpfw III and IV chassis, since the Pz Kpfw II chassis was acceptable as a mount for the leFH. Alkett was entrusted with the development of the vehicle, and presented a prototype to Hitler in October 1943. The Hummel (Bumble-Bee) was to be a mere 'Zwischenlösung' (interim solution) until chassis designed specifically as self-propelled gun-platforms could be developed and produced. By 12 May 1943, 100 Hummel were to be built for use in the planned summer offensive. On the same chassis, 157 Munitions Fahrzeuge (ammunition carriers) were produced to provide ammunition for the Hummel batteries.

Specific features: The Pz Kpfw III/IV chassis used a lengthened Pz Kpfw IV hull as the basic design, but with the motor moved forward to a central position. It retained the basic suspension of the Pz Kpfw IV except for the spacing between components. The drive sprocket was of the type designed for the Pz Kpfw III. The open-topped fighting compartment was enclosed on all four sides by slanted armour plates bolted to the hull. The glacis plate was extended, and a small compartment for the driver was fitted to it on the left-hand side. The Hummel, produced from early 1944, had a crew compartment for the driver and radio operator, extending across the full width of the hull. The 15cm sFH18/1 was mounted in the middle over the engine, and this gave the vehicle a very high silhouette. The Munitions Fahrzeuge varied from the Hummel by having a plate bolted over the front of the superstructure to close the gap normally filled by the gun and its shield, and its internal stowage was different.

Combat service: The Hummel were issued to the heavy batteries of the armoured artillery detachments (SP) of several Panzer divisions early in 1943, and first saw action at Kursk. Initially, each Panzer division had only six Hummel in a single heavy battery, then, two Munitions Fahrzeuge were added and, later, some Panzer divisions received a second heavy battery.

Plates 335-336. Hummel: Plate 335 shows a late production model, with redesigned front superstructure; Plate 336 (below) shows Hummel vehicles advancing in Russia.

Plate 337 (opposite page, top). The Hummel prototype vehicle.
Plates 338-339 (opposite page, top). The Hummel ammunition carrier: Plate 338, a vehicle captured by the Americans; Plate 339, the Munitions Fahrzeug crossing a river in Russia.

335

336

338

339

3.7cm FlaK auf Fahrgestell Panzerkampfwagen IV (Sf) (Sd Kfz 161/3)

Other designation: Möbelwagen (see also P.116)
Type: Self-propelled anti-aircraft gun on tank chassis

Manufacturer: Deutsche-Eisenwerke
Chassis Nos.: 93201–
240 produced from March 1944 to March 1945

Crew: 6	Engine: Maybach HL120TRM
Weight (tons): 24	Gearbox: 6 forward, 1 reverse
Length (metres): 5.92	Speed (km/hr): 38
Width (metres): 2.95	Range (km): 200
Height (metres): 2.73	Radio: FuG5 + FuG2

Armament:	One 3.7cm FlaK43 L/60	One 7.92mm MG42
Traverse:	360° (hand)	loose
Elevation:	−6° +90°	loose
Sight:	Flakvisier 3 × 8°	direct
Ammunition:	416	

Armour (mm/angle):	Front	Side	Rear	Top/Bottom
Superstructure:	50/9°	30/0°	20/11°	
Hull:	80/14°	30/0°	20/9°	10/90°
Gun shield:	25/0°	25/0°	25/0°	open

History: The Möbelwagen was developed to give the Panzer units mobile anti-aircraft protection which could accompany the Pz Kpfw into action. The vehicle was seen as a temporary solution, to be final solution, the 3.7cm Zwillingsflak (dual AA mount) on the Panther

replaced later by the Kugelblitz (Ball Lightning; AA tank) and, the chassis. Production was planned to start in February 1944 at 20 per month, later to increase to 30 per month. The chassis were provided by Krupp-Gruson.

Specific features: The 3.7cm FlaK43 was mounted on the basic Pz Kpfw IV hull. Protection was provided for the crew by a four-sided superstructure normally carried in the vertical position. The super-structure sides could be dropped to a horizontal position so that the gun could be traversed 360° at a low elevation.

Combat service: Issued to Flugabwehrzüge (AA platoons) of Panzer regiments in Panzer divisions.

Plates 340-341. Möbelwagen: right, with the superstructure sides lowered.

340

341

Flakpanzer IV/2cm Vierling

Other designations: Wirbelwind, Pz Fgst IV/3
Type: Anti-aircraft tank on obsolete tank chassis

Manufacturer: Ostbau
Chassis Nos.: 82001–90000
86 converted from Pz Kpfw IV from July to November 1944
1 prototype converted in May 1944

Crew: 5	Engine: Maybach HL120TRM
Weight (tons): 22	Gearbox: 6 forward, 1 reverse
Length (metres): 5.92	Speed (km/hr): 38
Width (metres): 2.9	Range (km): 200
Height (metres): 2.76	Radio: FuG5 + FuG2

Armament:	One 2cm Flakvierling 38	One 7.92mm MG34
Traverse:	360° (hand)	hand
Elevation:	−10° +90°	
Sight:	Flakvisier 38/40	KgZF2
Ammunition:	3,200	1,350

Armour (mm/angle):	Front	Side	Rear	Top/Bottom
Turret:	16/25°	16/36°	16/12°−22°	open
Superstructure:	80/10°	30/0°	20/11°	12/85°−90°
Hull:	80/12°	30/0°	20/9°	10/90°
Gun shield:	10/round			

History: The Wirbelwind was developed as a mount for anti-aircraft guns on Pz Kpfw IV chassis which had been returned from the front for major overhaul. They were intended to supplement production of the Möbelwagen. In the autumn of 1944, production of the Wirbelwind ceased, since the 2cm Flakvierling was not proving so effective as the 3.7cm FlaK.

Specific features: The turret was removed from normal Pz Kpfw IV and replaced by an open-topped turret, in which the Flakvierling 38 was mounted. Some vehicles had only 50mm frontal armour since early Ausf F to G were converted for use as the chassis.

Combat service: Issued to the Flugabwehrzug (AA platoons) of Panzer regiments in Panzer divisions.

Plates 342–345. Wirbelwind.

Flakpanzer IV/3.7cm FlaK

Other designations: Ostwind I, Gerät 582, Flakpanzerwagen 604/17
Type: Anti-aircraft tank on tank chassis

Plates 346-348. Ostwind I.

Manufacturer: Ostbau
Chassis Nos.: 82001–93000
1 prototype converted in July 1944
36 converted from Pz Kpfw IV plus 7 new production from December 1944 to March 1945

Crew: 6	Engine: Maybach HL120TRM112	
Weight (tons): 25	Gearbox: 6 forward, 1 reverse	
Length (metres): 5.92	Speed (km/hr): 38	
Width (metres): 2.95	Range (km): 200	
Height (metres): 3	Radio: FuG5 + FuG2	

Armament:	One 3.7cm FlaK43/1 L/60	One 7.92mm MG34	One 7.92mm MG34 or MG42
Traverse:	360° (hand)	hand	loose
Elevation:	−6° +90°		loose
Sight:	Flakvisier 3×8° KgZF2		direct
Ammunition:	1,000		

Armour (mm/angle):	Front	Side	Rear	Top/Bottom
Turret:	25/37°	25/30°	25/30°	open
Superstructure:	80/10°	30/0°	20/11°	12/85°–90°
Hull:	80/12°	30/0°	20/9°	10/90°
Gun shield:	25/round			

History: On 18 August 1944, an order for 100 Ostwind (east wind) was placed, after successful trials had been held in July. Replacing the Wirbelwind, Ostwind I provided the Panzer troops with the more effective 3.7cm FlaK43. Both Ostwind I and the Möbelwagen were to be replaced by Kugelblitz, but because of delays, only two Kugelblitz were produced, and seven of the chassis were used to produce Ostwind I.

Specific features: A six-sided open-topped turret was mounted, in place of the normal turret, on converted Pz Kpfw IV chassis. The turret could be traversed 360° to bring fast, effective fire on air or ground targets.

Combat service: Issued to the Flugabwehrzug (AA platoons) of Panzer regiments in Panzer divisions.

346

347

848

Leichte Flakpanzer IV (3cm) 'Kugelblitz'

Other designations: Gerät 556, Flakpanzerwagen 604/4
Type: Anti-aircraft tank

Manufacturer: Deutsche-Eisenwerke
2 delivered in February 1945
Production plan called for 30 per month from March 1945

Crew: 5	Engine: Maybach HL120TRM112
Weight (tons): 25	Gearbox: 6 forward, 1 reverse
Length (metres): 5.92	Speed (km/hr): 38
Width (metres): 2.95	Range (km): 200
Height (metres): 2.3	Radio: FuG5+FuG2

Armament: Two 3cm MK103/38   One 7.92mm MG34
Traverse: 360° (mechanical)   hand
Elevation: −5° +70°
Sight: KgZF2
Ammunition: 1,200   900

Armour (mm/angle):	Front	Side	Rear	Top/Bottom
Turret:	30/round +20/60°	20/round +20/60°		20/90°
Superstructure:	80/10°	30/0°	20/11°	12/85°−90°
Hull:	80/12°	30/0°	20/9°	10/90°

Gun mantlet: see turret

History: In April 1944, at a conference with Hitler, the possibility of arming a Pz Kpfw IV with a 3cm Doppelflak 303 (Dual AA Mount) turret, similar to that proposed for U-boats, was discussed. Col-General Guderian was demanding effective defence against fighter-bombers. Development was undertaken by Rheinmetall and Daimler-Benz and, as a result, an order was placed for production from September 1944. In November, production was ordered to start as soon as possible, but because of the cancellation of both Pz IV and Pz III/IV production in mid-1945, an order was placed for a similar

Plate 349. Kugelblutz (Ball lightning).

Kugelblitz based on the 38(d) chassis. The first prototypes were not delivered until February 1945.
Specific features: Pz Kpfw IV hull and superstructure were unchanged, but a Tiger turret-race was fitted (1.9m dia). The turret design was revolutionary. The mantlet, in the form of a great sphere, rotated within a low, open-topped turret. The two 3cm guns and three crew were carried inside the sphere. Traversing speed of 10° per second and 6° to 7° per second elevation were achieved. The 3cm MK103 was an adaptation of the aircraft gun, and was belt-fed (200 rds), rate of fire 650rpm.
Combat service: Two Kugelblitz were completed and intended for on the Western front. No record exists of any combat service.

10.5cm leFH18/1(Sf) auf Geschützwagen IVb (Sd Kfz 165/1)

Other designation: Pz Sf IVb (3 Serie)
Type: Self-propelled light field howitzer on tracked carriage

Manufacturer: Krupp-Gruson
Experimental series of 8 produced in November 1942

Crew: 4	Engine: Maybach HL66P
Weight (tons): 17	Gearbox: 6 forward, 1 reverse
Length (metres): 5.9	Speed (km/hr): 45
Width (metres): 2.87	Range (km): 250
Height (metres): 2.25	Radio: FuG Spr f

Armament: One 10.5cm leFH18/1 L/28
Traverse: 70° (hand)
Elevation: −10° +40°
Sight: SflZF/Rblf36
Ammunition: 60

Armour (mm/angle):	Front	Side	Rear	Top/Bottom
Turret:	20/20°	14.5/15°	14.5/10° open	
Superstructure:	30/10°	14.5/0°	14.5/20°	10/90°
Hull:	30/12°	14.5/0°	14.5/10°	14.5/90°
Gun mantlet:	20/0°−70°			

History: From 1941, various proposals had been made for a self-propelled version of the 10.5cm leFH18. Krupp designed a special vehicle based on the Pz Kpfw IV components, using a smaller engine, hull and three-station bogies per side, with larger road wheels. Krupp's Pz Sf IVb had a partly-traversing turret which was open-topped. A Test Series of eight units was ordered. Production vehicles were to have the Maybach HL90 which gave 320PS. Production was cancelled because, on the subject of self-propelled artillery, official thinking was tending towards carriages capable of all-round traverse, with ability to dismount the weapon. Alkett now proposed an interim solution of mounting the 10.5cm leFH18 on the Pz Kpfw II chassis, and this was accepted as the Wespe (wasp). In a final attempt to have their special GW IVb chassis utilized, Krupp offered the design as the basis for the Jagdpanzer IV, designated Panzerjäger IVb(E39) mit 7.5cm PaK39 L/48, but the normal Pz Kpfw IV chassis was again utilized.

Combat service: Troop-tested in Russia.

Plates 350-351. 10.5cm leFH18/1(Sf) auf Gesch IVb.

350

35

10.5cm leFH18/1 L/28 auf Waffenträger GW IVb

Other designation: 'Heuschrecke 10'
Type: Self-propelled light field howitzer on tracked weapon carriage

Manufacturer: Krupp
Chassis Nos.: 582501–582503
3 prototypes built in 1943

Crew: 5
Weight (tons): 23
Length (metres): 6
Width (metres): 3
Height (metres): 3

Engine: Maybach HL90
Gearbox: 6 forward, 1 reverse
Speed (km/hr): 45
Range (km): 300
Radio: FuG Spr f

Armament: One 10.5cm leFH18/1 L/28
Traverse: 360° (hand)
Elevation: −0° +68°
Sight: SflZF2
Ammunition: 60

Armour (mm/angle):	Front	Side	Rear	Top/Bottom
Turret:	30/30°	16/20°	16/25°	open
Superstructure:	30/20°	16/0°	16/20°	10/90°
Hull:	30/20°	16/0°	16/20°	10/90°
Gun mantlet:	30/round			

History: The Heuschrecke 10 was developed by Krupp from 1942. Unlike their earlier GW IVb, the turret was fully rotating and could be removed and emplaced on the ground. A lifting gantry was provided on the vehicle itself. Separate wheels and mounting-pad components were carried on the Heuschrecke. The chassis was built on the basis of the Pz III/IV chassis developed for the Hummel. A more powerful 10.5cm leFH43 was intended for the production vehicle, together with a HL100 motor. Another proposal was for a chassis based on the ill-fated Leopard design, but later, the chassis was to be based on the Panther, to give the Heuschrecke 15.

352

353

354

Plates 352-355.
Heuschrecke 10. Plate 353 shows the stowage position for the turret wheels; Plates 354 and 355 show the turret being removed from the chassis, to adopt the role of armoured pillbox.

355

Leichte PzH18/40/2 auf Geschützwagen III/IV (Sf)

Type: Self-propelled light field howitzer on tracked weapons carriage

Manufacturer: Deutsche-Eisenwerke
Prototype only
Crew: 5
Weight (tons): 25
Length (metres): 6.8
Width (metres): 3
Height (metres): 2.9

Engine: Maybach HL90
Gearbox: 6 forward, 1 reverse
Speed (km/hr): 45
Range (km): 300
Radio: FuG Spr f

Armament: One 10.5cm leFH18/40/2 L/28
Traverse: 360° (hand)
Elevation: −10° +70°
Sight: SflZF2
Ammunition: 80

Armour (mm/angle):	Front	Side	Rear	Top/Bottom
Turret:	10/25°	10/25°	10/12°	open
Superstructure:	30/20°	10/0°	10/10°	10/90°
Hull:	20/20°	20/0°	20/10°	10/90°
Gun shield:	10/0°			

356

History: This was the Rheinmetall-Borsig prototype built in competition with the Krupp Heuschrecke 10, and a similar vehicle proposed by Skoda on their T–25. Simpler than the Krupp, it featured a full leFH18/40 field-gun mounted in the rotating turret. The wheels and field trails for this gun were carried on the rear of the hull, for fitting when the gun was dismounted.

Plates 356-357. 10.5cm leFH18/40/2 auf Fgst Pz Kpfw III/IV (Sf); Plate 357 shows the two gun wheels and trails stowed at the rear of the vehicle.

357

Plates 358-363. Two projected designs based on the Pz Kpfw III/IV chassis. Plates 358-360: Mittlerer Waffenträger 12.8cm K81. Plates 361-363: Mittlerer Waffenträger 15cm sFH18 L/29.5.

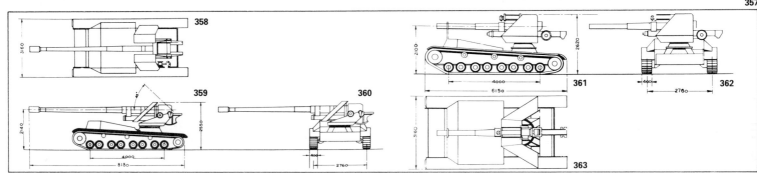

Brückenleger IV

Other designation: BL IV
Type: Bridge-layer on tank chassis

Plate 364. The Krupp version of BL IV.

Manufacturer: Krupp, Magirus
Chassis Nos.: 80301–80748
20 produced from February to May 1940 on Pz Kpfw IV Ausf C and D
Crew: 2
Weight (tons): 28
Length (metres): 11
Width (metres): 3
Height (metres): 3.54 (Krupp)
3.28 (Magirus)

Engine: Maybach HL120TRM
Gearbox: 6 forward, 1 reverse
Speed (km/hr): 40
Range (km): 200
Radio: FuG5

Armament: One 7.92mm MG34
Traverse: hand
Sight: KgZF2

Armour (mm/angle):	Front	Side	Rear	Top/Bottom
Superstructure:	30/7°	20/0°	20/9°	12/84°−90°
Hull:	30/12°	20/0°	20/10°	10/90°

History: The emphasis on fixed defence works led the Inspectorate of Engineers to demand an armoured bridge-layer. Early developments used the chassis of the Pz Kpfw I and II, which limited the

365/366

Plates 365–367.
Brückenleger IV. Top, the
Krupp version positioning
its bridge. Plates 366–367,
the Magirus version; left,
launching its bridge.

size and usefulness of the bridge carried. An order for fifty 9m bridges was placed, after success with bridges based on a mild steel BW (Pz Kpfw IV). In August 1939, four Pz Kpfw IV Ausf C chassis were delivered for conversion. Sixteen Ausf D chassis were set aside from September 1939. A report dated 17 January 1940 indicated that twelve BL IV would be ready by the end of March. Two were delivered in February, and ten in April. A demonstration was held at Klausdorf at the end of April. Two BL IV were carrying a bridge developed by Krupp, and the remainder, a Magirus design. The former used a forward pivoting gantry to launch its bridge, while the latter slid the bridge horizontally across the obstacle. With the expanding number of Panzer divisions, the original order was cut by thirty, and a new order was placed for an improved bridge to be built on sixty Pz Kpfw IV. The first twelve were to be delivered by September 1940, and the remaining 48 to be built at a rate of four per month. The lessons of the campaign in France and the Low Countries caused the cancellation of further BL IV production. Fifteen BL IV were re-converted to Pz Kpfw IV, two in August 1940, and thirteen in May 1941.

Combat service: Four BL IV were issued to the BL Zug (bridging platoon) of each Panzer division, starting with the 1st Panzer Division in early March 1940. Served with the 1st, 2nd, 3rd, 5th and 10th Panzer Divisions in 1940.

367

Panzerkampfwagen IV mit Schachtellaufwerk

Other designation: BW40
Type: Battle tank with experimental suspension

History: Prototype development of interleaving large road wheels on a Pz Kpfw IV of the 6/BW series (Ausf E). One prototype was built at the end of 1940, at the same time as a similar Pz Kpfw III was converted to Schachtellaufwerk.

Sonderausführung des Panzerkampfwagen IV

Other designation: Panzerkampfwagen IV mit hydrostatischen Antrieb
Type: Battle tank with experimental drive

History: Prototype development of a special version of the Pz Kpfw IV with hydrostatic drive, which was ordered by the SS in July 1944. Placing of this drive at the rear of the tank, gave additional space within the fighting compartment, and a drawing dated October 1944, indicated that sloping frontal armour was to be a feature of the project. A prototype was built from a Pz Kpfw IV Ausf G.

368

Plates 368-369. Pz Kpfw IV
modified with hydrostatic
drive.

369

Panzerkampfwagen IV mit Minenrollern (Pz. Minenräumgerät IV)

Type: Battle tank with mine-destroying rollers

History: Prototype development of mine rollers which could be attached to the front and rear of a tank. The front rollers cleared a path for the tracks, while the trailing rollers detonoted the mines between the path swept by the front rollers. An Ausf C was used for these tests.

Plate 370. Pz Kpfw IV mit Minenrollern.

2cm Flakvierling auf Fahrgestell Panzerkampfwagen IV (Sf)

Other designation: Möbelwagen (See also P.109 for 3.7cm Flak 43 version)
Type: Experimental self-propelled anti-aircraft gun

History: Designed early in 1943, the 2cm Flakvierling 38 on the Pz Kpfw IV chassis did not enter production. A normal tank chassis was fitted with a new wider superstructure on which hinged armoured shields surrounded the weapon. In action, these shields could be hinged outward to give room for all-round traverse, or could be folded flat when ground-level targets were to be engaged. Hitler saw a demonstration of the prototype in October 1943, but again refused permission for production. In January 1944, an order was given for an interim Flakpanzer of similar design, mounting the 3.7cm FlaK.

Plates 371–372. Möbelwagen (Furniture Van) left, with the armoured shields lowered.

Flakpanzer IV/3.7cm Flakzwilling

Other designation: Ostwind II
Type: Self-propelled anti-aircraft gun

History: As early as October 1943, Hitler had called for a Flakpanzer armed with two 3.7cm FlaK as the best interim solution until the Kugelblitz had been fully developed. In January 1945, Ostbau produced a prototype of the Ostwind II which had the 3.7cm Flakzwilling 44. This was the same basic weapon as the Flakzwilling 43, but the guns had to be mounted side-by-side in order to be accommodated in the Ostwind turret. Loss of the Ostbau facility and subsequent disruption ensured that no production followed.

Flakpanzer IV/3cm Flakvierling

Other designation: Zerstörer 45
Type: Self-propelled anti-aircraft gun

History: The Wirbelwind armed with the 2cm Flakvierling 38 was seen as a temporary solution, allowing the quick conversion to Flakpanzer of Pz Kpfw IV, returned from the front for overhaul. The limitations of the weapon were already known, and the Ostwind replaced the Wirbelwind before the end of 1944. To increase the effectiveness of existing Wirbelwind, a 3cm Flakvierling 103/38 was to replace the 2cm at the earliest possible time. However, only one prototype was built by Ostbau in December 1944.

Plate 373. Zerstörer 45.

Plate 374. Munitionsschlepper für Karlgerät, based on Pz Kpfw IV Ausf D chassis.
Plate 375. The carrier with its equipment stowed in travelling position.
Plate 376. The carrier based on Pz Kpfw IV Ausf F.
Plate 377. Because of shortage of fuel, many vehicles off the production lines were adapted to run on gas during trials. Gas canisters were carried in a rack above the engine.
Plate 533 (Pages 158–159) on test ground with Gerät 040.
Plate 536 (Page 159) with Gerät 041.

Munitionsschlepper für Karlgerät

Type: Ammunition carrier

History: During the testing of the prototype Gerät 040, the plan to have a fully-tracked ammunition-carrier was implemented. The Munitionsschlepper was built on the chassis of a Pz Kpfw IV Ausf D in October 1939. Racks for four 60cm rounds were mounted over the engine compartment. A crane for lifting these heavy rounds was fitted on the front right-hand side of the new superstructure. In 1941, thirteen Pz Kpfw IV Ausf F$_1$ chassis were converted to Munitionsschlepper, in addition to a number of rebuilt Pz Kpfw IV chassis.

374

375

376

377

Bergepanzer IV

Type: Recovery vehicle

History: From October 1944, Pz Kpfw IV chassis were converted to Bergepanzer. A large wooden box-body was mounted on top of the fighting compartment in place of the turret. A derrick crane was provided for, by mountings on the rear engine deck. These Bergepanzer were to be used in conjunction with the Bergeanker (recovery anchor). Thirty-six Bergepanzer IV were converted from October 1944 to December 1944.

Sturmgeschütz neuer Art (StuG nA Starr)

Type: Tank destroyer with experimental rigid mounted gun

History: At the beginning of 1944, Alkett was ordered to build two prototype Jagdpanzer IV with a rigid mounted gun – the 7.5cm PaK39 L/48. The first prototype rigid mount was tested at Kummersdorf in September 1944. Problems with seating of the sights and unmanageable handwheels were experienced and extensive trials of the second prototype were conducted by Wä Prüf 4 and 6. Many modifications were made to the mounting and sights to overcome these problems, but no satisfactory solution was reached. The knowledge gained, however, was applied to the rigid mounting of the 7.5cm in the Jagdpanzer 38(t), because production of the Jagdpanzer IV was to be replaced by the 38(t) and 38(d) during 1945.

Infanterie Sturmsteg auf Fahrgestell Panzerkampfwagen IV

Type: Assault bridge on tracked chassis

History: In 1939, having in mind the problems faced when assaulting fixed fortifications, the Waffenamt (Ordnance Department) ordered two Infanterie Sturmsteg built on to Pz Kpfw IV chassis. The bridge was built by Magirus on the same principle as a fire-fighting ladder of approximately 50m. Two bridges placed side-by-side were intended to form beams for a walkway. The two Pz Kpfw IV chassis were from Ausf C production, set aside in August 1939. Delivery of the Sturmsteg took place in February 1940, in time for the campaign in the West.

Plates 378-380. Infanterie Sturmsteg auf Fgst Pz Kpfw IV; above, disabled in 1940, during the campaign in France; below, a model showing the assault bridge extended and stowed.

379

380

Panzerfähre

Other designation: PzF
Type: Tracked amphibious armoured ferry

History: As a replacement for the unarmoured Land-Wasser-Schlepper, the Waffenamt placed an order with Magirus for the development of a lightly armoured vehicle capable of the same tasks. The Panzerfähre was based on the drive train, motor and running gear components of the Pz Kpfw IV Ausf F. Two prototypes were delivered in mid 1942.

Plates 381-382. PzF, on land and entering the water with a trailer in tow.

81

382

Plates 383-385 (right and below). Rocket projectors and recoilless gun mountings on Pz Kpfw IV chassis. Plate 383 shows the experimental Raketenwerfer. An old Pz Kpfw IV Ausf C chassis; the turret was replaced by a fixed armoured hatch and a box-type rocket projector containing four rockets. Plates 384 to 385 show front and rear views of a wooden mock-up of Pz Kpfw IV für zwei 7.5cm Rücklauflos Kanone 43 and 3cm MK103, a project to mount two 7.5cm recoilless guns and a 3cm automatic cannon on the Pz Kpfw IV chassis.

383

484

385

Panzerkampfwagen V (Panther)
and variants

Panzerkampfwagen V Ausf D (Sd Kfz 171)

Other designations: Panther I, VK3002, Gerät 46, Pz Kpfw Panther (Ausf D)
Type: Heavy medium tank

Manufacturer: MAN, Daimler-Benz, MNH, Henschel
Chassis Nos.: 210001–210254, 211001–214000
850 produced from January to September 1943

Crew: 5	Engine: Maybach HL230P30
Weight (tons): 43	Gearbox: 7 forward, 1 reverse
Length (metres): 8.86	Speed (km/hr): 46
Width (metres): 3.4	Range (km): 200
Height (metres): 2.95	Radio: FuG5

Armament: One 7.5cm KwK42 L/70 — One 7.92mm MG34 — One 7.92mm MG34

Traverse:	360° (hydraulic)	=	hand
Elevation:	−8° +18°	=	
Sight:	TZF12	=	direct
Ammunition:	79	5,100	

Armour (mm/angle):	Front	Side	Rear	Top/Bottom
Turret:	100/10°	45/25°	45/25°	16/83°–90°
Hull (upper):	80/55°	40/40°		16/90°
(lower):	60/55°	40/0°	40/30°	30–16/90°
Gun mantlet:	100/round			

History: After a study had been made of the Russian T–34, Hitler ordered the development of a similar vehicle in the 30 ton class. MAN and Daimler-Benz received orders to develop the chassis while the turret was being developed by Rheinmetall-Borsig. After reviewing the preliminary drawings, Hitler ordered preparations to be made for the development of a series of Daimler-Benz Panthers, and gave Daimler-Benz an order to produce 200. He thought that the Daimler-Benz Panther was better than the MAN design, and that it would be approved for production. On 14 May 1942, after comparing the prints and statistics of the MAN and Daimler-Benz designs, Hitler decided that the MAN version was superior and would go into production, since under no circumstances were two different designs to be produced at the same time. Production was to start in December 1942, with 250 to be built by 12 May 1943, in time for the summer offensive.

Specific features: The Panther suspension consisted of eight pairs of large road-wheels sprung on torsion bars, a rear idler and a front drive sprocket. The plates making up the hull were well angled to increase protection. The only verticle plate was the lower hull side plate. Direct vision was provided for the driver by an armoured flap. When this was closed the driver had to use the two periscopes mounted in the hull roof. No hull machine-gun mount was provided. A narrow port, covered by a flap, was provided in the hull front through which, the hull machine-gun could be fired. A decision had been made in the autumn of 1942 to increase the armour thickness of the upper hull front plate from 60mm to 80mm, but the first 20 Panthers produced by MAN still had 60mm frontal armour on the upper hull. The long 7.5cm KwK42 L/70 was mounted in an external, curved gun mantlet accompanied by a coaxial machine-gun. Pistol ports were provided in both turret sides and in the turret rear. Access to the turret was provided by a hatch in the turret rear, and through the cupola hatch. In addition, there was a small round hatch in the left turret side in the original turret design.

Combat service: Production of the Ausf D began in January 1943, and the first vehicles were issued during the following month. In April 1943, all issue was halted, and those that had been issued were recalled for major modifications. Finally, in May 1943, the 51st and 52nd Panzerabteilungen received the Panthers which were the first to go into action at Kursk in July 1943. Most of the Ausf D production was issued to these two independent units, plus the 23rd and 26th Independent Panzer Regiments, and the Panzer Regiments Das Reich and Leibstandarte Adolf Hitler.

386

387

388

Plates 386–388. Panther I. Plates 386 and 387: The prototype, with the cupola protruding through the turret side and a single-baffle muzzle-brake on the gun. The side view shows the smoke-dischargers on the side of the turret and its unique drive sprocket. Plate 388 shows the standard model, with cylindrical stowage box on the vehicle side, containing cleaning equipment for the gun.

Plates 389-390 (opposite page). A comparison of Pz Kpfw V Ausf D (top) and Ausf A. The top vehicle has armoured side-skirts and carries track links on the hull and turret for extra protection. Both vehicles are covered with Zimmerit (anti-magnetic paste).

Panzerkampfwagen V Ausf A (Sd Kfz 171)

Other designations: Panther I, VK3002, Pz Kpfw Panther (Ausf A)
Type: Heavy medium tank

Manufacturer: MAN, Daimler-Benz, Demag, MNH
Chassis Nos.: 151001–160000, 210254–211000
2,000 produced from August 1943 to May 1944

Crew: 5	Engine: Maybach HL230P30
Weight (tons): 44.8	Gearbox: 7 forward, 1 reverse
Length (metres): 8.86	Speed (km/hr): 46
Width (metres): 3.42	Range (km): 200
Height (metres): 2.98	Radio: FuG5

Armament: One 7.5cm KwK42 L/70		One 7.92mm MG34	One 7.92mm MG34
Traverse: 360° (hydraulic)	=		5° left 5° right (hand)
Elevation: −8° +18°	=		−10° +15°
Sight: TZF12a	=		KgZF2
Ammunition: 79		5,100	

Armour (mm/angle):	Front	Side	Rear	Top/Bottom
Turret:	110/11°	45/25°	45/25°	16/84°−90°
Hull (upper):	80/55°	40/40°		16/90°
(lower):	60/55°	40/0°	40/30°	30–16/90°
Gun mantlet:	100/round			

History: The Ausf A was the second series of the Panther production. The basic design remained the same as the Ausf D, the difference being a series of modifications to improve performance.

Specific features: The important changes on the Panther Ausf A were the introduction of the new cupola for the commander, and strengthened running gear. The number of wheel-rim bolts was doubled to prevent failures. Several modifications were made to the drive-train to improve reliability. Engine exhaust cooling was modified. The hull design remained unchanged, but a new ball-mount was designed to replace the letter-box flap MG port. These ball-mounts were fitted to a proportion of Ausf A from August 1943, and were fitted to all Ausf A from late 1943. The turret had many modifications. In addition to the new cupola, an episcope for the loader was provided on the right side of turret roof. The small ammunition-loading hatch in the left side was eliminated, and during the production run, the turret side pistol ports were eliminated in favour of the roof-mounted 'Nahverteidigungswaffe' (close-defence weapon). The TZF12 binocular telescope was gradually replaced by the monocular TZF12a during the Ausf A production.

Combat service: When the Panther Ausf A was first introduced, it saw service in Russia and Italy. Most of the Panther detachments deployed to meet the Allied invasion of France in mid 1944 were equipped with Panther Ausf A, and many of them were still in service at the end of the war.

391

Plate 15 (Page 7) Pz Kpfw V Ausf A
Plates 391–393. Pz Kpfw V Ausf D and A. (Above, a late model D.) Note the new type of turret, with no side opening and with the new pattern of cupola, featuring periscopes and a semi-circular rail to mount the MG34. Plate 393. Front view, showing the ball-mount for the hull machine-gun, plus vision devices.
Plate 394-395. Rear views, showing two sorts of exhaust system and jack stowage (which varied on this model, as on Ausf D and G).
Plate 396. Left elevation of Pz Kpfw V Ausf A.
Plate 397. Two Ausf A vehicles under fire on the Russian Front.
Plate 945 (Page 246) Cupola of Pz Kpfw V Ausf A

392

393

395

394

396

Panzerkampfwagen V Ausf G (Sd Kfz 171)

Other designations: Panther I, VK3002, Pz Kpfw Panther (Ausf G)
Type: Heavy medium tank

Manufacturer: MAN, Daimler-Benz, MNH
Chassis Nos.: 120301–, 124301–, 214001–
3,126 produced from March 1944 to April 1945
Crew: 5
Weight (tons): 45.5
Length (metres): 8.86
Width (metres): 3.4
Height (metres): 2.98

Engine: Maybach HL230P30
Gearbox: 7 forward, 1 reverse
Speed (km/hr): 46
Range (km): 200
Radio: FuG5

Armament: One 7.5cm   One 7.92mm MG34   One 7.92mm MG34
  KwK42 L/70
Traverse: 360° (hydraulic) =   5° left 5° right (hand)
Elevation: −8° +18°   =   −10° +15°
Sight: TZF12a   =   KgZF2
Ammunition: 81   4,800

Armour (mm/angle):	Front	Side	Rear	Top/Bottom
Turret:	110/11°	45/25°	45/25°	16/84°−90°
Hull (upper):	80/55°	50/30°		40 & 16/90°
(lower):	60/55°	40/0°	40/30°	30−16/90°
Gun mantlet:	100/round			

History: The Ausf G was the third series of the Panther. Many design changes were made with this model, brought about by recommendations from the troops in the field manning the Ausf D and A.

Specific features: The major external difference between the Panther Ausf G and the earlier Ausf A and Ausf D was the redesigned hull. Side armour was increased on the upper hull side, and the side plate was now a single piece. The driver's vision port was removed from the front plate to increase strength. Vision was now provided through a rotating periscope, and the driver's seat could be raised and the controls extended so that he could drive with his head out of the hatch. The pivoting hatches over the driver and radio operator were replaced by hinged versions. Suspension remained much the same as before, but on late production vehicles, the rearmost damper was deleted. A trial production series in September 1944 featured the steel-rimmed 'silent bloc' wheels that were to be standardized on the Ausf F in 1945. Many minor changes were made to improve reliability during the production run, especially to the drive-train. A gearbox oil cooler was fitted. 3mm armoured ammunition bins were installed for the first time. From October 1944 vehicles were equipped with a fighting compartment heater system which drew warm air from a tower-like device.

Plates 398-399. Pz Kpfw V Ausf G. Note the hit on the drive sprocket sustained by the lower vehicle.
Plates 400-402 (opposite page). Pz Kpfw V Ausf G showing the 1944 modification to the gun mantlet (Plate 400), with new vision devices (Plate 401) and with steel-rimmed wheels (Plate 402).
Plates 403-404. (opposite page, below). During the fighting in the Ardennes, the Germans converted a number of Panthers to simulate American M10 tank destroyers, by the addition of sheet-metal superstructures and false side-aprons.

399

fitted over the left side engine fan. Effective flame-trap exhaust mufflers were introduced. In September 1944, a proportion of the turrets delivered were fitted with a new gun mantlet on which the under curve was eliminated (by a forward angled projection) to prevent downward deflection of hits through the thin hull roof armour.

Combat service: The Ausf G saw action on eastern, south-eastern and western fronts until the end of the war. It generally comprised over half the tank strength of the Panzer divisions, making itself felt in the last offensives in East Prussia, Hungary and Belgium. Approximately 450 Panthers were available with units under Army Group B at the start of the Ardennes offensive.

400

401

402

403

404

Panzerkampfwagen V Ausf F (Sd Kfz 171)

Other designation: Pz Kpfw V neuer Art, Pz Kpfw Panther nA
Type: Heavy medium tank

Manufacturer: Daimler-Benz
The Ausf F did not go into series production. Reports indicate that 8 hulls were produced by Daimler-Benz in 1945, but only prototype turrets had been completed at this time

Crew: 5	Engine: Maybach HL230P30
Weight (tons): 45	Gearbox: 7 forward, 1 reverse
Length (metres): 8.86	Speed (km/hr): 55
Width (metres): 3.44	Range (km): 200
Height (metres): 2.92	Radio: FuG5

405

Armament: One 7.5cm   One 7.92mm MG42   One 7.92mm MG44
KwK42/1 L/70
Traverse: 360° (hydraulic)   =   hand
Elevation: −8° +20°   =
Sight: EM 1.25 R(Pz)TZF13 =   KgZF2
Ammunition: 79

Armour (mm/angle):	Front	Side	Rear	Top/Bottom
Turret:	120/20°	60/25°	60/25°	40/90°
Superstructure:	80/55°	50/30°		25/90°
Hull:	60/55°	40/0°	40/30°	30–16/90°
Gun mantlet:	120/Saukopfblende			

History: Daimler-Benz was given the task of developing the 'Schmal' (narrow) Panther turret. This design was to have a small frontal area, thicker armour, to prevent penetration under the gun mantlet, and to have the same size turret ring as previous Panther turrets. It was to be mounted on the Ausf F and the Panther II. Only a prototype of the turret was completed, and the Ausf F series was never produced. Further development of this 'Schmal' turret was planned, with provision for mounting an 8.8cm KwK and a stabilized sight. Neither goal had been reached by the end of the war. The designation of the Schmal turret was Gerät 710 (Schmal Turm 605).

Specific features: The differences between the Ausf F and the Ausf G designs were: 1. The new 'Schmal' turret design with range-finder bulges in the turret side, conical gun mantlet with 7.5cm KwK42/1, coaxial MG42 and thicker armour plate. 2. 25mm hull roof instead of the 16mm of the normal Panther series. 3. Driver's and hull gunner's hatches designed to be lifted slightly and moved to the side. 4. Hull machine-gun mount designed for the MP44 instead of the MG. 5. Radios, weapons and stowage arranged so that the troops in the field could make the conversion to a command tank. This conversion entailed the mounting of an additional radio set in the turret. The required second antenna was already on each turret. 6. The Flugabwehrgerät (anti-aircraft mount) installation was prepared to such an extent that the crew could install the rest of the parts. The fighting strength of the vehicle was unimpaired by the addition of the wireless set or the anti-aircraft mount. The steel-rimmed 'silent bloc' wheels were to become standard during the production of the Ausf F.

Plates 405-408. The 'Schmal' turret, on the tank and in detail.
Plate 409. Pz Kpfw V Ausf F.

Plate 964 (Page 249) 7.5cm KwK 42/1 armament of the Ausf F on a proof mount.

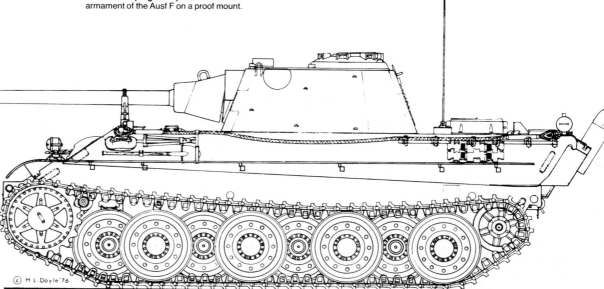

409

Panzerbefehlswagen mit 7.5cm KwK42 L/70 and Panzerbeobachtungswagen Panther

Other designation: Pz Kpfw Panther (Sd Kfz 171) (als Pz Bef Wg),
Pz Bef Wg Panther, and Pz Beob Wg Panther
Type: Heavy medium command tank / observation post tank

329 converted from Pz Kpfw Panther from May 1943 to February 1945
41 Beob Wg converted from Pz Kpfw Panther in late 1944/1945

Crew: 5	Engine: Maybach HL230P30
Weight (tons): 44.5	Gearbox: 7 forward, 1 reverse
Length (metres): 8.86	Speed (km/hr): 46
Width (metres): 3.4	Range (km): 200
Height (metres): 2.98	Radio: FuG5 & FuG8
	FuG5 & FuG7

Armament: One 7.5cm KwK42 L/70	One 7.92mm MG34	One 7.92mm MG34
Traverse: 360° (hydraulic)	=	5° left 5° right (hand)
Elevation: −8° +20° (Ausf D) −8° +18° (Ausf A/G)	=	−10° +15°
Sight: TZF12 (Ausf D) TZF12a (Ausf A/G)	=	KgZF2
Ammunition: 64	5,100 (Ausf D/A) 4,800 (Ausf G)	

Armour (mm/angle):	Front	Side	Rear	Top/Bottom
Turret:	100/10°	45/25°	45/25°	16/83°−90°
Superstructure:	80/55°	40/40°	40/30°	16/90°
(Ausf G)		50/30°		40−16/90°
Hull:	60/55°	40/0°	40/30°	30−16/90°
Gun mantlet:	100/round			

History: The command vehicle for Panther units was developed so as to be inconspicuous when in action. The additional radio was fitted by reducing the number of ammunition rounds carried for the 7.5cm gun. The FuG5 radio was located in the turret, and the FuG7 or FuG8, in the hull over the gearbox. A proportion of all versions of the Panther were produced as command tanks. In late 1944, a 'Beobachtungs Panzerwagen Panther' was converted from rebuilt Panther tanks. The main armament, the 7.5cm KwK, was removed and the front of the turret plated over. In the centre of this front plate were attached a dummy gun and mantlet, and to the right, a ball-mounted MG34 (traverse 5° left 5° right, elevation −10° +15°). On the extremities of the new front plate, armoured flaps covered the openings for an EM 1.25m R (Pz) stereoscopic range-finder. Additionally, the Beob Pz Wg carried a Blockstelle 0 range-plotting table and other instruments for use with artillery observation.

Specific features: The Pz Bef Wg and the Pz Beob Wg were fitted with two additional radio aerials: a star aerial in the centre rear of the engine deck, and a 1.4m rod on the right side of the turret roof.

Combat service: Pz Bef Wg Panther served alongside the Panther on all fronts.

Plates 410-411. Pz Bef Wg Panther. (Plate 411 shows an early model Ausf D.)
Plate 412. Panther equipped with infra-red equipment. This vehicle worked in conjunction with the Sd Kfz 251/20, mittlerer Schützenpanzerwagen (Infrarotscheinwerfer), which carried the 60cm infra-red searchlight. (See page 177).
Plate 413. Pz Beob Wg Panther.

Jagdpanther (Sd Kfz 173)

Other designation: Panzerjäger für 8.8cm PaK43 auf Fgst Panther I,
Pz Jäg Panther, 8.8cm PaK43 (L/71) auf Pz Jäg Panther

Type: Heavy tank destroyer

Manufacturer: MIAG, MNH
Chassis Nos.: 300001–300392
392 produced from January 1944 to March 1945

Crew: 5	Engine: Maybach HL230P30
Weight (tons): 46	Gearbox: 7 forward, 1 reverse
Length (metres): 9.9	Speed (km/hr): 46
Width (metres): 3.42	Range (km): 160
Height (metres): 2.72	Radio: FuG5 + FuG2

Armament:	One 8.8cm PaK43/3 L/71	One 7.92mm MG34
Traverse:	13° left 13° right (hand)	5° left 5° right (hand)
Elevation:	$-8°$ $+14°$	$-10°$ $+15°$
Sight:	SflZF5	KgZF2
Ammunition:	57	600

Armour (mm/angle):	Front	Side	Rear	Top/Bottom
Superstructure:	80/55°	50/30°	40/35°	25/83° + 16/90°
Hull:	60/55°	40/0°	40/25°	25–16/90°
Gun mantlet:	100/Saukopfblende			

History: On 2 October 1942, the order was issued to develop a heavy assault gun by using the long 8.8cm Pak L/71 mounted on the Panther chassis. A wooden mock-up was completed by October 1943, and the prototype was shown to Hitler on 16 December 1943. Production started at MIAG in January 1944, and at MNH in November 1944, and continued until March 1945. Originally, there were two designation listed, the above and 'Sturmgeschütz fur 8.8cm StuK43 auf Fgs Panther I (Sd Kfz 172).

Specific features: The fighting compartment was designed by extend ing the upper hull and side plates of the normal Panther chassis. Th 8.8cm PaK43/3 was installed in a gun mount in this sloping fror plate. Earlier production vehicles had the gun mount welded to th superstructure front plate; later production vehicles had a protrudin gun mount which was bolted in place. The driver was provided wit a periscope in the front superstructure next to the gun mount, whil all other crew vision was by periscopes mounted in the superstruc ture roof. Close defence was provided by a 'Nahverteidigungsgerä' (close-defence weapon) mounted in the superstructure roof, and machine-gun in a hull mount in the superstructure front. The suspen sion was unchanged from that installed on the Panther, but the drive train was improved by the installation of a heavy-duty transmission.

Combat service: The first Jagdpanthers were issued to the 559th an 654th Panzerjägerabteilungen in June 1944. Only the latter uni was issued a sufficient number to fill the complete establishment of 42 The other Pz Jag Abt had only a company strength of from ten to fourteen Jagdpanthers. The largest collection of Jagdpanthers built during the wa were assembled in December 1944 to participate in the Ardenne: offensive. From January 1945 until the end of the war, they were also issued to the tank detachments of seven different Panzer divisions, to The Führer Grenadier Division and to a Panzer brigade.

414

415

Plate 414–415. Early and middle production Jagdpanthers, respectively.
Plate 416. A late production model, with bolted gun mount.
Plates 417–419 (opposite page). Top, an early pro-duction vehicle, with two vision slots for the driver and a monobloc gun barrel. Centre, a middle production vehicle, with two-piece barrel. Bottom, a late pro-duction Jagdpanther, with two-piece barrel.

416

17

18

420

42

421

4.

422

423

4

Panzer-Bergegerät (Panther I) (Sd Kfz 179)

Other designations: Bergepanther, Pz Berge Wg Panther
Type: Armoured recovery vehicle

Manufacturer: MAN, Henschel, Demag
Chassis Nos.: 210125–210137, 212086–212200, 175501–
232 Ausf A produced from June 1943 to September 1944 plus 8 converted from Panther in August 1944
107 Ausf G produced by Demag from September 1944 to March 1945

Crew: 5	Engine: Maybach HL230P30
Weight (tons): 43	Gearbox: 7 forward, 1 reverse
Length (metres): 8.82	Speed (km/hr): 46
Width (metres): 3.27	Range (km): 320
Height (metres): 2.74	Radio: FuG5

Armament:	Two 7.92mm MG34 or MG42	One 2cm KwK38 (on early Ausf A only)
Traverse:	loose	hand
Elevation:	loose	
Sight:	direct	TZF3a
Ammunition:	4,800	

Armour (mm/angle):	Front	Side	Rear	Top/Bottom
Gunshield:	8/0°	8/0°	8/0°	open
Superstructure:	80/55°	40/40°	40/30°	16/90°
Ausf G		50/30°		
Hull:	60/55°	40/0°	40/30°	30 & 16/90°

History: The problems of recovering heavy tanks had become clear since the commitment of the Tiger in late 1942. In view of the large number of Panthers it was intended to deploy in mid 1943, plans were made for a recovery vehicle based on the Panther chassis. In June 1943, the first twelve were built by simply providing a turretless tank chassis from the MAN production. Normal production was then undertaken by Henschel from July 1943, and they built 70 before their Panther production ceased in November 1943. The need of Bergepanther continued, and in February 1944, Demag converted their entire Panther production to Bergepanther. After an additional 150 Ausf A units, the Ausf G went into production in September 1944. In April 1944, Hitler ordered that Bergepanthers be built from Panthers

sent for rebuild, and the plan was for thirteen in April, eighteen in May, twenty in June and ten in July. This programme did not materialize, and only eight conversions were made in August 1944.

Specific features: The original twelve Bergepanther were turretless Panther Ausf D, but those built by Henschel in 1943 were fully equipped with a 40 ton winch, spade and 1.5 ton derrick. Again, the chassis was Ausf D. The Demag vehicles built from February to September 1944 used the Panther Ausf A chassis with the 'letter-box' MG port in the hull front plate. The 2cm KwK38 mounting was eliminated from this series, and the spade was extended.

Combat service: The Panzer Regiment Lauchert had four of the first twelve, so-called Schlepper, at Kursk in July 1943, while the 51st and 52nd Panzerabteilungen each had four Bergepanther. The normal establishment of the workshop and recovery company of each tank detachment was from two to four Bergepanther. The workshop and recovery company of heavy tank detachments was two Bergepanther.

427

Plates 420-426 (opposite page).
Plates 420-421. Bergepanther based on Ausf D chassis. Plate 421 shows the armoured shield for the machine-guns.
Plates 422-423. Bergepanther production vehicle based on Ausf A. The rear view shows the spade lowered to hold the vehicle firmly while carrying out recovery operations.
Plate 424. The dismountable jib in the erected position.
Plate 425. Top view of the Bergepanther, showing the winch motor and the stowage of equipment.
Plate 426. Munitionspanzer Panther—a Bergepanther, with the winch and recovery gear removed, adapted to carry ammunition.

Plate 427. Panzer-Bergegerät Ausf G.
Plate 428. The Bergepanther in operation, towing a Panther tank. Note the open machine-gun mounting on the front of the recovery vehicle.

428

Flakzwilling 3.7cm auf Panzerkampfwagen Panther

Other designation: Gerät 554 / Flakpanzer 341 'Coelian'
Type: Anti-aircraft tank

Plates 429-430. The mock-up Flakzwilling 3.7cm auf Pz Kpfw Panther.

History: In December 1943, Rheinmetall-Borsig started a project to mount two 3.7cm FlaK43 in a fully-armoured turret, on the chassis of a normal Panther. A wooden mock-up turret was mounted on a Panther Ausf D chassis. The final design for the turret had sloping armour similar to the schmal turms of the Panther Ausf F. Production of this tank was continually delayed.

429

430

Sturmpanther

Type: Assault tank

History: In late 1944, plans were made to mount the 15cm StuH43/1 in the Panther, but production had not begun when the war ended in 1945.

Jagdpanther Starr

Type: Tank destroyer with experimental rigid mounted gun

History: When the war ended, Krupp were working on a prototype of a rigid mounted 8.8cm PaK43/1 L/71 in the Jagdpanther. Success with prototypes of the rigid mounted guns in the Jagdpanzer 38(t) indicated that the Jagdpanther mounting was more suitable because of the vehicle's mass, and the possibility existed of mounting the gun along the centre-line of the fighting compartment. Krupp envisaged mounting the gun farther back in the vehicle.

Panzerkampfwagen Panther II

Type: Battle tank

Plate 431. Pz Kpfw Panther II.

History: Even as production of the Panther I commenced in 1943, plans were laid down to create a Panther II which would have heavier armour (100mm front and 60mm side), but capable of the same performance despite a weight of 47 tons. It was decided that this Panther II design was to be co-ordinated with that of the Tiger II, a decision that led to delays in production of the latter. Pressure for production of the Panther I and an order from Speer reduced the priority of the Panther II project at MAN. However, two prototypes were ordered in 1944 and one of these, fitted with a normal Panther I turret was delivered by MAN in 1945. This vehicle is currently at Fort Knox in the USA. With its 100mm front and 60mm sides, it weighed 55 tons. The running gear was based on the steel-rimmed wheels, drive and idler sprockets of the Tiger II. Only seven wheel-stations per side were used, and these were staggered to accommodate the single torsion bar which was used instead of the double torsion bars of the Panther I. New tracks were used. A steering-wheel now controlled the hydraulic steering, and a reinforced AK 7–200 gearbox was used. Despite the two prototypes, the Panther II project remained at a low priority, and work had already commenced on the E–50 design which was to replace Panther I and Panther II. The E–50 project indicated a common hull layout with the E–75, except for armour thickness. The

E-50 was to have had 3 Adler 'Belleville Washer' suspension units giving six wheels per side. The heavier E–75 had four units. The angles of armour were increased on these hulls, while the 900PS of the Maybach HL234 motor was transferred by an eight-speed hydraulic transmission.

Geschützwagen Panther für sFH18/4(Sf)

Other designation: Gerät 811
Type: Weapons carrier

History: Ordered early in 1944, the GW Panther used a shortened Panther suspension. It was equipped with a lifting beam for placing the 15cm sFH18 on the ground in a similar fashion to the Heuschrecke. The prototype, built by Daimler-Benz, was completed just before the war ended. Armour thicknesses of 20mm and 30mm were used in this design. Various other designs for Waffenträger (weapons carriage) using the Panther components were considered for mounting the heavier weapons, but little progress was made towards prototypes

VK3002(DB) — Panzerkampfwagen V

Type: Battle tank prototype

History: On 25 November 1941, the Waffenamt ordered Daimler-Benz and MAN to develop the tank that subsequently became known as the Panther. During 1942, the MAN design was accepted for production, but in the meantime, Daimler-Benz had partially completed their VK3002(DB) prototype. This vehicle closely followed the layout of the Russian T–34, with its turret far forward. Daimler again offered one of their own engines, the MB507 diesel. Drive was to the rear sprocket. Suspension was leaf-spring operating on paired bogie wheels, but other forms of suspension were considered.

432

433

434

435

436

437

Plates 432-433. The Daimler-Benz VK3001(DB) and VK3002(DB) (Plate 433).
Plate 434. Gerät 5-1028, a model of 10.5cm leFH Rheinmetall design for a Waffenträger based on the Panther chassis.
Plate 435. A model of Krupp's design for a Waffenträger on the Panther chassis.
Plate 436. Gerät 5-12, Krupp's model of the 12.8cm K43 on the Panther chassis. (Gerät 5-1228 was a project to mount the 15cm sFH.)
Plate 437. Gerät 5-1213, Rheinmetall's design to mount the 12.8cm gun on the Panther chassis.
Plate 438. Design to mount the 8.8cm FlaK41 on the Panther chassis.

438

Panzerkampfwagen VI (Tiger)
and variants

Panzerkampfwagen VI—DW I und DW II

Other designation: Henschel Durchbruchwagen I und II
Type: Battle tank prototype

History: In 1937, the Waffenamt entrusted Henschel with the development of a heavy breakthrough tank which would be about 50 per cent heavier than the Pz Kpfw IV, and which would be protected by 50mm armour. The DW I was the first prototype resulting from this work. The running gear featured five road wheels and was sprung by torsion bars. The hull side armour was made in two pieces and was joined at the rear of the fighting compartment. The DW II which followed an order in 1938, was basically an improved DW I featuring different tracks and one-piece side armour in a single length. A speed of 35km/hr could be reached. The engine was a Maybach HL120 coupled to a Maybach Variorex eight-speed gearbox. The same hull arrangement was retained with the subsequent VK3001(H).

VK3001(H)

Other designation: Panzerkampfwagen VI
Type: Medium tank

Manufacturer: Henschel
4 prototype chassis produced between March and October 1941

Crew: 5	Engine: Maybach HL116
Weight (tons): 32	Gearbox: 6 forward, 1 reverse
Length (metres): 5.81	Speed (km/hr): 25
Width (metres): 3.16	
Height (metres): 1.85	

Armament:	One 7.5cm KwK L/24 or	One 10.5cm KwK L/28	One 7.92mm MG34	One 7.92mm MG34
Traverse:	360° (hydraulic)	=		hand
Sight:	TZF9	=		KgZF2

Armour (mm/angle):	Front	Side	Rear	Top/Bottom
Turret:	50/	30/		
Superstructure:	50/10°	30/0°	50/0°	25/
Hull:	50/13½°	30/0°	50/5½°	20/90°
				35/20° & 22°

History: On 9 September 1938, the Waffenamt (Ordnance Department) authorized Henschel to start work on a proposal to meet the VK3001 specification. Henschel based their VK3001(H) on the DW II prototype; however, dry pin tracks were used in place of the needle-bearing tracks. Early in 1940, the first trials took place and a test series of eight was ordered. The first VK3001(H) were ready in March 1941, but in May, it was decided to abandon this development in favour of the heavier VK3601. Two more VK3001(H) were completed in October 1941. The existing chassis were used extensively during the testing of the VK3601 and, later, the VK4501(H). After the war had ended, a VK3001(H) was recovered from the Henschel proving ground, intact and in running order. Twelve turrets were built by Krupp. Six, armed with the KwK L/24 were issued for mounting in permanent emplacements.

Combat service: None. Used as trial and test vehicle and in tank driver training schools.

Plates 439-440. VK3001(H): left, with weights to simulate the turret; above, the chassis on trials.

12.8cm Selbstfahrlafette L/61 (Panzerselbstfahrlafette V)

Other designation: VK3001(H), Pz SfIV
Type: Heavy self-propelled gun on tracked carriage

Plates 441-442. 12.8cm Sf L/61 (Pz Sf V).

441

Manufacturer: Henschel, Rheinmetall-Borsig
2 produced from VK3001(H) components early in 1942

Crew: 5	Engine: Maybach HL116
Weight (tons): 35	Gearbox: 6 forward, 1 reverse
Length (metres): 9.7	Speed (km/hr): 25
Width (metres): 3.16	Radio: FuG5
Height (metres): 2.7	

Armament: One 12.8cm K L/61   One 7.92mm MG34
Traverse: 7° left 7° right (hand)   loose
Elevation: −15° +10°   loose
Sight: SflZF   direct
Ammunition: 18

Armour (mm/angle):	Front	Side	Rear	Top/Bottom
Turret:	50/14½°	15/10°	15/14½°	open
Superstructure:	50/8°	30/0°	15/16°	15/90°
Hull:	50/13½°	30/0	30/45°	20/90°
				35/20° & 22°
Gun mantlet:	50/40°			

History: As a result of the decision to abandon the VK3001 project, the Waffenamt had on hand several of the Henschel VK3001 chassis. Two were allocated for conversion to a heavy Panzerjäger mounting the Rheinmetall 12.8cm K which was based on the 12.8cm FlaK. The gun was mounted on a pedestal ahead of the engine and was surrounded by a heavily armoured superstructure. The hull was extended back to carry this fighting compartment; an additional road-wheel was fitted. Photographs of a completed 12.8cm Sf L/61 are dated 9 March 1942. The 12.8cm Gerät 40 had been developed since 1936 as a FlaK weapon. The order for the anti-tank gun version was placed in 1939.

Combat service: The 12.8cm Sf L/61 was used in action in Russia, and one was captured almost intact late in 1943. It was subsequently displayed at exhibitions held in 1944. Photographs of a vehicle in action indicate 22 victory rings painted on the gun barrel.

442

VK3601(H)

Other designation: Panzerkampfwagen VI
Type: Heavy tank

Manufacturer: Henschel
1 prototype plus trial series of 6 chassis produced early in 1942

Crew: 5	Engine: Maybach HL174
Weight (tons): 40	Gearbox: 8 forward, 4 reverse
Length (metres): 6.05	Speed (km/hr): 40
Width (metres): 3.14	Radio: FuG5
Height (metres): 2.7	

Armament: One 7.5cm   One 7.92mm MG34   One 7.92mm MG34
  Gerät 725
Traverse: 360°   =   hand
  (hydraulic)
Sight: KgZF2

Armour (mm/angle):	Front	Side	Rear	Top/Bottom
Turret:	100/10°	80/0°	80/0°	26/90°
Superstructure:	100/8°	60/0°	60/0°	26/90°
Hull:	100 & 60/23° & 60°	60/0°	80/0°	26/90°
Gun mantlet:	100/0°			

History: The VK3601 was ordered from Henschel in May 1941 to meet a specification for a tank mounting a weapon capable of penetrating 100mm armour at 1,500 metres, while having adequate protection to withstand attack by a similar weapon. Henschel based their design on the VK3001(H), but used larger road wheels on eight axles. At the end of July 1941, the VK3601 had to be abandoned, since the squeeze-bore weapon 0725 could not be used because of its dependence upon tungsten-cored ammunition. The alternative weapon was the 8.8cm KwK36, already available for the Porsche VK4501(P). The VK 3601 was quickly adapted, however, to meet the new requirement, as the VK4501(H). The six turrets built for the VK3601(H) were made available for building into permanent fortifications.

Combat service: None. Chassis were to be issued as Bergewagen and Schlepper.

443

444

Plates 443-444. VK3601(H) undergoing trials.

Panzerkampfwagen VI Ausf E (Sd Kfz 181)

Other designations: Tiger I, VK4501(H)
Type: Heavy tank

Manufacturer: Henschel, Wegmann
Chassis Nos.: 250001–251357
1,354 produced from July 1942 to August 1944

Crew: 5	Engine: Maybach HL210P45
Weight (tons): 57	Gearbox: 8 forward, 4 reverse
Length (metres): 8.45	Speed (km/hr): 38
Width (metres): 3.7	Range (km): 140
Height (metres): 2.93	Radio: FuG5

Armament: One 8.8cm KwK36 L/56	One 7.92mm MG34	One 7.92mm MG34
Traverse: 360° (hydraulic)	=	15° left 15° right
Elevation: $-9°+10°$	=	$-7°+20°$
Sight: TZF9b; later, TZF9c	=	KgZF2
Ammunition: 92 Pzgr+	4,800 Patr SmK Spgr	

Armour (mm/angle):	Front	Side	Rear	Top/Bottom
Turret:	100/8°	80/0°	80/0°	25/81°–90°
Superstructure:	100/10°	80/0°		25/90°
Hull:	100/24°	60/0°	80/8°	25/90°
Gun mantlet:	100–110/0°			

History: The order to design the VK4501(H) was issued on 26 May 1941. Henschel und Sohn, of Kassel, were to develop the chassis. Krupp was to develop the turret for both the VK4501(H) and the VK4501(P). Rheinmetall also developed a turret for the VK4501(H) to mount the 7.5cm KwK L/70, but it never advanced beyond the prototype stage. Lessons learned in the development of the VK3001 and VK3601 were beneficiently applied to the design of the VK4501(H). Production was planned to start in July 1942, with 285 to be completed by 12 May 1943, in time for the summer offensive. When the VK4501(P) production was halted, the VK4501(H) production order was increased by 50 to make up for the loss.

Specific features: The Tiger I had eight sets of interleaved road wheels with torsion bar suspension to support its 57 tons. The hull and superstructure were welded together, with the superstructure extending over the tracks to allow the installation of a wide turret. The 8.8cm KwK36 was mounted coaxially with a MG34 in the external gun mantlet. The turret was formed from a plate bent to the shape of a horseshoe. Originally, the turret had two machine-pistol ports in the rear, and a cylindrical cupola with vision slits. In December 1942, the right-hand pistol port was replaced by an escape hatch, and in July 1943, the cupola was replaced by a newer design with periscopes. In May 1943, the automotive performance was improved by the installation of the HL230P30, and in January 1944, new steel-tyred, rubber-cushioned road wheels replaced the dished type. Eighty-four Tiger I were equipped as 'Pz Bef Wg mit 8.8cm KwK L/56'. These had additional radio sets, which reduced ammunition stowage to 66 rounds for the 8.8cm and 4,050 Patr for the machine-guns.

Combat service: The first unit to be equipped with Tigers was the 1st Platoon of the 502nd schwere Panzerabteilung which was hurriedly assembled and rushed to the Leningrad area in August 1942.

The Tiger I was issued to the heavy tank detachments and heavy tank companies of three SS divisions, and to the Grossdeutschland Division. Still in service at the end of the war, the Tiger I had taken a heavy toll of enemy armour on all fronts.

Plates 445-446. Overhead views of Pz Kpfw VI Ausf E, showing the massive horseshoe-shaped turret and the 'Feifel' air-cleaner system (which was later discontinued).

Plates 447-454 (opposite page).

Plate 447. Pz Kpfw VI Ausf E with schnorkel tube erected. This allowed the vehicle to wade to a depth of 13ft, but it was discarded on later vehicles. Subsequent Tigers had a wading capability limited to 4ft.

Plate 448. Ausf E with the narrow tracks that were put on for travel or transportation; in this model, the outer wheels were removed from each suspension unit.

Plate 449. Replenishing ammunition; 'S' mine dischargers, which fired a small anti-personnel mine, are mounted on each corner of this Ausf E's hull and in Plate 448.

Plate 450. Pz Kpfw VI Ausf E with the new type of cupola.

Plates 451-453. Late production Pz Kpfw VI Ausf E vehicles, characterized by their periscope-equipped cupolas and all-steel disc wheels. Plate 453 shows vehicles in France in 1944, with wide battle tracks, Zimmerit coating and an anti-aircraft machine-gun on the cupola.

Plate 454. Pz Bef Wg mit 8.8cm KwK L/56.

Plate 963 (Page 249) Interior of turret of Pz Kpfw VI Ausf E.

447

451

448

452

449/450

453/454

38cm RW61 auf Sturmmörser Tiger

Other designation: Tiger-Mörser
Type: Assault rocket mortar on heavy tank chassis

Manufacturer: Alkett
Chassis Nos.: 250001–251357
18 converted from Tiger 1 from August to December 1944

Crew: 5	Engine: Maybach HL230P45
Weight (tons): 65	Gearbox: 8 forward, 4 reverse
Length (metres): 6.28	Speed (km/hr): 40
Width (metres): 3.57	Range (km/hr): 120
Height (metres): 2.85	Radio: FuG5

Armament: One 38cm Stu M RW61   One 7.92mm MG34
   L/5.4

Traverse: 10° left 10° right (hand)	15° left 15° right (hand)
Elevation: −0° +85°	−7° +20°
Sight: PaK ZF3 × 8	KgZF2
Ammunition: 14	600

Armour (mm/angle):	Front	Side	Rear	Top/Bottom
Superstructure:	150/45°	80/30+0°	80/0°	40–25/90°
Hull:	100/25°	60/0°	80/9°	25/90°

History: On 5 August 1943, a self-propelled vehicle was proposed, based on the Tiger I chassis, but mounting a 38cm mortar. Alkett was in charge of the design and had completed a prototype by 20 October 1943, when it was run through its paces for approval. Brandenburger Eisenwerke produced the superstructures and Alkett converted the Tiger I and completed the Sturmmörser at their Berlin-Spandau plant.

Specific features: The hull and suspension remained unchanged from the Tiger I. The superstructure front was cut down and a larger box superstructure housing the 38cm mortar was fitted. The large mortar was an unusual design which fired rocket-assisted ammunition and had vents in the gun tube wall to exhaust the propellant gases forward. The range of the RW61 was 4,600m.

Combat service: The Sturmmörser were issued to Sturmmörser Companies 1001, 1002 and 1003, and were employed mainly in the defence of the German homeland.

Plate 33 (Page 13) Loading ammunition with crane.
Plates 455-457. 38cm Sturmmörser; Plate 455 shows the loading hatch in the roof.
Plates 1004–1007 (Page 253) Interior and other details of 38cm Sturmmörser.

455

456

457

VK3001(P)

Other designation: Typ 100, 'Leopard', Sd Fz 1
Type: Medium tank

Manufacturer: Nibelungenwerke
2 prototype chassis produced between 1940 and 1941

Crew: 5	Engine: 2x Porsche Typ–100
Weight (tons): 30	Gearbox: electric drive
Length (metres): 6.58	Speed (km/hr): 60
Width (metres): 3.8	Radio: FuG5
Height (metres): 3.05	

Armament: One 7.5cm   One 10.5cm KwK L/28   One 7.92mm MG34
     KwK L/24 or
Traverse: 360° (electric) =
Elevation: −10° +20° =

Armour (mm/angle):	Front	Side	Rear	Top/Bottom
Turret:	80/21½°	60/0°	60/0°	40/10° & 15°
Superstructure:	75/15°	60/0°		26/90°
Hull:	75/20° & 45°	60/0°	40/31½° & 0°	26/90°
Gun mantlet:	80/0°			

458

History: As a result of an order placed in 1939, the design bureau of Dr.-Ing.h.c.F. Porsche, KG, of Stuttgart began work on their first armoured vehicle design. The subsequent vehicle was designated VK3001(P), but was known within the Porsche and Nibelungenwerke organizations as the 'Typ 100' or Leopard. Dr. Porsche attempted to solve many problems in the design of the VK3001(P): longitudinal torsion bars mounted externally for suspension, air-cooled engines and electric transmission. Extensive tests in 1940 and 1941 proved the VK3001(P) satisfactory, but the engines were unreliable. The turret, which was being developed by Krupp, had not been completed when the VK3001 project was abandoned in 1941. The existing VK3001(P) vehicles were used extensively during development of the VK4501(P).

459

Tiger (P)

Other designations: Pz Kpfw VI, VK4501(P), Porsche Typ 101
Type: Heavy tank

Manufacturer: Nibelungenwerke
Chassis Nos.: 150001–150010
5 produced in July 1942

Crew: 5	Engine: Two Porsche Typ 101/1
Weight (tons): 57	Gearbox: electric drive
Length (metres): 9.34	Speed (km/hr): 35
Width (metres): 3.38	Radio: FuG5
Height (metres): 2.8	

Armament: One 8.8cm   One 7.92mm MG34   One 7.92mm MG34
  KwK36 L/56
Traverse: 360° (electric) =   15° left 15° right
                                        (hand)
Elevation: −9° +18° =   −7° +20°
Sight: TZF9b =   KgZF2

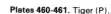

Armour (mm/angle):	Front	Side	Rear	Top/Bottom
Turret:	100/8°	80/0°	80/0°	25/81°–90°
Superstructure:	100/12°	80/0°		20/90°
Hull:	100/35°	60/0°	80/0°	20/90°
Gun mantlet:	100–110/0°			

History: The VK4501(P) was developed by Dr.-Ing.h.c.F. Porsche, KG, the order having been issued on 26 May 1941. The prototype was completed in April 1942, and, without preliminary testing, production was put in hand, with delivery scheduled to start in July 1942. Problems with the motor and suspension brought production to a halt in August 1942, after only five had been completed. In October 1942, Nibelungenwerke was ordered to cease production of the Tiger(P) because Porsche had been unable to solve the technical problems.

Specific features: The suspension for the Tiger(P) consisted of six pairs of steel-tyred rubber-cushioned road wheels with drive sprockets in the rear instead of at the front. The drive-train consisted of two V-10 air-cooled engines which drove generators to provide power for the electric motors which drove the sprockets. The turret, which was designed by Porsche and built by Krupp, was later developed for the Henschel VK4501(H), by modifying the roof angles.

Combat service: In September 1942, an order established that, since they had air-cooled motors, the first series of Tiger(P) were to equip two tank detachments destined for North Africa. However, drive-train problems halted production, and the five completed Tiger(P) were issued for training and testing at Döllersheim.

460

461

Sturmgeschütz mit 8.8cm PaK43/2 (Sd Kfz 184)

Other designations: Ferdinand, Elefant, Pz Jäg Tiger (P)
Type: Heavy assault gun / tank destroyer

Manufacturer: Nibelungenwerke
Chassis Nos.: 150001–150100
90 produced in April and May 1943

Crew: 6
Weight (tons): 65
Length (metres): 8.14
Width (metres): 3.38
Height (metres): 2.97

Engine: Two Maybach HL120TRM
Gearbox: electric drive
Speed (km/hr): 30
Range (km): 150
Radio: FuG5

Armament:	One 8.8cm PaK43/2 L/71	One 7.92mm MG34*	One 7.92mm MG34
Traverse:	28° (hand)	hand	loose
Elevation:	−8° +14°		loose
Sight:	SflZF	KgZF2	direct
Ammunition:	50 Pzgr +Spgr	600 Patr SmK	

Armour (mm/angle):	Front	Side	Rear	Top/Bottom
Superstructure:	200/25°	80/30°	80/20°	30/86°
Hull (upper):	100+100/12°	80/0°	80/40°	30/90°
(lower):	100+100/35°	60/0°	80/0°	50–20/90°
Gun mantlet:	25/0° +100/round			

*Rebuilt vehicles only

History: During the development of the Tiger(P) and Tiger(H), Hitler had agitated for a turret design which would be large enough to mount the 8.8cm KwK L/71. This had not materialized and on 22 September 1942 it was decided that a StuG with 200mm frontal armour and the long 8.8cm gun should be immediately designed, with the Tiger(P) as the basis, and part of the Tiger(P) production diverted for the vehicle. Alkett was to design and produce the Ferdinand, with Nibelungenwerke supplying the completed chassis. Despite the shortage of suspension parts and lack of test runs, on 6 February 1943 Hitler ordered that 90 Ferdinands were to be supplied for the front as quickly as possible by all available means. This resulted in the order for Nibelungenwerke to complete the Sturmgeschütz Ferdinand instead of Alkett. All 90 were completed by the end of May 1943, in time for use in the summer offensive at Kursk.

Specific features: The hull of the Ferdinand was that of the Tiger(P), but with 100mm plates bolted to the front, and an addition to the rear to support the superstructure and vent cooling air for the electric motors. The superstructure housed the long 8.8cm gun in a limited traverse mount. No secondary armament was mounted until late 1943, when those returned from the front were modified to carry a hull machine-gun. The superstructure was also changed at this time to provide the commander with a cupola. Forty-eight Ferdinands were so modified.

Combat service: Ferdinands were issued to Panzerjägerabteilungen 653 and 654 in April and May 1943. These units fought at Kursk during the limited offensive and helped plug holes in the line for the rest of the summer and autumn. The units were pulled out late in 1943 to overhaul the vehicles, after which, the 653rd Panzerjäger-the 614th Panzerjägerkompanie. These vehicles were also used in Italy in 1943/44.

462

Plates 462-463 and 464 (opposite page, top). Ferdinand; Plate 463 (below) shows a rebuilt model, with hull machine-gun and commander's cupola.

463

464

Bergepanzer Tiger (P)

Type: Recovery vehicle

Plates 465-466. Bergepanzer Tiger (P).

History: In September 1943, three Bergepanzer Tiger(P) were converted from the Tiger(P) chassis. The conversion was completed in a similar manner to the Ferdinand self-propelled gun. The engines were mounted in the centre of the tank chassis, and a new superstructure was added at the rear. A ball-mount was provided for the sole armament, a 7.92mm MG34. Other than a small derrick crane, rams and timber beams, no special recovery equipment was fitted.

465 **466**

Bergepanzer Tiger Ausf E

Other designation: Berge-Wg Tiger
Type: Recovery vehicle

Plates 467-468. Bergepanzer Tiger Ausf E; right, close-up of winch.

History: In 1944, three Tiger Ausf E were converted to Berge-Wg by the removal of the main armament and the fitting of a small tubular crane on the turret.

467 **468**

Panzerkampfwagen VI Ausf B (Sd Kfz 182)

Other designations: Tiger II, VK4503, Königstiger, Pz Kpfw Tiger, Ausf B.
Type: Heavy tank

Manufacturer: Henschel
Chassis Nos.: 280001–280489
489 produced from January 1944 to March 1945

Crew: 5	Engine: Maybach HL230P30
Weight (tons): 68	Gearbox: 8 forward, 4 reverse
Length (metres): 10.3	Speed (km/hr): 35
Width (metres): 3.76	Range (km): 170
Height (metres): 3.08	Radio: FuG5

Armament: One 8.8cm   One 7.92mm MG34   One 7.92mm MG34
  KwK43 L/71

Traverse: 360° (hydraulic)	=	hand	
Elevation: −7.4° +15°	=	−8° +17°	
Sight: TZF9b later TZF9d	=	KgZF2	
Ammunition: 72 Pzgr & Spgr	5,850 Patr SmK		

Armour (mm/angle):	Front	Side	Rear	Top/Bottom
Turret:	180/9°	80/21°	80/21°	40/78°–90°
Porsche turret:	60–110	80/30°	80/30°	40/77°–90°
	/round			
Superstructure:	150/50°	80/25°		40/90°
Hull:	100/50°	80/0°	80/30°	40–25/90°
Gun mantlet:	Saukopfblende			

History: In January 1943, a new Tiger was ordered which was to have a turret large enough to mount the 8.8cm L/71 gun, since this had not been achieved with the Tiger I. Frontal armour thickness was to be increased to 150mm, but the side armour was to remain at 80mm. A wooden mock-up showing the immense size of the vehicle was displayed on 20 October 1943. The turret chosen to mount the long 8.8cm gun was a design by Porsche for the VK4502(P), with a curved front plate. On 6 December 1943, the shot-trap, formed by the curved front of the turret, was ordered to be eliminated. This was achieved by Henschel redesigning the turret and gun mantlet, in such a manner as to decrease the frontal area and incorporate a bell mantlet.

Specific features: The• Tiger II had a hull similar in design to the Panther series. The frontal armour was well sloped to increase protection. The suspension consisted of nine sets of interleaved road wheels sprung on torsion bars. The first fifty Tiger II had the turret with the curved front plate, designed by Porsche for his VK4502, Project 180. The remainder had the newly-designed turret. From November 1944, a proportion of Tiger II were converted to Command tanks by the installation of additional radio sets, at the expense of ammunition stowage. The designation of these was Pz Bef Wg mit 8.8cm KwK43 L/71.

Combat service: The first Tiger II were issued to training units in February and May 1944. The first deliveries to combat units did not take place until June 1944, five months after production had started. Apart from five issued to the Feldherrnhalle division in March 1945, all Tiger II were issued to the independent schwere Panzer detachments of the Army and the SS. The Tiger II eliminated its opponents with ease, on both Eastern and Western fronts, but insufficient were produced to arrest the flood of enemy armour.

Plates 469–470. Pz Kpfw VI Ausf B prototype, with Porsche turret and exhaust system designed for submersion similar to the early Tiger I Ausf E.
Plate 471. The Porsche turret on its test rig.
Plates 472-473. Pz Kpfw VI Ausf B production model, with Porsche turret.
Plates 959–961 (Page 248) Details of alternative guns and turrets.

470

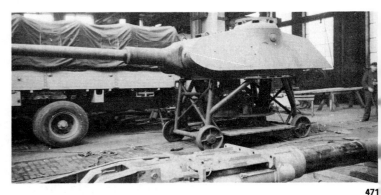

471

472

473

469

474

475

Plate 16 (Page 8) Pz Kpfw IV Ausf B.
Plates 474-475. Pz Kpfw VI Ausf B.
Plate 476. Tiger II with wide battle tracks and track guards.
Plate 477. A line-up of Tiger II vehicles, in the first battalion to receive them.
Plate 478. Pz Bef Wg mit 8.8cm KwK43 L/71.

476

477

478

Jagdtiger (Sd Kfz 186)

Other designation: Jagdpanzer VI, Pz Jäg Tiger, 12.8cm PaK44 auf Pz Jäg Tiger
Type: Heavy tank destroyer

Manufacturer: Nibelungenwerke
Chassis Nos.: 305001–305077
77 produced from July 1944 to March 1945

Crew: 6	Engine: Maybach HL230P30	
Weight (tons): 70	Gearbox: 8 forward, 4 reverse	
Length (metres): 10.65	Speed (km/hr): 38	
Width (metres): 3.63	Range (km): 170	
Height (metres): 2.95		

Armament: One 12.8cm PaK44 L/55	One 7.92mm MG34	One 7.92mm MG42
Traverse: 10° left 10° right (hand)	hand	loose
Elevation: −7.5° +15°	−8° +17°	loose
Sight: WZF2/7	Kg ZF2	direct
Ammunition: 40 Pzgr & Spgr	1,500 Patr SmK	

Armour (mm/angle):	Front	Side	Rear	Top/Bottom
Superstructure:	250/15°	80/25°	80/5°	40/85°
Hull (upper):	150/50°			40/90°
(lower):	100/50°	80/0°	80/30°	40–25/90°

History: Early in 1943, orders were given to design a heavy, self-propelled anti-tank gun, by mounting the 12.8cm gun on a Tiger II chassis. A wooden model of the enormous vehicle was displayed on 20 October 1943, and the finished prototype, in April 1944. Two Jagdtiger (Nos. 305001 and 305004) were built with the Porsche-designed longitudinal torsion-bar suspension. This proved unsatisfactory and delayed production until the Jagdtiger had been redesigned with a torsion-bar suspension. The initial series was for 150, but an order issued in October 1944 stipulated that when these had been completed, production capacity was to be used for building the Panther. However, this was reversed in January 1945, with an order to continue the assembly of Jagdtiger as fast as possible. A Jagdtiger mounting the 8.8cm L/71 was designated Sd Kfz 185, but this never went into production.

Specific features: The Jagdtiger had the same suspension as the Tiger II, but its hull was lengthened. The superstructure had a very box-like appearance, with the sides being formed by the continuation of the upper hull sides. The hull machine-gun mount was retained in the hull front, as secondary armament to the 12.8cm PaK44 mounted in the superstructure front.

Combat service: The Jagdtiger was issued to only two combat units Panzerjagerabteilung 653 and schwere Panzerabteilung 512. The 653rd was employed on the Western Front during the Ardennes offensive, and later with the 512th in the defence of Germany proper in such actions as that of the Remagen Bridgehead on 10 March 1945

479

480

Plate 953 (Page 24) Interior of the Jagdtiger.

Plate 479 (above). Rear view of Jagdtiger.
Plates 480-481. Jagdtiger with Henschel suspension (left) and Porsche suspension (below).

481

Plates 965–967 (Page 249). Interior and armament of Jagdtiger.

Geschützwagen Tiger für 17cm K72 (Sf), für 21cm Mrs18/1 (Sf) und für 30.5cm GrW Sf 1-606/9

Other designations: 17cm—Gerät 809, 21cm—Gerät 810, 30.5cm—Gerät 817, Grille
Type: Heavy self-propelled gun on tracked carriage

One prototype chassis completed by May 1945; production was due to commence mid-1945

Crew: 7
Weight (tons): 58
Length (metres): 13
    (11 with 21cm Mrs18/1)
Width (metres): 3.27
Height (metres): 3.15

Engine: Maybach HL230P30
Gearbox: 8 forward, 4 reverse
Speed (km/hr): 35
Range (km): 200
Radio: FuG Spr Ger f

Armament:	Traverse (hand):	Elevation:	Sight:	Ammunition:
One 17cm K72 (Sf) L/50 or	5° left 5° right	− 0° +50°	Rblf36	5
One 21cm Mrs18/1 (Sf) L/31 or	5° left 5° right	− 0° +50°		3
One 30.5cm GrW (L/16)	5° left 5° right	+40° ±75°		
One 7.92mm MG34		− 3° +17°	KgZF2	
One 7.92mm MG42	loose	loose	direct	

Armour (mm/angle):	Front	Side	Rear	Top/Bottom
Superstructure:	16/30°	16/20°	open	open
Hull:	30/50°	16/0°	16/45°	16/90°
Gun shield:	16/30°			

History: As early as June 1942, it was decided to design self-propelled mounts for the heavier type of artillery so that the latter could be brought into action as quickly as possible, avoiding the break-down into small loads that transport by normal tractors entailed. In January 1943, such a carriage, based on the proposed Tiger Ausf B was ordered. Initially, the 360° traverse was to be achieved by putting the complete vehicle on a turntable, but eventually it was decided to simplify the design by making provision for winching the weapon off the rear of the carriage on to a 360° traverse platform carried on the back. The first prototype was at Sennelager for testing at the end of the war. Concern at the length of time needed to produce conventional heavy artillery, led to an order in January 1945 for the production of heavy, smooth-bore mortars, capable of firing fin-stabilized projectiles over long ranges. Krupp and Skoda competed in the design, and Skoda produced a 30.5cm GrW (mortar) prototype by the beginning of April 1945. A 42cm GrW project was also underway. These mortars automatically returned to 40° elevation for loading. The Grille, mounting this weapon, was to have four hydraulic jacks for stability when firing.

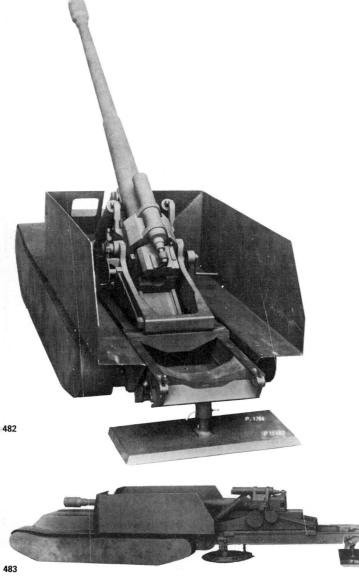

482

483

484

485

Plates 482-483. Wooden model of GW Tiger für 17cm K72 (Sf). In the lower photograph, the gun is in the process of being winched off the carriage on to the traverse platform.
Plates 484-485. The completed GW Tiger für 17cm K72 (Sf), Plate 485 showing the rear of the carriage.

Miscellaneous fully-tracked vehicles

3.7cm WD Schlepper 25PS

Type: Self-propelled anti-tank gun

History: This self-propelled gun was ordered in 1927. It used a 25PS WD tractor with lightly armoured engine covers. The pedestal-mounted anti-tank gun was the 3.7cm PaK L/45. Traverse was 30° and elevation −5°+15°. An MG was carried for defence. Overall length of the vehicle was 3.3m and width, 1.45m. The gun was adopted by the German Army.

7.7cm WD Schlepper 50PS

Type: Self-propelled gun

History: The Hanomag 50PS fully-tracked tractor was adopted in 1927 to carry the 7.7cm K light gun of the German Army. A full 360° traverse was provided, and elevation was −7°+15°. This self-propelled gun was adopted by the German Army.

Leichtertraktor

Type: Light tank

History: In 1929, the firms of Krupp and Rheinmetall-Borsig were given orders to develop a fully-tracked light armoured vehicle. The Leichtetraktor (Rh-B) prototype was ready by May 1930. This was a load-carrier. Tests with the prototype led to an order for two vehicles, one with a fully-rotating turret, and one as a pedestal mounting for a self-propelled gun. The turreted version was started in 1934. With weights varying between 8 tons and 9.5 tons, these Rheinmetall vehicles were powered by a 100PS motor. The armament was a 3.7cm KwK L/45 and a light MG with elevation of −10°+25°. The 3.7cm PaK L/45 Sf had greater elevation, −10°+30°. Overall length was 4.21m and height 3m. The Krupp developments were for the load-carrier, and in 1931 and 1932 they designed a turreted version with two variations of suspension. The Krupp vehicle was smaller and lighter, with a weight of 7.9 tons, length 4.18m and a height of only 2.13m. It carried a crew of three.

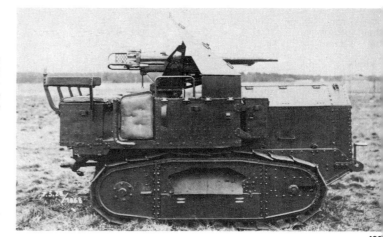

Plate 486. 3.7cm WD Schlepper 25PS.
Plate 487. 7.7cm WD Schlepper 50PS.
Plate 488. Leichtetraktor.

Grosstraktor

Type: Medium tank

Manufacturer: Rheinmetall-Borsig, 2; Krupp, 2 in 1928 and 1929; Daimler-Benz, 2 in 1929 and 1930

Crew: 6	Engine: BMW Va 6cyl 250PS
Weight (tons): 19.32	Gearbox: 6 forward, 2 reverse
Length (metres): 6.6	Speed (km/hr): 40
Width (metres): 2.81	Range (km): 150
Height (metres): 2.3	

Armament: One 7.5cm KwK L/24	One 7.92mm sMG	Two 7.92mm sMG
Traverse: 360° (hand)	=	360° (hand)
Elevation: −12° +60°	=	−15° +80°
Ammunition: 104		6,000

Armour: 13mm mild steel only

History: The original order for the development of the Grosstraktor series was placed with the three firms in 1925. Rheinmetall began their prototype in 1926, and Krupp and Daimler-Benz (Porsche) began shortly after. Trials were planned for 1929 and 1930, with a view to ordering a medium tank for the German Army. The first Krupp and Rheinmetall prototypes were delivered in 1928, and the second, in 1929. The Daimler-Benz vehicle suffered numerous defects and the prototype was not delivered until 1929. The second vehicle was delivered in 1930. Assembly took place at the Rheinmetall Werke at Unterluess.

Specific features: Cletrac-steering was used on the Rheinmetall prototype and the second vehicle was capable of swimming. The Daimler-Benz vehicle was lighter (15 tons) and was powered by a Daimler M182206 6-cylinder 255PS motor.

Combat service: All vehicles were taken to Kama in Russia for tests outside the area of the Armistice control. For the August manoeuvres in 1935, the 1st Panzer Division had a medium Company equipped with the Grosstraktor vehicles. One Grosstraktor was issued to each Panzer regimental headquarters as a parade monument when their useful life had ended.

489

490

Plates 489-490. Grosstraktor: the Rheinmetall (top) and Daimler-Benz prototypes.

Neubaufahrzeug (Nb Fz)

Type: Medium tank

Manufacturer: Rheinmetall-Borsig

2 prototypes produced in 1934, 3 experimental vehicles produced in 1935

Crew: 6	Engine: BMW Va
Weight (tons): 23.41	Gearbox: 6 forward, 1 reverse
Length (metres): 6.6	Speed (km/hr): 30
Width (metres): 2.19	Range (km): 120
Height (metres): 2.98	Radio: FuG

Armament: One 7.5cm KwK L/24	One 3.7cm KwK L/45	One 7.92mm MG13	Two 7.92mm MG13
Traverse: 360° (hand)	=	=	14° left 20° right (hand)
Elevation: −10° +22°	=	=	−10° +25°
Ammunition: 80	50		6,000

Armour (mm/angle):	Front	Side	Rear	Top/Bottom
Turret:	15/	13/	13/	13/90°
Superstructure:	13/	13/0°	13/	13/90°
Hull:	20/	13/0°	13/	13/90°
Gun mantlet:	15/round			

History: The Neubaufahrzeug was ordered from Rheinmetall-Borsig in 1933, and was to be a development of their earlier Grosstraktor to provide the German Army with a 20 ton multi-turreted main tank. Tests on two mild steel prototypes in 1934 led to the construction of three armoured vehicles in 1935. These were fitted with a Krupp-designed turret and gun mount which simplified construction and set the 7.5cm KwK and 3.7cm KwK side by side.

Specific features: Vehicles 1 and 2 had mild steel armour and the rounded Rh-B turret and vertical gun mount. Before being used in action in 1940, vehicles 3, 4 and 5 were refitted with an extra turret similar to that of the Pz Kpfw I, but armed with only one MG34.

Combat service: The prototypes were used by the tank training school at Putlos until 1940. The three armoured vehicles were attached to the Pz Abt z b V 40 (z b V = for special employment). In April 1940, they were shipped direct to Oslo in Norway and were used in action during that month. One vehicle was destroyed and the two surviving NbFz were returned to Germany at the end of 1940.

491

492

Plate 34 (Page 13) Neubaufahrzeug in action.
Plate 491. The mild steel Neubaufahrzeug prototype, with Rheinmetall turret mounting the 3.7cm gun above the 7.5cm.
Plate 492. The armoured version, with Krupp-designed turret.

VK6501(H)

Other designations: Panzerkampfwagen VII, Henschel SW
Type: Heavy tank

Manufacturer: Henschel
1 prototype chassis produced in 1941

Crew: 5
Weight (tons): 65
Length (metres): 7
Width (metres): 3.2
Height (metres): 2.92

Engine: Maybach HL224
Gearbox: 5 forward, 1 reverse
Speed (km/hr): 20

Armament: One 7.5cm KwK L/24 — One 7.92mm MG34 — One 7.92mm MG34
Traverse: 360° (hydraulic) = hand
Sight: = KgZF2

Armour (mm):	Front
Turret:	80
Superstructure:	80
Hull:	80
Gun mantlet:	80/round

History: Ordered on 1 September 1939 as a heavier development of the so-called Panzerkampfwagen VI, VK3001(H). The initial prototype was built of mild steel. The two main features of the VK6501(H)

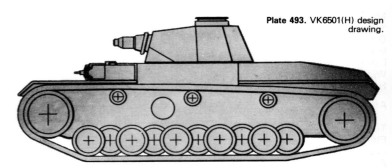

Plate 493. VK6501(H) design drawing.

were the separate small turret for the hull MG, and the fact that the vehicle could be broken down into three sub-sections for transport: the forward, driver's section with the transmission, the fighting compartment and the engine compartment. A special Faun truck was developed as a crane vehicle to accompany the VK6501. The prototype was finally delivered for testing at Sennelager in mid 1941. Production models were to have armour of 100mm.

Panzerkampfwagen 'Maus'

Other designation: Porsche 205
Type: Super heavy tank

Manufacturer: Alkett
Chassis Nos.: 351451–
2 prototypes, 9 under construction

Crew: 5
Weight (tons): 188
Length (metres): 10.09
Width (metres): 3.67
Height (metres): 3.66

Engine: MB509 V12 1,080PS or MB517 Diesel
Gearbox: 2 forward, 2 reverse
Speed (km/hr): 20
Range (km): 186
Radio: FuG5

Armament: One 12.8cm KwK44 L/55 — One 7.5cm KwK44 L/36.5 — One 7.92mm MG34
Traverse: 360° (power) = =
Elevation: −7° +23° = =
Sight: ZF = =
Ammunition: 32 — 200

Armour (mm/angle):	Front	Side	Rear	Top/Bottom
Turret:	240/round	200/30°	200/7°	40/90°
Superstructure:	200/55°	180 + 100/0°	180/38°	80–40/90°
Hull:	200/35°	180/0°	180/30°	100–40/90°
Gun mantlet:	240/Saukopfblende			

History: In June 1942, Porsche of Stuttgart were ordered by Hitler to start designing a superheavy tank, mounting a 12.8cm gun, and having maximum possible armour. Trials were to commence in May 1943. Many difficulties arose. For example, the air-cooled motor did not materialize, and the V1 vehicle had to be fitted with a modified MB509 aircraft engine, the V2 with a MB517 diesel. The Porsche longitudinal torsion bar suspension had to be abandoned as there was insufficient space for the number of stations needed to carry the continually growing weight. Meanwhile, an order had been placed for a production series of 150, but in October 1943, this was cancelled. The V1 prototype was tested with a simulated turret in December 1943, and with a turret and armament in June 1944. The turretless V2 started tests in September 1944, but the engine was destroyed in an accident and was not replaced until April 1945. Both prototypes were blown up at Kummersdorf.

Specific features: The Maus ran on Skoda-designed volute suspension, and was designed to be fitted with either a 15cm KwK44 or a 17cm KwK44. For river crossing, the Maus was expected to submerge to a maximum of 8m taking power, via cable, from another Maus on the bank, for its electric drive.

Plate 494. Pz Kpfw 'Maus' prototype on trials, with simulated turret. (See also Plate 27, Page 12.)

Panzerkampfwagen E-100

Other designation: Gerät 383
Type: Super heavy tank

Manufacturer: Henschel
1 prototype built at Paderborn

Crew: 5		Engine: Maybach HL234
Weight (tons): 140		Gearbox: 8 forward, 4 reverse
Length (metres): 10.27		Speed (km/hr): 40
Width (metres): 4.48		Range (km): 120
Height (metres): 3.29		Radio: FuG5

Armament:	One 15cm KwK44 L/38	One 7.5cm KwK44 L/36.5	One 7.92mm MG34
Traverse:	360° (power)	=	=
Elevation:	−7° +23°	=	=
Sight:	ZF	=	=
Ammunition:	32	200	

Armour (mm/angle):	Front	Side	Rear	Top/Bottom
Turret:	240/round	200/30°	200/7°	40/90°
Superstructure:	200/60°	60+120/20° & 0°	150/30°	40/90°
Hull:	150/40°	120/0°	150/30°	80/90°
Gun mantlet:	240/Saukopfblende			

History: In June 1943, the E–100 was ordered by the Waffenamt from Adlerwerke, as a parallel development to the Porsche 205–Maus. In 1944, Hitler put a stop to all development of superheavy tanks and the project went on to a very low priority, and only three Adler employees were available to assemble the prototype at a small Henschel facility near Paderborn. The chassis of the prototype was virtually complete when the war ended, only the turret was missing. For initial test runs, a normal Tiger B engine HL230P30 had been fitted, with Olvar transmission. The final version was to have had the HL234 motor, and Mekydro transmission. A 17cm KwK44 was proposed as the final armament.

Specific features: Unlike other E series developments, the E–100 had a front drive and conventional layout. The suspension was of the externally-mounted, Belleville Washer type. The side armour shields and the battle tracks could be removed to reduce the width to 3.29m for rail transport.

Plates 495-496. Pz Kpfw E-100: the completed chassis and the chassis being removed on a trailer after the war by the British Army.

495

Minenräumwagen (Sd Kfz 300)

Other designation: Borgward B I und B II
Type: Expendable remote-controlled mine clearing vehicle

Manufacturer: Borgward
50 B I produced from 1939 to May 1940

Crew: none	Engine: Borgward 4M 1.5 RII 1.51
Weight (tons): 1.5	29PS at 2,500rpm
	Gearbox: 2 forward, 1 reverse
	Speed (km/hr): 5

Armour:	Front
Superstructure:	mild steel
Hull:	mild steel

History: The B I was designed in 1939 to act as a minefield-clearance vehicle. It was radio-controlled, and towed mine-detonation rollers. It was cheaply constructed so as to be expendable. In 1940, an order was placed for 100 of the B II, which was a larger vehicle powered by a six-cylinder motor. Only prototypes of the B II were completed, both types being eventually replaced by the wire-guided Goliath. A further experimental amphibious vehicle called 'Ente' was based on the B II.

Specific features: The B I had three road wheels and a silencer on the left-hand side of the hull. The B II had greater ground contact with four road wheels, and the silencer was placed on the hull rear. The motor in the B I was a Borgward 6M 2.3 RTBV six-cylinder 2.3lit of 49PS at 3,500rpm. The overall vehicle weight was 2.3 tons.

Combat service: Experimental field trials only.

497

498

499

Plate 497. The experimental amphibious vehicle 'Ente'.
Plates 498-499. Borgward B I (left) and B II (above).

Leichte Ladungsträger (Sd Kfz 302) (E-Motor)

Other designations: Goliath, Gerät 67
Type: Expendable remote-controlled tracked demolition charge

Manufacturer: Borgward, Zündapp
2,650 produced from April 1942 to January 1944

Crew: none	Engine: Two Bosch MM/RQL
Weight (tons): 0.37	electric 2.5kw
Length (metres): 1.5	Gearbox: 1 forward, 1 reverse
Width (metres): 0.85	Speed (km/hr): 10
Height (metres): 0.56	Range (km): 1.5

Armament: 60Kg Sprengladung

Armour (mm/angle):	Front
Hull (upper):	5/48° mild steel
(lower):	5/30° mild steel

History: Tests carried out with the Borgward B I and B II Minenräumwagen (Sd Kfz 300) remote-controlled minefield-clearance vehicle, led to an order at the end of 1940 for a similar small vehicle which would carry an explosive charge, and which could be used for wider applications than minefield clearance. The initial prototype had four large wheels and trackwork based on the B II. The production model, however, had smaller wheels, which allowed room for battery-carrying sponsons on either side, and left more space for the explosive charge. Guidance was by a three-strand wire, two for steering and one for detonating the charge.

Specific features: The E–Motor version of the Goliath can be recognized by the flat top plate, three return rollers and disc-type idler. The hull had three compartments separated by transverse bulkheads, the explosive charge to the front, control unit in the centre and drum of wire at the rear. The batteries (12 Volt) and the separate electric motor for each track were in sponsons on each side.

Plate 500. Le Ladungsträger Ausf A, prototype series.

Combat service: The first units to be issued with the Goliath were Panzerpionier Kompanien (Goliath) 811–815, which were part of the Heerespionierbataillon (mot) zbV 600 (Taifun). Also in service with Pioniersturmbrigade 627. An example of action involving the Goliath was the clearance of minefields at Kursk for the 654th schwere Panzerjägerabteilung (Ferdinand unit).

Plates 501-502. Goliath production machines; right, being manhandled with the aid of a two-wheeled trailer.

502

Leichte Ladungsträger (Sd Kfz 303) (V-Motor)

Other designations: Goliath, B V, Gerät 671 und 672
Type: Expendable remote-controlled tracked demolition charge

Plates 503-505. Goliath Ausf a (Plate 504) and Ausf b. Plate 503 shows the petrol engine and the front compartment for the explosive charge.

Manufacturer: Zündapp, Zachertz
4,604 produced from April 1943 to September 1944
325 modified vehicles produced from November 1944 to January 1945

Crew: none	Engine: Zündapp SZ7 2cyl 703cc
Weight (tons): 0.43	12.5PS at 4,500rpm
Length (metres): 1.63	Gearbox: 2 forward, 1 reverse
Width (metres): 0.91	Speed (km/hr): 12
Height (metres): 0.62	Range (km): 12

Armament: 75Kg Sprengladung   100Kg Sprengladung
(Sd Kfz 303a)   (Sd Kfz 303b)

Armour (mm/angle):   Front
Hull (upper):   10/48° mild steel
     (lower):   10/60° mild steel

History: In 1942, a new version of the Goliath was ordered, which would allow a heavier charge to be carried over a greater distance. Zündapp therefore developed a version powered by their 703cc motorcycle engine. Two models of the Sd Kfz 303 were built: the initial version carried a 75kg demolition charge and was smaller (1.62m x 0.84m x 0.60m), and lighter (0.37 tons) than the final model. Approximately 650m of guidance wire was carried on the drum in each Goliath. For normal long-distance transport, the Goliath was mounted on a two-wheeled trailer.

Specific features: Raised air-intake cowl on the hull top, a spoked idler and two return rollers identified the Goliath (V-Motor). The

503

dimensions of the special trailer for carrying Goliath to the battle zone were: length 3.15m, width 1.50m, height 0.60m.

Combat service: As for Goliath (E-Motor).

504

505

Schwere Ladungsträger (Sd Kfz 301) Ausf A und B

Other designations: Sonderschlepper B IV, Gerät 690
Type: Tracked demolition charge layer

Manufacturer: Borgward
Chassis Nos.: 360001–
12 Versuchsfährzeuge produced in April 1942, 616 Ausf A produced from May 1942 to June 1943. 260 Ausf B produced from July to November 1943

Crew: 1
Weight (tons): 3.6
Length (metres): 3.65
Width (metres): 1.8
Height (metres): 1.19

Engine: Borgward 6M RTBV 2.31 lit 49PS at 3,300rpm
Gearbox: 1×2 forward, 1×2 reverse
Speed (km/hr): 38
Range (km): 212
Radio: EP3 mit UKE6

Armament: 500Kg Sprengladung

Armour (mm/angle):	Front	Side	Rear	Top/Bottom
Turret:	8/24°	8/21°	open	open
Superstructure:	10/47°	5+8/0°	5+8/19°	3/90°
Hull:	10/79°	5+8/0°	5+8/55°	4/90°

History: The Ladungsträger was designed to carry a heavy demolition charge to a specific target, where the charge was dropped, the vehicle backed off, and the charge detonated. The B IV could be remotely controlled by radio for the final phase of such an operation. The technique of depositing charges for destroying minefields and demolishing fortifications and pillboxes had been practised during the campaign in France in 1940, using a modification to the Pz Kpfw I. In October 1941, Borgward were ordered to develop a special-purpose vehicle with the radio-control feature. The resultant design was based on their Munitionsschlepper VK301.

Specific features: Originally, the B IV had 5mm side armour which was increased by adding 8mm plates during the production run. The side and rear armour were increased to 10mm, and this was the main feature of the Ausf B. The radio aerial was moved forward on this model, and the radio-control device was improved. During the Ausf B production, the dry pin steel track was introduced.

Combat service: Issued to Panzerkompanien (Funklenk) 311, 312, 313 and 314 and to Panzerabteilungen (Funklenk) 301 and 302. In July 1943, the 312th Panzerkompanie (Funklenk), which was subordinated to Army Group Centre, used the B IV successfully when clearing minefields at Kursk.

508

509

506

507

510

Plate 506. Schwerer Ladungsträger Borgward B III, forerunner of the B IV series.
Plates 507-510. Schwerer Ladungsträger Ausf A. In Plate 507, the explosive charge is on the front of the vehicle, and the driver's shields are up. These shields were folded down when the machine was radio-controlled; Plate 509 shows the explosive charge being released. Plate 510, the driver has just the side-shields up.

Schwere Ladungsträger (Sd Kfz 301) Ausf C

Other designation: Sonderschlepper B IV
Type: Tracked demolition charge layer

Manufacturer: Borgward
Chassis Nos.: 360001–
305 produced from December 1943 to September 1944

Crew: 1	Engine: Borgward 6B 3.8lit
Weight (tons): 4.85	78PS at 3,000rpm
Length (metres): 4.1	Gearbox: 1×2 forward,
Width (metres): 1.83	1×2 reverse
Height (metres): 1.25	Speed (km/hr): 40
	Range (km): 212
	Radio: EP3 mit UKE6

Armament: 500Kg Sprengladung

Armour (mm/angle):

	Front	Side	Rear	Top/Bottom
Turret:	15/22°	8/22°	open	open
Superstructure:	20/57°	20/0°	20/30°	6/90°
Hull:	20/79°	20/0°	20/55°	6/90°

History: The Ausf C was introduced in December 1943 and featured increased armour protection and simplified construction. To increase the performance of this heavier version, a larger engine had to be used, which in turn, increased the overall length. One of the major disadvantages of the vehicle was that it was often difficult for the operators to see the target from any safe distance. Experiments were carried out using a TV camera mounted on the front of the vehicle, but little came of this project. Towards the end of the war, a number of B IV were converted to small self-propelled weapons by the mounting of rocket-launchers, Raketen Pz B 54.

Specific features: Simpler construction using a smaller number of armour plates. The driving position was moved to the left-hand side of the vehicle.

Combat service: In August and September 1944, twenty-one Tiger Ausf E were issued to the 301st Panzerabteilung to control their B IV, in place of StuGIII. Each Zug (platoon) had a Tiger for the platoon leader and three Tigers, each controlling three B IV. One Sd Kfz 251 was attached to the platoon to carry additional 'Sprengladung' (explosive charges) and backup crews.

Plates 511-512. A rather battered schwerer Ladungsträger Ausf C; this machine featured all-steel tracks.
Plate 513. Kleinpanzer Wanze: this consisted of four 8.8cm Raketen Panzerbüchse 54 (rocket-launchers) mounted in a metal frame on the Borgward IV chassis.

512

513

Mittlere Ladungsträger 'Springer' (Sd Kfz 304)

Other designation: Gerät 680
Type: Expendable tracked demolition charge vehicle

Plate 514. Mittlerer Ladungsträger 'Springer'.

Manufacturer: NSU
50 produced from October 1944 to February 1945

Crew: 1	Engine: Opel Olympia 1.5lit
Weight (tons): 2.4	37PS at 3,400rpm
Length (metres): 3.17	Speed (km/hr): 42
Width (metres): 1.43	Range (km): 200
Height (metres): 1.45	Radio: KE6 mit UKE6

Armament: 330Kg Sprengstoff

Armour (mm/angle):

	Front	Side	Rear	Top/Bottom
Driver's shield:	9/20°	9/15°	open	open
Hull (upper):	10/30°	3+5/0°	9/45°	8/75°–90°
(lower):	10/45°	3+5/0°	9/45°	8/90°

History: The 'Springer' was ordered as a replacement for the light Goliath and the heavy B IV, being more effective than the former, and cheaper than the latter which were scheduled to go out of production in 1944. Production facilities for the NSU Kettenkrad were to be used for the Springer. It had also been intended to use this vehicle as a chassis for a 10.5cm IG recoilless gun in the Kleinpanzer Wanze (small tank) project, but this never materialized. The technique for using the Springer was to drive it as close as possible to the target, the driver dismounted and closed the turret sides down to protect the radio, which was then used to guide the Springer. *(Continued overleaf.)*

Specific features: The Springer used the drive-train, motor, and parts of the running gear of the Kettenkrad.

Combat service: The Springer was issued to normal radio-controlled armoured companies which had a StuG40 Ausf G to direct them to the target area. Each Zug had a command StuG40, plus three StuG40 each controlling three Springer.

Plates 515-516. Mittlerer Ladungsträger 'Springer': below with the turret sides down; right, a rear view of the prototype.

Gepanzerte Munitionsschlepper (VK302)

Other designation: Sonderschlepper B III
Type: Tracked armoured ammunition carrier

Manufacturer: Borgward
Chassis Nos.: 330001–
28 produced from October 1941 to February 1942

Crew: 2	Engine: Borgward 6M RTBV 2.3lit
Weight (tons): 3.5	49PS at 3,300rpm
Length (metres): 3.57	Gearbox: 1 forward, 1 reverse
Width (metres): 1.83	Speed (km/hr): 30
Height (metres): 1.44	Range (km): 150

Armour (mm/angle):	Front	Side	Rear	Top/Bottom
Superstructure:	14.5/20°	10/0°	10/40°	8/90°
Hull:	14.5/15°	10/0°	10/0°	8/90°

History: This special ammunition carrier was ordered as early as September 1937, to provide a fully-tracked ammunition supply vehicle. A pre-production series of 20 was ordered after tests with the prototypes. A second order for 100 improved vehicles was placed, but production was continually delayed in favour of more important equipment. Finally, in December 1941, the first deliveries took place. Only 28 of the original order were delivered, because in January 1942, production was suspended in favour of the proposed Ladungsträger RK4, which had been designed by Saurer.

Specific features: The engine was mounted to the rear, and two armoured panniers for ammunition were mounted on each side. Minor modifications were made to the running gear and armour layout. The lubricated track and running gear were used as the basis for the Sd Kfz 301.

Combat service By 1 July 1942, twenty VK302 had been issued to the troops, three were still with Wa Prüf 6 (Ordnance Proving Department 6), and five were still to be delivered by the manufacturer. Three of these were to have had new armour.

Plate 517. Gep Mun Schl VK302.
Plates 518-519. VK302 chassis with a wooden mock-up of the 10.5cm LG L/32.

Plate 520. VK302 chassis with a wooden mock-up of the 10.5cm LG L/32.

Panzer Selbstfahrlafette 1a 5cm PaK38 auf Gepanzerter Munitionsschlepper

Other designation: Leichte Panzerjäger
Type: Self-propelled anti-tank gun

History: A number of experimental Panzerjäger vehicles were ordered in July 1940. Included were two based on the Borgward ammunition carrier. The 5cm PaK38 was mounted on top of the engine compartment, with one man on each side. Ammunition was stored alongside the driver in the place formerly occupied by the helper. To cope with the recoil loads imposed on the very small chassis, a spade was lowered at the rear of the vehicle. These prototypes were ready in August 1941 and were issued to the troops for testing. The chassis number of one vehicle was 330033. The unsuitability of the 5cm PaK38 for conditions prevailing in 1942, precluded any further orders, but in September 1941, another light fighting vehicle was ordered. This was to mount the 10.5cm IG2.540 recoilless gun designed by Rheinmetall for paratroops. A limited traverse mount, similar to the 5cm PaK38, allowed 40° traverse and −10°+20° elevation. A Krupp proposal indicated a 360° traverse turret configuration. Only mock-ups on the Munitionsschlepper chassis were completed.

Plates 521-523. Pz Sf la 5cm PaK38 auf gep Mun Schl.

521

522

523

7.5cm PaK40/4 auf Raupenschlepper, Ost (Sf)

Type: Self-propelled anti-tank gun on tracked lorry chassis

Manufacturer: Steyr-Daimler Puch
60 converted in 1943

Crew: 4	Engine: Steyr V8 3.5lit
Weight (tons): 5.2	85PS at 3,000rpm
Length (metres): 4.57	Gearbox: 4 forward, 1 reverse
Width (metres): 1.99	Speed (km/hr): 17.2
Height (metres): 2.6	Range (km): 250

Armament: One 7.5cm PaK40/4 L/46
Traverse: 30° left 30° right (hand)
Elevation: −5° +22°
Sight: ZF3×8

Armour (mm/angle):	Front	Side	Rear	Top
Hull:	5/	5/0°	open	open
Gun shield:	5+5/30°			

525

History: In August 1943, Steyr Werke indicated to the Waffenamt (Ordnance Department) the possibility of using the RSO as a self-propelled carriage for the PaK40. As a result, a Test Series of fifty was ordered on 30 September 1943, to be ready within one month. Hitler saw a demonstration of this vehicle early in October, and the fifty were sent for troop trials with Army Group South. In January 1944, Hitler stated that he was most interested in this equipment and a production plan was formulated, giving projected figures of: from March 1944—60, April—100, May—150, June—200 and from July—400 per month.

Specific features: Normal RSO with wooden load platform on which the PaK40 turntable was mounted. The cab was replaced by a lightly armoured cab, with folding top and open driving position.

Combat service: Troop trials with Army Group South early in 1944.

Plates 524-526. 7.5cm PaK40/4 auf RSO (Sf).

526

524

Panzerkampfwagen E-25

Type: Tank destroyer

History: The E-25 was an armoured vehicle in the 25 ton to 30 ton class, ordered in 1944. Argus-Werke carried out the design work, and Alkett were in the process of building five prototypes when the war

Gepanzerter Mannschaftstransport-wagen 'Kätzchen'

Type: Armoured personnel carrier

History: In 1944–45, Auto-Union delivered two prototypes of the fully-tracked armoured personnel carrier. Overlapping steel-rimmed wheels were used with front drive. The engine was a Maybach HL50 of 180PS.

Manufacturer: Auto-Union
2 Prototypes in 1944

Length (metres): 4.22	Engine: Maybach HL50
Width (metres): 2.34	
Height (metres): 1.45	

Armament: One 7.92mm MG34

Armour (mm/Angle):	Front	Side	Rear	Top
Superstructure:	20/60°	15/45°	20/30°	open
Hull:	20/20°–55°	20/0°	20/30	

One example captured by American forces in early 1945.

ended. The E−25 was, in outline. like the Jagdpanzer Hetzer, but was to be armed with the 7.5cm L/70. The main technical features were the large diameter road wheels, Belleville Washer suspension units, and hydrostatic drive coupled to a transverse-mounted HL230 motor. The drive was to the rear sprocket. Panther tracks were used.

Plate 527. Gep MTW 'Kätzchen'.

Land-Wasser-Schlepper

Other designation: LWS
Type: Tracked amphibious vehicle

History: In 1936, Rheinmetall-Borsig received an order to develop a fully-tracked amphibious tractor, and, working with various firms, including Alkett, the LWS was built. Powered by a Maybach HL120 engine, the LWS could achieve 35km/hr on roads, and 12km/hr in water. A conventional boat rudder and propeller were used, and the hull was boat-shaped. The total weight was 17 tons and up to 20 men could be accommodated. The normal function was seen as towing, and a powerful winch was fitted. By mid 1940, a pre-production series of seven had been completed and a further 14 were on order. The LWS saw service in the East.

528

529

530

Plates 528-530. The LWS: Plate 528 shows the prototype.

531

532

Plates 531-532. Two Waffenträger design models: left, Rheinmetall design for 10.5cm leFH on Leopard Waffenträger; right, a self-propelled gun based on the Skoda T25. (For details of the Leopard project, see page 37). (For details of Skoda T25, see Page 43).

Gerät 040 und Gerät 041

Other designation: Karlgerät
Type: Self-propelled heavy siege mortar on tracked carriage

Manufacturer: Rheinmetall-Borsig
Chassis Nos.: I–VI
1 prototype completed in early 1940
6 production vehicles delivered between November 1940 and August 1941

Weight (tons): 124	Engine: Daimler-Benz MB503 V12
Length (metres): 11.37	44.5lit 580PS, later MB507
Width (metres): 3.16	Gearbox: 4 forward, 1 reverse
Height (metres): 4.78	Speed (km/hr): 10

Armament: One 60cm Gerät 040 L/8.44, later one 54cm Gerät 041 L/11.5
Traverse: 4° left 4° right (hand)
Elevation: −0° +70°

Armour: mild steel superstructure and hull

534

History: The self-propelled version of the 60cm siege mortar was ordered in June 1937. General Karl Becker of the Artillery was involved in the development, hence the name Karl was used to describe the gun. The driving trials were held at Unterlüss in May 1940. Delivery of the six production vehicles took place from November 1940 to August 1941. In February 1941, discussions commenced, concerning increasing the range of the weapon, and in May 1942, 54cm barrels (Gerät 041) were ordered for the six vehicles. At a conference with Hitler in March 1943, it was stated that the first 54cm Gerät 041 would be delivered by June 1943, and the third, by mid-August. The 60cm and 54cm barrels appear to have been interchanged as required. In 1945, US forces captured vehicle II with a 60cm, and vehicle V with a 54cm.

Specific features: The prototype chassis, built in 1939, had eight road wheels with external swing arms. Production Karl had eleven road wheels. Ammunition was transported in a tracked Munitionsschlepper converted from the Pz Kpfw IV, four rounds in each Schlepper. For the 60cm 040, the s Be Granate weighed 2.17 tons and the le Be Granate, 1.70 tons; in the case of the 54cm Gerät 041, 1.58 tons and 1.25 tons respectively. Maximum rate of fire was 6rph.

Combat service: Guns I-IV went to the Russian Front in July 1941 with the 628th schwere Artillerie Abteilung. They saw action at various sites, including Lemberg in that year. The best known action was against Sevastopol in 1942. Later, four guns were issued to the 833rd schwere Artillerie Abteilung (mot). These guns had the names Adam, Eve (1st Batt) and Thor, Odin (2nd Batt). The names for guns V and VI were Loki and Ziu.

535

536

537

538

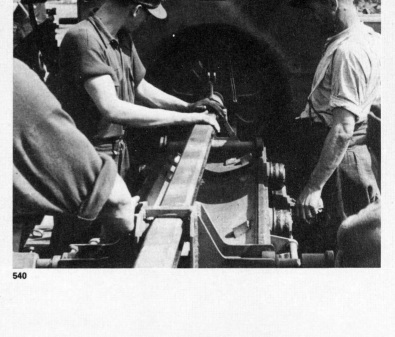

539

540

Plate 9 (Page 5) Gerät 040 crew preparing to fire.
Plates 533-534. Gerät 040 (60cm) mortars on the test ground. Note Pz Kpfw IV Munitions-träger vehicles (data page 117).
Plate 535. Prototype chassis for Gerät 040.
Plates 536-537. Gerät 041 (54cm) mortars 'Thor' (top) and 'Loki'.
Plates 538-539. Moving Karl. Plate 538 shows rail transportation—two special trucks which suspended the vehicle between them on cantilevered beams. A pair of jacks was used to lift the vehicle into the travelling position. Plate 539 shows road transportation, where the vehicle was partially dismantled and put on to special trailers. The chassis was carried on a 24-wheeled trailer. (See also overleaf.)
Plate 540. Loading a 60cm shell into the breech of 'Ziu'.

Plates 1008—1009 (Page 254) Details of weapon.

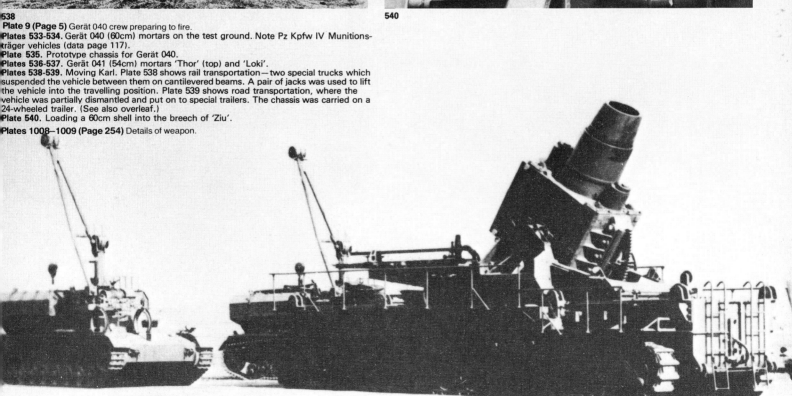

Plates 541-543. The 16-wheeled transport for Mörser Karl: the top recoil system and loading mechanism (Plate 541); the tube and breech assembly (Plate 542); the gun cradle and top carriage (Plate 543).

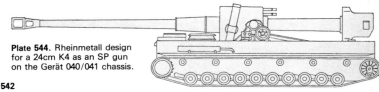

Plate 544. Rheinmetall design for a 24cm K4 as an SP gun on the Gerät 040/041 chassis.

8.8cm FlaK auf Sonderfahrgestell

Other designation: Flakpanzer für s FlaK
Type: Self-propelled anti-aircraft gun on tracked chassis

Manufacturer: Krupp
3 prototypes produced in late 1942

Crew: 8	Engine: Maybach HL90
Weight (tons): 26	Gearbox: 6 forward, 1 reverse
Length (metres): 7	Speed (km/hr): 35
Width (metres): 3	Range (km): 250
Height (metres): 2.8	

Armament: One 8.8cm FlaK37 L/56 later one 8.8cm FlaK41 L/75
Traverse: 360° (hand)
Elevation: −3° +85°
Sight: FlaK

Armour (mm/angle):	Front	Side	Rear	Top/Bottom
Superstructure:	50/30°	10/0° & 30°	10/24°	open
Hull:	50/12°	20/0°	20/15°	10/90°
Gun shield:	10/10°			

History: The history of the Flakpanzer für schwere FlaK began in 1941 when the Waffenamt ordered yet another heavy Panzerjäger vehicle, the 8.8cm K (Pz Sf) auf Sonderfahrgestell. The chassis was also known as the Pz Sf IV c. A special version of the 8.8cm L/56 was planned to be mounted in an open turret carried by the Sonderfahrgestell. Later, it was envisaged to mount the L/71 version of the 8.8cm PaK. The chassis were built, but the requirement for this Panzerjäger was cancelled and the chassis were used for the development of the heavy FlaK vehicle. In 1944, the FlaK41 was mounted, and plans were in hand to mount the Gerät 042. Krupp also proposed this as the chassis for the 10.5cm leFH43 Waffenträger.

Specific features: The Sonderfahrgestell was based on the Pz Kpfw IV, but was a very much modernized vehicle. The Flakpanzer could lower the superstructure sides to allow 360° traverse. New, wide (520mm) tracks were used in conjunction with Schachtellaufwerk (interleaved suspension).

Plate 545 (left) and 546-547 (opposite page). 8.8cm FlaK37 auf Sd Fgst.

Plates 548-549 (opposite page). 8.8cm FlaK41 auf Sd Fgst. Plate 549 shows the armoured sides lowered to afford all-round traverse.

546

547

548

549

550

551

552

Plates 550-552 (above). Three project designs: top, Gerät 42 auf Sd Fgst, a project to mount the 8.8cm FlaK42 on a special chassis; centre, 10.5cm leFH43(K) Waffenträger; bottom, Krupp's projected Pz Sf IVc, to mount the 8.8cm PjK43.

Semi-tracked vehicles

Leichte Gepanzerte Kraftwagen (Sd Kfz 250) (later) Leichte Schutzenpanzerwagen (Sd Kfz 250)

Other designations: D7p, le SPW Alte, Gerät 89
Type: Semi-tracked light armoured personnel carrier

Manufacturer: Büssing-NAG, Weserhütte, Wumag, Wegmann (Evans+
    Pistor), Ritscher, Deutsche Werke
Chassis Nos.: 95001– , 201001– ͺ310001–
4,250 produced from June 1941 to October 1943

Crew: 2	Engine: Maybach HL42TRKM
Weight (tons): 5.8	Gearbox: 7 forward, 3 reverse
Length (metres): 4.56	Speed (km/hr): 60
Width (metres): 1.95	Range (km): 320
Height (metres): 1.66	Radio: FuG Spr Ger f

Armament: see list of variants

Armour (mm/angle):	Front	Side	Rear	Top/Bottom
Superstructure:	10/30°	8/35°	8/17°	open
Hull:	14.5/12°	8/30°	8/45°	6/90°

History: In 1939, after successful trials of the light semi-track troop-carrier, the Army indicated their requirement of a similar vehicle capable of transporting a Halbgruppe (half platoon), thereby increasing the flexibility of reconnaissance units. Büssing-NAG were entrusted with the development of the armoured body, and Demag, with the chassis, which was to be based on their existing Zgkw It (Sd Kfz 10). Prototypes were already available, powered by the Maybach NL38 motor. Because of delays, the production series was not started until June 1941 when the first thirty-nine vehicles were completed. Up to October 1943, only minor modifications were incorporated in the production vehicles, but twelve official sub-variants existed, each having a special-purpose configuration. After October 1943, this version of the le SPW was known as 'Alte' (old).
Specific features: The Sd Kfz 250 consisted of a modified Demag D7 tractor chassis, mounting an armoured body. In order to maintain the performance of this limited payload vehicle when fitted with the armoured superstructure, Demag shortened the chassis and removed the forward wheel and torsion bar. The lubricated tracks provided

some of the steering, though for normal road use, the front wheels were sufficient.
Combat service: The bulk of the sub-variants were issued to Panzer Aufklärungs detachments of Panzer and Panzergrenadier divisions. The light reconnaissance company which used these vehicles was normally issued with twenty-eight when attached to a Panzer division, or eighteen when with a Panzergrenadier division. The ammunition carriers and observation vehicles were attached to Sturmgeschütz units.

553

Plates 553-554. Rear and side view of le SPW Sd Kfz 250 'Alt'.

554

Leichte Schützenpanzerwagen (Sd Kfz 250)

Other designations: D7p, le SPW Neu, Gerät 89
Type: Semi-tracked light armoured personnel carrier

Manufacturer: Weserhütte, Deutsche Werke, Evans+Pistor to 1945, Wumag to July 1944
Chassis Nos.: 95001– , 201001– , 310001–
2,378 produced

Crew: 2
Weight (tons): 5.38
Length (metres): 4.61
Width (metres): 1.95
Height (metres): 1.66

Engine: Maybach HL42TUKRM
Gearbox: 7 forward, 3 reverse
Speed (km/hr): 60
Range (km): 300
Radio: FuG Spr Ger f

Armament: see list of variants

Armour (mm/angle):	Front	Side	Rear	Top/Bottom
Superstructure:	10/30°	8/35°	8/10°	open
Hull:	15/12°	8/30°	8/45°	6/90°

Plate 555. Le SPW Sd Kfz 250 'Neu'.

History: The armoured body of the Sd Kfz 250 (Alte Ausf) was complex in shape and required considerable manhours for construction. During 1943, it was decided to simplify the body so that as many flat armour plates as possible could be used. In October 1943, the Sd Kfz 250 Neu entered production. By mid-July, the production plan for industry in 1945, indicated that the le SPW was to be dropped in favour of increased production of the m SPW (Sd Kfz 251).

Specific features: The 19 main armour plates of the old model were reduced to nine, and the vehicle was easily recognizable by the slab-sided appearance of the permanent stowage boxes along each side.

555

Combat service: Served with the Panzer Aufklärungs detachments of Panzer and Panzergrenadier divisions. The 1944 Establishment for Panzer divisions indicated a requirement of fifty-five le SPW. The Sd Kfz 250 also was issued to the armoured reconnaissance vehicle companies of Panzer divisions during 1944.

Leichte Schützenpanzerwagen (Sd Kfz 250 Variants)

Sd Kfz 250/1 leichter Schützenpanzerwagen. Gerät 891. Weight: 5.38 tons Crew: 6. Built continuously from 1941 to 1945, the main purpose of this version was to transport the Halbgruppe of 4. The armament was two MG34. The height of this vehicle including the MG shield was 1.98m. Ammunition: 2,010.

Sd Kfz 250/1 leichter Schützenpanzerwagen (s MG). Crew: 6. This version carried the support Halbgruppe with two MG34 in heavy field mountings.

Sd Kfz 250/2 leichter Fernsprechpanzerwagen. Gerät 892. Weight: 5.44 tons. Crew: 4. Used for cable-laying by communications troops in the creation of telephone networks. The crew was 4 and armament was one MG34.

Plate 556. Le SPW Sd Kfz 250/1.

557

Plates 557-558. Sd Kfz 250/2 leichte Fernsprechpanzerwagen; above, the cable drum in the rear of the vehicle. Three cables could be laid simultaneously—one from each front mudguard and one from the rear. Right, a telephone cable being run out from the drum on the front right mudguard.

558

Sd Kfz 250/3 leichte Funkpanzerwagen. Gerät 893. Weight: 5.35 tons. Crew: 4. For control of motorized formations, and was equipped with the FuG12 radio which used the 2 metre rod and, later, the 2 metre star aerial. The armament of all Funkpanzer versions was one MG34.

Sd Kfz 250/3 leichte Funkpanzerwagen. Weight: 5.35 tons. Crew: 4. Issued to Luftwaffe ground units for air support control. FuG7 with 2 metre rod.

Sd Kfz 250/3 leichte Funkpanzerwagen. Weight: 5.35 tons. Crew: 4. Luftwaffe ground-to-air communications post, fitted with FuG7, and the FuG8 for main divisional command link-up. The antenna for the

Plates **559-561**. Sd Kfz 250/3 leichter Funkpanzerwagen. Plates 559 and 561 show the ground-to-air communications vehicle based on the 'Neu' Sd Kfz 250, carrying rod and star aerials in Plate 559, and a frame aerial in Plate 561. Plate 560 shows the interior of the vehicle with the radio equipment at top right.

559

FuG8 was frame in the early vehicles, and 8 metre star mast later.

Sd Kfz 250/3 leichte Funkpanzerwagen. Weight 5.35 tons. Crew 4. General-purpose radio vehicle with radios to suit use.

Sd Kfz 250/4 leichte Truppenluftschützpanzerwagen. Gerät 894. Originally envisaged as a light anti-aircraft vehicle armed with Zwillingslafette (dual mount) 36 (2 x MG34), but this version was not put into production.

Sd Kfz 250/4 leichte Beobachtungspanzerwagen. Weight: 5.7 tons. Crew: 4. In 1943, this version was introduced to act as an observation vehicle for the Sturmgeschütz detachment. Radio equipment was the FuG15 and FuG16. Armament was one MG34 or 42.

Sd Kfz 250/5 leichte Beobachtungspanzerwagen. Gerät 895. Weight: 5.35 tons. Crew: 4. Armoured observation post equipped with FuG4 and FuG8. Early vehicles had the frame antenna, later, the 2 metre star, for the FuG8.

Sd Kfz 250/5 leichte Beobachtungspanzerwagen. Weight: 5.35 tons. Crew: 4. FuG12 replaced the earlier radio. In 1944, this version was redesignated Leichter Aufklärungspanzerwagen to differentiate from the Sd Kfz 250/4.

Sd Kfz 250/6 leichte Munitionspanzerwagen Ausf A für Sturmgeschütz 7.5cm Kanone (Kurz) Ausf A bis E. (Gerät 896). Weight: 5.95 tons. Crew: 2. Armament: one 7.92mm MG34. Ammunition: 1,100. Issued to Sturmgeschütz Abt after the Sd Kfz 252 went out of production in September 1941. These Munitionspanzerwagen carried 70 rounds of 7.5cm ammunition for the StuK (L/24). An ammunition trailer was normally attached. The radio was FuG16.

Sd Kfz 250/6 leichte Munitionspanzerwagen Ausf B für Sturmgeschütz 40 Ausf F and G. Weight: 6.09 tons. Crew: 2. Carried 60 rounds of 7.5cm StuK40 (L/48) ammunition. The armament of these vehicles was one MG34 or 42.

Sd Kfz 250/7 leichte Schützenpanzerwagen (schwerer Granatwerfer). Gerät 897. Height: 1.8m. Weight: 5.61 tons. Crew: 5. Issued to the fourth platoon of Leichter Panzer Aufklärungs companies. The 8cm GrW34 was used to support the other platoons in action with fire from its mortar. An MG34 or 42 completed the armament. Forty-two rounds of mortar ammunition were stored.

Sd Kfz 250/7 leichte Schützenpanzerwagen (Munitionsfahrzeug). Armament: two 7.92mm MG34. Weight: 5.38 tons. Crew: 4. Ammunition: 2,010. Carrying 66 rounds of mortar ammunition, these vehicles were issued to section leaders or platoon commanders and frequently carried additional radio equipment.

560

561

562

Plate 562. Sd Kfz 250/4 leichte Beobachtungspanzerwagen, here acting as observation vehicle for 15cm Panzerwerfer vehicles (data page 180).

563

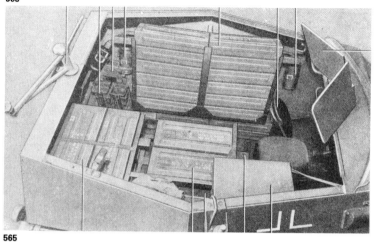

565

566

568

Plates 563-564. Sd Kfz 250/5 leichte Beobachtungspanzerwagen. The interior view shows the scissors telescope and the radio equipment.

564

Plates 565-566. Interior views of Sd Kfz 250/6 leichte Munitionspanzerwagen Ausf A (Plate 565) and Ausf B, showing stowage of ammunition.

Plates 567-568. Sd Kfz 250/7 schwere Granatwerfer. Plate 568 shows the 8cm GrW34 mortar within the vehicle.

Plate 569. Interior of Sd Kfz 250/7 Munitionsfahrzeug.

567

569

Sd Kfz 250/8 leichte Schützenpanzerwagen (7.5cm). Gerät 898. Height: 2.07m. Weight: 6.30 tons. Crew: 3/4. Armament: one 7.5cm KwK37 L/24, later, one 7.5cm K51 (Sf). Ammunition: 20. A small number of Sd Kfz 250/8 using the Alte chassis were issued in the spring of 1943. In October 1944, the Sd Kfz 250/8 was re-introduced with the gun mounted in the new unified mount 7.5cm K51 (Sf). These vehicles were issued to the 4th Platoon of the Leichter Panzer Aufklärungs companies.

Sd Kfz 250/9 leichte Schützenpanzerwagen (2cm). Gerät 883. Weight: 6.02 tons. Crew: 3. Height: 2.16m. Armament: one 2cm KwK38. Sight: TZF3a. Ammunition: 100. One 7.92mm MG34 or 42. Elevation: $-10°+85°$. The order for 30 of these semi-tracked armoured cars was issued in March 1942. In the same year, three prototypes were sent to Russia to see if the cross-country performance were better than that of the wheeled armoured cars, and as a result, the Sd Kfz 222 was discontinued and replaced by the Sd Kfz 250/9 which began mass-production in May 1943. Early versions used the complete turret assembly of the Sd Kfz 222, and later models, the Hängelafette (swinging mount) 38. The radio equipment was the FuG12.

Sd Kfz 250/10 leichte Schützenpanzerwagen (3.7cm PaK). Gerät 881. Weight: 5.67 tons. Crew: 4. Height: 1.97m. Armament: one 3.7cm PaK 35/36. Sight: ZF2 × 16°. Ammunition: 216. One 7.92mm MG34. Ammunition: 1,100. Elevation: $-8°+25°$. Traverse: 30° left 30° right. The Sd Kfz 250/10 was issued to platoon leaders to provide heavy support. Various configurations of gun shield were used with the 3.7cm PaK.

Sd Kfz 250/11 leichte Schützenpanzerwagen (schwere Panzerbüchse 41) Gerät 882. Height: 2.13m. Weight: 5.53 tons. Crew: 6. Armament: one 2.8cm sPzB41. Ammunition: 168. One 7.92mm MG34 or 42. Ammunition 1,100. The Sd Kfz 250/11 was an alternative to the Sd Kfz 250/10 and was issued to platoon leaders. The sPzB41 was a high-velocity cone-bore weapon. A light-weight field carriage designed for airborne troops was carried on the vehicle so that the sPzB41 could be dismounted.

Sd Kfz 250/12 leichte Messtruppanzerwagen. Gerät 899. Weight: 5.80 tons. Crew: 3/5. Armament: one 7.92mm MG34 or 42. Ammunition: 1,100. This was a survey and range-plotting vehicle used by artillery troops. The radio equipment consisted of a FuG8 in the early versions; the FuG12 became standard in later models.

Sd Kfz 250/–. There existed both Alt and Neu versions mounting the 2cm FlaK. although no official record exists.

Sd Kfz 250/–. A Sfl 5cm PaK38 L/60 is still on display in Yugoslavia. It used the (Neu Ausf) chassis which was lengthened to accommodate the PaK38.

Sd Kfz 250/–. Lastkraftwagen. A number of armoured vehicles were modified by removing the rear armoured body to provide a load-carrier.

Plate 570. Sd Kfz 250/8 leichte Schützenpanzerwagen mit 7.5cm KwK37.

Plates 571-574. Sd Kfz 250/9 leichte Schützenpanzerwagen (2cm). That in Plate 573 is based on the 'Neu' vehicle, as well as having the later Hängelafette turret (see page 192). Below, vehicles operating in Russia.

575

576

577

578

Plates 575-576. Sd Kfz 250/10 leichte Schützenpanzerwagen (3.7cm PaK). Note that the **Plate 1037 (Page 268)** Sd Kfz 250/10.
Plates 577-578. Sd Kfz 250/11 leichte Schützenpanzerwagen (schwere Panzerbüchse 41).

Plates 579-580. Sd Kfz 250/12 leichte Messtruppanzerwagen, a survey/range-plotting vehicle.

579

580

Plate 581. Sd Kfz 250 mounting the French 25mm Hotchkiss anti-tank gun.

Plate 582. Sd Kfz 250 'Neu Ausf' with 5cm PaK38.

581

582

Leichte Gepanzerte Munitionskraftwagen (Sd Kfz 252)

Type: Semi-tracked light armoured ammunition carrier

Manufacturer: Demag/Wegmann from June 1940, Deutsche Werke from January to September 1941
413 produced

Crew: 2	Engine: Maybach HL42TRKM
Weight (tons): 5.73	Gearbox: 7 forward, 3 reverse
Length (metres): 4.7	Speed (km/hr): 65
Width (metres): 1.95	Range (km): 320
Height (metres): 1.8	Radio: FuG15 or FuG16

Armament: One 7.92mm MG34
Traverse: loose
Elevation: loose
Sight: direct

Armour (mm/angle):	Front	Side	Rear	Top/Bottom
Superstructure:	18/30°	8/30°	8/55°	8/90°
Hull:	18/12°	8/30°	8/45°	8/90°

History: Developed together with the Sd Kfz 253, the Munitionskraftwagen did not enter production until the former vehicles had been completed. The initial series consisted of 30 vehicles, built between June and August 1940. When production ceased in September 1941, the vehicle was replaced by the Sd Kfz 250/6.

Specific features: The Sd Kfz 252 was distinguished by its fully enclosed armoured body which was sloped at a considerable angle to the rear, to reduce weight. Pistol ports were provided under the side vision ports. Normally trailer Sonder Anhänger 3 1/1 was towed, so as to increase the ammunition load.

Combat service: Issued to Sturmartillerie batteries.

583

584

Plates 583-584. Sd Kfz 252 leichte gepanzerte Munitionskraftwagen with its Sd Ah 3 1/1 trailer (left, passing a Sturmgeschütz).

Plate 1033 (Page 268) overhead view of Sd Kfz 252 in action.

Leichte Gepanzerte Beobachtungskraftwagen (Sd Kfz 253)

Type: Semi-tracked light armoured observation post

Manufacturer: Demag/Wegmann
285 produced from March 1940 to June 1941

Crew: 4	Engine: Maybach HL42TRKM
Weight (tons): 5.7	Gearbox: 7 forward, 3 reverse
Length (metres): 4.7	Speed (km/hr): 65
Width (metres): 1.95	Range (km): 320
Height (metres): 1.8	Radio: FuG15 & FuG16

Armament: One 7.92mm MG34
Traverse: loose
Elevation: loose
Sight: direct

Armour (mm/angle):	Front	Side	Rear	Top/Bottom
Superstructure:	18/30°	8/30°	8/23°	8/90°
Hull:	18/12°	8/30°	8/45°	8/90°

History: During the late thirties, trials were held of the pre-production series of the Sturmgeschütz and it was concluded that these vehicles would have to be supported by an armoured ammunition carrier and observation vehicle. These were to be based on the Demag semi-track chassis. Shortly after the Sturmgeschütz had gone into production in 1940, an order for 25 le gep Beob Wg was placed, and these were built between March and June 1940. As these were the very first production vehicles using the Demag-developed D7p, shortened version of the 1 ton tractor, some manufacturing difficulties were experienced. Further series were ordered as the number of Sturmgeschütz was increased, but this specialized model was abandoned in favour of the normal Sd Kfz 250.

Specific features: Heavier armour and a fully-enclosed crew compartment were features of these Sd Kfz 253. Observation was from a large circular hatch in the roof. The radio aerial on the right-hand side folded forward into a protective channel when not in use.

Combat service: Served with Sturmartillerie Batterien 640, 659, 660 and 665 in France in 1940, and later with other assault artillery batteries in Russia.

Plates 585-586. Sd Kfz 253 leichte gepanzerte Beobachtungskraftwagen: below, the circular hatch cover can be seen atop the hull superstructure; right, in Russia.

585

586

587

Plates 587-590. Sd Kfz 251 mittlere Schützenpanzerwagen Ausf A (Plate 587), Ausf B (Plate 588) and Ausf C (Plates 589 and 590). Note that the vehicle in Plate 590 has a riveted body.

588

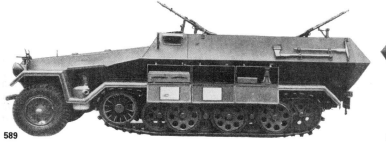

589

590

Mittlere Gepanzerte Mannschaftskraftwagen (Sd Kfz 251), later Mittlere Schützenpanzerwagen Ausf A, B und C

Other designations: HL KL 6p, Gerät 90
Type: Semi-tracked medium armoured personnel carrier

Manufacturer: Hanomag, MNH, Schichau, Wumag, Weserhütte, Borgward
Chassis Nos.: 221001– , 540001– , 625001– , 320001– , 720001– , 725001– , 796001– , 811001–
4,650 produced from June 1939 to September 1943

Crew: 2	Engine: Maybach HL42TUKRM
Weight (tons): 7.81	Gearbox: 4 × 2 forward,
Length (metres): 5.8	1 × 2 reverse
Width (metres): 2.1	Speed (km/hr): 53
Height (metres): 1.75	Range (km): 300
	Radio: FuG Spr Ger f

Armament: see list of variants

Armour (mm/angle):	Front	Side	Rear	Top/Bottom
Superstructure:	10/33°	8/35°	8/40°	open
Hull:	14.5/21°	8/35°	8/30°	6/90°

History: During the period when the concept of the Panzer Division was being planned, requirements were detailed for an armoured personnel carrier, capable of accompanying tanks into battle. As early as 1935, it was suggested that the requirement could be filled by fitting an armoured body on a medium semi-track tractor. In 1937 development was begun, with Hanomag being entrusted with the chassis design and Büssing-NAG, with the armoured body. The Zgkw 3t (Sd Kfz 11) was the basis of the new vehicle. The Ausf A and B were superseded in 1940 by the Ausf C which was manufactured continuously until late 1943.

Specific features: The Ausf A can be identified by three early-pattern vision slits on each side, and a radio aerial mounted on the front right-hand mudguard. The Ausf B had a single vision port for the driver and commander only. Both models had an unprotected MG mount over the crew compartment. The Ausf C featured a single-plate nose armour, and armoured cowls to cover the engine side intakes, and an armoured shield for the forward MG was introduced. All vehicles had a well-designed and shaped armoured body, and wide-opening double doors at the rear, to facilitate quick exit. Various styles of manufacture were used by different producers, so that there existed Sd Kfz 251 Ausf C with both welded and riveted bodies.

Combat service: See list of variants.

Mittlere Schützenpanzerwagen Ausf D (Sd Kfz 251)

Other designations: HL KL 6p, Gerät 90
Type: Semi-tracked medium armoured personnel carrier

Manufacturer: Hanomag, MNH, Schichau, Wumag, Weserhütte,
  Borgward from September 1943 to March 1945, Evans + Pistor,
  Deutsche Werke, Büssing-NAG from 1944
Chassis Nos.: as for Ausf A, B, C
10,602 produced

Crew: 2
Weight (tons): 8
Length (metres): 5.98
Width (metres): 2.1
Height (metres): 1.75

Engine: Maybach HL42TUKRM
Gearbox: 4 × 2 forward,
  1 × 2 reverse
Speed (km/hr): 53
Range (km): 300
Radio: FuG Spr Ger f

Armament: see list of variants

Armour (mm/angle):	Front	Side	Rear	Top/Bottom
Superstructure:	10/33°	8/35°	8/33°	open
Hull:	15/22°	8/35°	8/33°	6/90°

History: The Sd Kfz 251 Ausf D was developed in order to simplify construction so that output could be increased as much as possible. The number of separate armour plates was reduced wherever possible.
Specific features: Simplified armoured body with reverse sloped rear plate, engine air-intakes incorporated under the engine side armour, and light metal stowage boxes permanently fitted along each side in place of mudguards.
Combat service: See list of variants.

Mittlere Schützenpanzerwagen (Sd Kfz 251 Variants)

Sd Kfz 251/1 mittlere Schützenpanzerwagen. Weight: 9 tons. Crew: 12. Height with MG shield: 2.16m. Armament: Two 7.92mm MG34 or 42. Ammunition: 2,010. Standard armoured personnel carrier for the Panzergrenadier Gruppe. When co-operating with Panzer units, the FuG5 radio was sometimes fitted. Other designation was Gerät 901.
Sd Kfz 251/1 mittlere Schützenpanzerwagen. Weight: 9 tons. Crew: 11. Armament: Two 7.92mm sMG34, one 7.92mm MG34 or 42. Ammunition: 2,010. Carrier for the Heavy MG Group of the Armoured Infantry Detachment.
Sd Kfz 251/1 mittlere Schützenpanzerwagen (Wurfrahmen 40). Crew: 7. Armament: Two 7.92mm MG34 or 42. Ammunition: 2,010. 6–Wurfrahmen 40. Five 28cm Sprengranate (HE round). One 32cm Flammgranate (incendiary round). After the campaign in France in 1940, J. Gast KG. Berlin were ordered to develop a projector for the Wurfgerät 40, which would be fitted on the m SPW. The resulting vehicle could be traversed by the driver, and elevation of +5° +40° could be set on each projector frame. Firing took 10 seconds and gave the 3rd Panzerpionier Zug heavy bombardment capability up to 1.9km for Sprengranate and 2.2km for Flammgranate.
Sd Kfz 251/1 mittlere Schützenpanzerwagen (IR) 'Falke'. Crew: 12. Standard armoured personnel carrier, fitted with infra-red equipment, for use by Panzergrenadier units attached to the infra-red Panther detachments.
Sd Kfz 251/2 mittlere Schützenpanzerwagen (Granatwerfer). Weight: 8.64 tons. Crew: 8. Armament: 8cm Gr W 34; 7.92mm MG34 or 42. Ammunition: 66 (Gr W 34), 2,010 (MG34 or 42). This mortar vehicle

was issued to the heavy platoon of armoured infantry companies. Gerät 892 was its other designation.
Sd Kfz 251/3 mittlere Funkpanzerwagen. Gerät 893. Weight: 8.50 tons. Crew: 7. Armament: Two 7.92mm MG34 or 42. Ammunition: 2,010. Height: 1.75m. A total of eight different types of radio equipment were carried by the m Funkpanzerwagen depending upon the unit for which it was issued. As follows:
FuG8 + FuG5 + FuG4, Divisional and artillery link to Panzer units. Until 1942, the FuG8 required a frame antenna.
FuG8 + FuG4, Division-to-artillery link vehicle. Until 1942, frame antenna fitted for FuG8.
FuG8 + FuG5, Division-to-Panzer unit link vehicle. Until 1942, frame antenna fitted for FuG8.
FuG7 + FuG1, Ground-to-air link and transmission listening monitor.
FuG12 + FuG11 + Kdo FuG Tr Command-post vehicle. The original frame antenna was subsequently replaced by a 9m winch mast.
FuG Tr 100mw Command-post.
FuG Tr 80mw Command-post.
FuG Tr 30mw Command-post.
FuG Tr 15kzw Command-post.
Sd Kfz 251/4 mittlere Schützenpanzerwagen (IG). Gerät 904. Weight: 8.75 tons. Crew: 7. Armament: One 7.92mm MG34. Ammunition: 1,100. Ammunition carrier and tractor for the 7.5cm leIG18. This vehicle was replaced by the Sd Kfz 251/9 with its self-propelled 7.5cm gun in 1942. 120 rounds of ammunition were carried.

Plates 591 and 592 (opposite page). Sd Kfz 251 mittlere Schützenpanzerwagen Ausf D.
Plates 593–595. Sd Kfz 251 mittlere Schützenpanzerwagen (Wurfrahmen 40) Ausf B
Plates 596-597. Exterior and interior views of Sd Kfz 251/2 mittlere Schützenpanzerwagen (Granatwerfer) Ausf C.
Plates 598-599. Sd Kfz 251/3 mittlere Funkpanzerwagen Ausf C. Plate 599 shows the radio equipment.
Plate 600. Ammunition carrier/tractor Sd Kfz 251/4 mittlere Schützenpanzerwagen (IG) Ausf C.

592

597

593

Antenne für Fu 8

Antenne für Fu 5

Antenne für Funksprechgerät f

598

594

Mittelwellenempfänger c
(Fu 4)

10 Watt Sender c

30 Watt Sender a
(Fu 8)

(Fu 5)

UKW Empfänger e
(Fu 2)

599

595

596

600

601

602

603

604

605

Plates 601-602. Sd Kfz 251/6 mittlere Kommandopanzerwagen Ausf A. (Plate 601 shows an early vehicle.)

Plate 603. Command vehicle Sd Kfz 251/6 Ausf C equipped with the 2.8cm Panzer-büchse 41.

Plate 604. A command vehicle (Ausf A) with an extension built on top of the super-structure for map reading.

Plate 605. The interior of Guderian's command vehicle. (Note the early 'Enigma' code machine.)

Plate 606. The command vehicle (an Ausf B) of the commander of the infantry division 'Grossdeutschland'.

Sd Kfz 251/5 mittlere Schützenpanzerwagen (Pi). Gerät 905. Weight: 8.87 tons. Crew: 9. Armament: Two 7.92mm MG34. Ammunition: 4,800. FuG8+FuG4. Radio-command vehicle for the Engineer Platoon (a), discontinued in 1943.

Sd Kfz 251/5 mittlere Schützenpanzerwagen (Pi). FuG8 + FuG5. Radio-command vehicle for the Heavy Platoon of the Panzerpionier Gruppe, discontinued in 1943.

Sd Kfz 251/6 mittlere Kommandopanzerwagen. Weight: 8.50 tons. Crew: 8. Armament: One 7.92mm MG34. Ammunition: 1,100. FuG11 + FuG Tr 100mw. Fully-equipped command-post vehicle, discontinued in 1943. Later version of the command-post was equipped with the FuG19 + FuG12.

Sd Kfz 251/7 mittlere Pionierpanzerwagen. Weight: 8.07 tons. Crew: 7/8. Height: 2.70m. Armament: Two 7.92mm MG34 or 42; one 7.92mm Pz B39. Ammunition: 4,800 (MG), 40 (PzB). Special carriers fitted with racks to carry small assault bridges, mines, and other heavy equipment of the Panzerpionier company (gp). When issued to the HQ Company, these vehicles were fitted with a FuG5. Other designation was Gerät 907.

Sd Kfz 251/8 mittlere Krankenpanzerwagen. Gerät 908. Weight: 7.47 tons. Crew: 3. Armoured ambulance designed to carry two stretcher cases and four seated wounded. Later versions had modified rear doors to facilitate entry and exit. When issued to the HQ Company or Panzer detachment, the FuG5 was fitted.

607

610

608

611

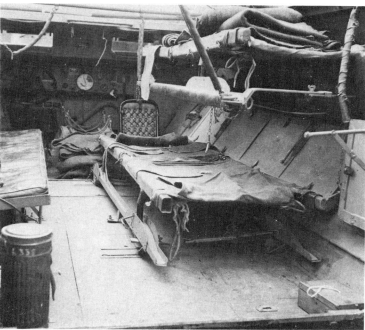

Plate 607. Sd Kfz 251/7 Ausf C mittlere Pionierpanzerwagen.
Plate 608. Sd Kfz 251/7 towing a 2.8cm sPzB41 anti-tank gun.
Plate 609. Sd Kfz 251/7 Ausf D mittlere Pionierpanzerwagen.
Plates 610-612. Armoured ambulance Sd Kfz 251/8 mittlere Krankenpanzerwagen: Ausf C (Plate 610), a late version Ausf D (Plate 611) and an interior view (Plate 612).

612

Plates 613-616. Sd Kfz 251/9 mittlere Schützenpanzer-wagen (7.5cm): an early version Ausf C (Plate 613), Ausf D (Plate 614), and Ausf D (Plate 615). Plates 615 and 616 show the new gun mounting.

Opposite page: Plates 617-622
Plates 617-619. Sd Kfz 251/10 mittlere Schützenpanzer-wagen (3.7cm PaK). Plate 617 shows an Ausf A, mounting the gun in a large shield; in Plate 618 the Ausf C vehicle carries a small gun shield.
Plates 620-621. Sd Kfz 251/11 mittlere Fernsprechpanzer-wagen. Plate 620 shows the cable drum on the front mudguard; Plate 621 shows the drum mounted in the rear of the vehicle.
Plate 622. Sd Kfz 251/15 mittlere Lichtauswertepanzer-wagen.

613

614

615

616

Sd Kfz 251/9 mittlere Schützenpanzerwagen (7.5cm). Gerät 909. Weight: 8.53 tons. Crew: 3. Height: 2.07m. Armament: One 7.5cm KwK37 (L/24). Traverse: 12° left 12° right. Elevation: −10°+12°. Sight: SflZF1. Ammunition: 52. Two 7.92mm MG34 or 42. Ammunition: 2,010. Designed to provide more flexible support for the Heavy Armour Infantry Company (gp). On 31 March 1942, Büssing-NAG were ordered to develop an armoured superstructure to mount the old 7.5cm KwK, redundant since the un-gunning of the Pz Kpfw IV with the KwK40 (L/43). In June 1942, two prototypes were sent to Russia for field tests and as a result, an order for 150 units was placed in the same month. In 1944, a new design of mounting was introduced which could be fitted on a number of vehicles without major modification. The 7.5cm was redesignated K51(Sf) when fitted in the new mounting. The unofficial name sometimes used for this vehicle was 'Stummel' (stump).

Sd Kfz 251/10 mittlere Schützenpanzerwagen (3.7cm PaK). Gerät 910. Weight: 8.02 tons. Crew: 5. Height: 2.17m. Armament: One 3.7cm PaK35/36 (L/45), one 7.92mm MG34 or 42, one 7.92mm PzB39. Ammunition: 168 (PaK), 1,100 (MG), 40 (PzB). From 1940, the Sd Kfz 251/10 was issued as the Zugführerwagen to platoon leaders,

so as to provide some heavy support. Minor variations existed in the arrangement of the 3.7cm PaK shield.

Sd Kfz 251/11 mittlere Fernsprechpanzerwagen. Gerät 911. Weight: 8.50 tons. Crew: 5. Height: 2.17m. Armament: Two 7.92mm MG34 or 42. Ammunition: 2,010. Medium telephone exchange and cable-laying vehicle similar to the Sd Kfz 250/2. Two versions existed, one, with the leichter Feldkabelträger 6 (gp) and another, with the mittlerer Feldkabelträger 10 (gp). Ordered in January 1942, the first units were delivered 15 August 1942.

Sd Kfz 251/12 mittlere Messtrupp und Gerätpanzerwagen. Gerät 912. Crew: 6. Artillery survey vehicle to carry the survey section and their equipment. Carried the FuG8 radio with a frame antenna. Discontinued in 1943.

Sd Kfz 251/13 mittlere Schallaufnahmepanzerwagen. Gerät 913. Artillery sound-recording equipment vehicle. Discontinued in 1943.

Sd Kfz 251/14 mittlere Schallauswertepanzerwagen. Gerät 914. Weight: 8.50 tons. Crew 8. Height: 2.50m. Artillery sound-ranging vehicle. Discontinued in 1943.

Sd Kfz 251/15 mittlere Lichtauswertepanzerwagen. Gerät 915. Artillery-flash-spotter vehicle. Discontinued in 1943.

617

618

619

620

621

622

Sd Kfz 251/16 mittlere Flammpanzerwagen. Gerät 916. Weight: 8.62 tons. Crew: 5. Armament: Two 1.4cm Flammenwerfer, two 7.92mm MG34 or 42. Ammunition: 700 litres flame fuel, 2,010 (MG). Height: 2.10m. Delivered from January 1943, the Sd Kfz 251/16 carried sufficient flame fuel to allow about 80 bursts of up to two seconds' duration. The projectors, fitted on either side of the vehicle, had a traverse of 90° and elevation up to +40°. Range was about 35m depending on wind conditions. The earlier versions were also armed with a 7mm Flammwerfer 42, a portable projector, attached to 10m of hose pipe.

Sd Kfz 251/17 mittlere Schützenpanzerwagen (2cm). Gerät 917. Weight: 8.80 tons. Crew: 4/6. Height: 2.25m. Armament: One 2cm KwK38 mit Flakrohr, two 7.92mm MG34 or 42. Ammunition: 600 (KwK), 600 (MG). Already, by 26 October 1943, there was an Ausf A and Ausf B of the Sd Kfz 251/17. Photographic evidence shows three different models using the Sd Kfz 251 Ausf C chassis. Two of these involved considerable rebuilding of the superstructure to allow all-round traverse. On the Sd Kfz 251 Ausf D chassis, a modified gun mounting was introduced which could be fitted into the normal super-structure. Later versions of this were fitted with a small turret sur-rounding the 2cm KwK38, which had a FlaK barrel.

Sd Kfz 251/18 mittlere Beobachtungspanzerwagen. Crew: 6. Obser-vation vehicle using the Sd Kfz 251 chassis instead of the Sd Kfz 250. The radio equipment was the FuG12. The Gerät number 918 was entered in lists from 24 August 1944.

Sd Kfz 251/19 mittlere Fernsprechbetriebspanzerwagen. Gerät 919. Mobile telephone exchange—Telephone Switchboard troop.

Sd Kfz 251/20 mittlere Schützenpanzerwagen (Infrarotscheinwerfer). Gerät 920. Crew: 4. In late 1944, the Sd Kfz 251/20, known also as UHU (eagle owl), was introduced as the command and observation vehicle of the five-tank Infra-red Panther Platoons. The infra-red equip-ment fitted to each Panther tank had a range of only 400m. Each UHU with its 60cm Beobachtungs Gerät 1251 and telescope Beobachtungs Gerät 1221 was capable of illuminating and sighting at ranges of 1,500m. The UHU commander then controlled the five Panthers, in their attack of such targets, over the usual FuG5 radio. The main searchlight had a traverse of 360° and could be folded down when not in use. In August 1944, 600 UHU were ordered, but only about 60 were delivered before the end of the war.

Sd Kfz 251/21 mittlere Schützenpanzerwagen (Drilling MG151S). Gerät 921. Crew 4/6. Armament: Three 1.5cm MG151/15 or 2cm MG151/20. Ammunition: 2,000. This anti-aircraft vehicle was created by mounting three heavy machine-cannon from fighter aircraft on a pedestal. Each gun was fed by belt from a separate ammunition box. The rate of fire was 700rpm. Production of the Sd Kfz 251/21 com-menced in August 1944.

Plates 623-625. Sd Kfz 251/16 mittlere Flammpanzerwagen; Plates 624 and 625 show Ausf C vehicles; Plates 623 is a close-up of the flame-throwers mounted on each side of the vehicle.
Plate 626. Sd Kfz 251/17 (2cm FlaK)—the Luftwaffe crew preparing for action.

627

631

Plates 631–632. Sd Kfz 251/20 mittlere Schützenpanzerwagen (Infrarotscheinwerfer) — or 'UHU'.

Plates 633–634. Sd Kfz 251/21 mittlere Schützenpanzerwagen (Drilling MG151S) anti-aircraft vehicle.

628

632

629

633

630

634

Plates 627-630. Sd Kfz 251/17 (2cm FlaK). Plate 627 shows the first version, Plate 628 the Luftwaffe version, and Plate 629 the third version mounting the 2cm KwK38 mit Flakrohr. The vehicle in Plate 630 is a field modification with the gun inside the vehicle.

Sd Kfz 251/22 mittlere Schützenpanzerwagen (7.5cm PaK40). Gerät 922. Crew: 4. Armament: One 7.5cm PaK40 L/46. Ammunition: 22. Traverse: 20° left 18° right. Elevation: −3° +22°. Production of the so-called Kanonen–SPW began in December 1944, as a result of a personal order from Hitler that as many anti-tank guns as possible be mounted on self-propelled carriages. The complete PaK40 (minus wheels) was fitted in the Sd Kfz 251/22, and only part of the roof had to be removed to allow adequate traverse. The Sd Kfz 251/22 were issued to the 1945 Establishment Panzer divisions as follows: nine to Panzerjäger detachments, three to Panzer Aufklärungs detachments and six to gun platoons.

Sd Kfz 251/23 mittlere Schützenpanzerwagen (2cm KwK). Gerät 923. Crew: 4. Armament. One 2cm KwK38 in Hängelafette 38. Ammunition: 100. Elevation: −10° +85°. One 7.92mm MG42. Ammunition: 2,010. Semi-tracked armoured car, similar to the smaller Sd Kfz 250/9. and using the Hängelafette (swinging mount) 38 turret installation, as on the Sd Kfz 234/1 armoured cars. FuG12 radio set was carried. The Sd Kfz 251/23 was listed from 28 December 1944.

Sd Kfz 251 Munitionspanzer. The Sd Kfz 251 was used to transport ammunition for many different armoured formations.

Sd Kfz 251 7.5cm PaK42 L/70 auf 3t Zgkw. During discussions with Hitler on 30 September 1943, it was decided that the proposed new 7.5cm PaK44 L/70 be mounted on a motorized carriage as well as on the normal cruciform towed carriage. A 3t Zgkw was to be used. and the resulting vehicle was to be troop tested. The prototype was shown on 28 January 1944, and consisted of an adapted KwK42 mounted on the stripped down chassis of a m SPW. The Pak44 project, however, came to nothing and it was realised that the 3t Zgkw was not a suitable carriage in any event.

Plates 635–636. Sd Kfz 251/22 mittlere Schützenpanzerwagen (7.5cm PaK40).
Plate 637. Sd Kfz 251/23.
Plates 638-639. An experimental mounting: the 7.5cm PaK42 L/70 auf 3t Zgkw.
Plate 640. Field modification of an Sd Kfz 251 to mount a U.S. .50 calibre machine-gun.
Plate 641. An American T-34 (Calliope) 60-barrel rocket-launcher mounted on a modified Sd Kfz 251. This equipment was mounted previously on an M4 medium tank.

638

639

635

640

636

637

641

Panzerspähwagen RK Ausf A

Other designation: Saurer RK9
Type: Wheel-cum-track armoured car

History: In 1938, the Waffenamt issued an order for Saurer in Vienna to develop a reconnaissance vehicle in the wheel-cum-track configuration. The resulting vehicle was of 6.5 tons, with 14.5mm to 5.5mm armour. It was powered by a Saurer OKD diesel motor of 100PS. On wheels, a speed of 80km/hr, and on tracks, 30km/hr could be achieved. Two prototypes were built. The first, with an open-topped superstructure, was delivered by June 1942, and the second, with a turret, was delivered shortly afterwards. The turret was similar to contemporary reconnaissance vehicle designs such as the VK901. Armament was the EW141 and an MG34. During 1942, a pre-production series of 15 was under manufacture, but had not been completed when the order was cancelled as a result of changing requirements.

Plates 642-643. Pz Sp Wg RK Ausf A: right, with turret.

Mittlere Gepanzerte Beobachtungskraftwagen (Sd Kfz 254)

Other designation: RR-7/2
Type: Wheel-cum-track medium armoured observation post

Manufacturer: Saurer
128 produced from June 1940 to March 1941

Crew: 7
Weight (tons): 6.4
Length (metres): 4.56
Width (metres): 2.02
            2.20 (on wheels)
Height (metres): 1.88

Engine: Saurer CRDv 4cyl 70PS diesel
Gearbox: 5 forward, 1 reverse
Speed (km/hr): 60
Range (km): 500 (on wheels)
Radio: FuG8, FuG4, FuG Spr Ger f

Armament: One 7.92mm MG34
Traverse: loose
Elevation: loose
Sight: direct

Armour (mm/angle):	Front	Side	Rear	Top/Bottom
Superstructure:	15/40°	8/35°	8/15°	6/90°
Hull:	15/20°	8/0°	8/15°	6/90°

History: From 1936, the RR–7 was developed by Saurer as an artillery tractor for the Austrian Bundesheer (Army). Testing was completed and in 1937, an order was placed for tractors, which were manufactured in 1938. After the incorporation of Austria into the Reich in 1938, the RR–7 chassis was developed by the Wehrmacht as a light troop-carrier, but was subsequently issued as a light armoured observation and radio vehicle from late 1940. Records indicate that a total of 140 RR–7 type vehicles were ordered, so it can be assumed that the Sd Kfz 254 were all newly-constructed for the Wehrmacht.

Specific features: Armoured superstructure similar to that of the Sd Kfz 253 le gep Beob Kw semi-track vehicle, with fully enclosed roof and large rear-opening doors. The frame aerial was for the powerful FuG8 radio. The most unusual feature of the Sd Kfz 254—apart from the unique wheel-cum-track configuration—was the diesel motor.

Combat service: Served in Russia and Africa with the Panzarartillerie detachments from 1941.

Plates 644–645. Sd Kfz 254 mittlere gep Beob Kw in its two travelling modes.

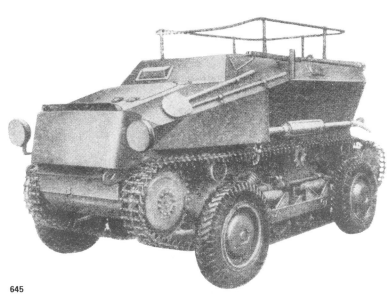

644

645

646

648

647

649

650

Munitionskraftwagen für Nebelwerfer (Sd Kfz 4)/ 15cm Panzerwerfer 42 auf Sf (Sd Kfz 4/1)

Other designation: Maultier
Type: Semi-tracked armoured lorry as ammunition carrier and self-propelled carriage for multiple rocket launcher

Manufacturer: Opel
289 Munitionskraftwagen, 300 Panzerwerfer produced from April 1943 to March 1944
19 Panzerwerfer converted from Mun Kw in June 1944

Crew: 3	Engine: Opel 3.6lit 6cyl 68PS at 3,000rpm
Weight (tons): 7.1	
Length (metres): 6	Gearbox: 5 forward, 1 reverse
Width (metres): 2.2	Speed (km/hr): 40
Height (metres): 2.5	Range (km): 130
	Radio: FuG Spr G f

Armament: One 15cm Nebelwerfer 42 — One 7.92mm MG34 or 42

Traverse: 270° (hand)	loose	
Elevation: −12° +80°	loose	
Sight: RA35	direct	
Ammunition: 20	2,000	

Armour (mm/angle):	Front	Side	Rear	Top/Bottom
Turret (Panzerwerfer):	10/45°	10/40°	10/40°	
Superstructure:	8/35°	8/35°	8/30°	6/90°
Hull:	8/6°	8/0°	8/30°	6/90°

History: In 1942, an order was placed for the conversion to semi-tracked lorries of the three ton LKW, built by Opel, Ford and KHD. The rear wheels were replaced by a simple Horstmann tracked suspension and running gear. The production of Opel Maultier vehicles reached 4,000 and during 1943, Opel were ordered to build an armoured-body vehicle to act as an Sf for the 15cm Nebelwerfer, or as an ammunition carrier. Conspicuous smoke trails, which resulted from the firing of a Nebelwerfer, made it imperative for the battery to change position frequently. The armoured Maultier was to give mobility and protection. A new ten-barrelled Nebelwerfer 42 was designed for use on the Maultier. Photographic evidence shows that some Maultiers were fitted with the 24-rail 8cm R–Vielfachwerfer (multiple rocket-launchers) of the Waffen SS.
Specific features: Three minor variations in the suspension components existed. Some vehicles were fitted with smoke-dischargers as standard. The Munitionskraftwagen were identical with the Panzerwerfer, with the exception of the 15cm Panzerwerfer 42. The Panzerwerfer version weighed 8.50 tons and had a height of 3.05m.
Combat service: Nebelwerfer brigades.

Illustrations, top of page.
Plates 646-648. 15cm Panzerwerfer 42 auf Sf (Sd Kfz 4/1) versions A (Plate 646), B (Plate 647) and C (Plate 648).
Plate 649. Loading the rocket tubes.
Plates 650 (detail, above) and **651** (below). Maultier mounting the 8cm R-Vielfachwerfer.
Plate 652. Munitionskraftwagen für Nebelwerfer (Sd Kfz 4).

651

652

2cm FlaK auf Fahrgestell Zugkraftwagen 1t (Sd Kfz 10/4)

Other designation: Demag D7
Type: Self-propelled anti-aircraft gun on light semi-tracked vehicle

Chassis No.: 95001– , 201001– , 300001– , 402001–,
  600001– , 701001–
610 produced

Crew: 7
Weight (tons): 5.5
Length (metres): 4.75
Width (metres): 1.93
Height (metres): 2

Engine: Maybach HL38TRKM
Gearbox: 7 forward, 3 reverse
Speed (km/hr): 65
Range (km): 300

Armament: One 2cm FlaK30
  L/112.5 or
Traverse: 360° (hand)
Elevation: −12° +90°
Sight: Flakvisier 35
Ammunition: 280

One 2cm FlaK38 L/112.5

360° (hand)
−20° +90°
Flakvisier 38

Armour: later models had 8mm armoured cabs and/or gun shields

History: In 1938, a 2cm FlaK30 was mounted on the Demag D II 3 a predecessor of the D7. The D7 was built from 1938 to 1944, by various firms, including Mechanische Werke-Cottbus, Saurer, MNH, Büssing-NAG, Adler and Demag. The Zgkw 1t was the earliest self-propelled mounting for the FlaK troops. A special superstructure with folding sides was designed to give room for all-round traverse.
Specific features: The original vehicles were totally unarmoured, but eventually an armoured cab was provided and an armoured shield was fitted to the 2cm FlaK. A small supply of ammunition was carried in bins attached to the folding sides of the superstructure, but generally, a single-axle ammunition-trailer was towed.
Combat service: Issued to the FlaK units of both Luftwaffe and Wehrmacht.

653

655

Plate 653. 2cm FlaK38 auf Maultier—the 2cm FlaK38 carried on a Gleisketten-LKW 2t Maultier Ford.
Plate 654. 2cm FlaK30 auf leichte Selbstfahrlafette (Demag D II 3), an experimental mounting on the third prototype of the Sd Kfz 10 series.
Plates 655-656. 2cm FlaK auf Fgst Zgkw 1t (Sd Kfz 10/4); below, in action, with the sides down to permit full traverse for the weapon.

654

656

Plates 657-658. Sd Kfz 10/5; right, with armoured cab and 2cm FlaK38.

3.7cm PaK35/36 auf Zugkraftwagen 1t

Type: Self-propelled anti-tank gun

History: Panzerjäger units provided mobility for their 3.7cm PaK by mounting them on the rear of Zgkw 1t. Generally, the complete gun with its field carriage was carried, but versions existed which had a pedestal mount. Some of these conversions had improvised armour.

Plates 659-661. 3.7cm PaK35/36 on the Sd Kfz 10; right, with pedestal mount; below right, with additional armour plates on the front of the engine and at the side of the gun.

659

661

5cm PaK38(Sf) auf Zugkraftwagen 1t

Type: Self-propelled anti-tank gun

Plates 662-663. 5cm PaK38(Sf) auf Zgkw 1t.

History: During 1941, a number of light self-propelled anti-tank guns were created, by mounting a 5cm PaK38 L/60 on a Zgkw 1t. The gun was carried without its wheels, but was otherwise complete. Light armour was added to the engine compartment and driver's cab. Photographic evidence indicates that these light Panzerjäger were supplied to Waffen SS units.

662

663

7.62cm FK36(r) auf Panzerjäger Selbstfahrlafette Zugkraftwagen 5t (Sd Kfz 6)

Other designations: Diana, Büssing-NAG BN9
Type: Self-propelled captured anti-tank gun on semi-tracked vehicle

Chassis Nos.: 3001–3617
9 converted in late 1941
Crew: 5

Weight (tons): 10.5
Length (metres): 6.33
Width (metres): 2.26
Height (metres): 2.98

Engine: Maybach HL54TUKRM
Gearbox: 4 × 2 forward,
    1 × 2 reverse
Speed (km/hr): 50
Range (km): 317

Armament: One 7.62cm FK36(r) L/51.5`
Traverse: 30° left 30° right (hand)
Ammunition: 7.62cm Pzgr 39, Pzgr 40, Spgr 39

Armour (mm/angle):	Front	Side	Rear	Top/Bottom
Superstructure:	10/0°	10/0°	10/0°	open
Gun shield:	10/			

History: During the initial phases of operation Barbarossa, the Germans captured huge numbers of the Russian 76.2mm M1936 field gun. Designated 7.62cm FK36(r) or FK296(r) by the Germans, it was issued in large numbers to Panzerjäger detachments, unmodified and using Russian ammunition. In late 1941, an attempt was made to self-propel this heavy anti-tank gun, by mounting it in an armoured box on the rear of a five ton semi-track. Nine such conversions were sent to Africa.

Combat service: Served with the 605th Panzerjägerabteilung in North Africa. Six guns were delivered in January, and three in February 1942. They were prominent in the battle of Gazela in May/June 1942.

Plates 664-665. 7.62cm FK36(r) auf Pz Jag Sf Zg kw 5t.
Plate 5 (Page 4). 7.62cm FK36(r) auf Pz Jag Sf Zg Kw 5t in action.

3.7cm FlaK36 auf Fahrgestell Zugkraftwagen 5t (Sd Kfz 6/2)

Other designation: Büssing-NAG BN9/BN9b
Type: Self-propelled anti-aircraft gun on semi-tracked vehicle

Chassis Nos.: 3001–3617
339 produced until 1943
Crew: 7

Weight (tons): 10.4
Length (metres): 6.32
Width (metres): 2.26
Height (metres): 2.5

Engine: Maybach HL54TUKRM
Gearbox: 4 × 2 forward,
    1 × 2 reverse
Speed (km/hr): 50
Range (km): 317

Armament: One 3.7cm FlaK36 L/98
Traverse: 360° (hand)
Elevation: −8° +85°
Sight: Flakvisier 40

History: The Büssing-NAG BN9 (Zgkw 5t) was built from 1939 to 1943, and was used as the basis of the self-propelled 3.7cm FlaK36. The rear superstructure of the vehicle was specially designed for the FlaK gun so that the sides folded down to provide an adequate platform for all-round traverse. Ammunition for the 3.7cm FlaK was carried in a single-axle trailer behind the Zgkw 5t. When the latter was phased out of production in 1943, the 3.7cm was mounted on the Zgkw 8t, as a temporary solution. The sWS was intended to carry the 3.7cm FlaK43.

Combat service: Issued to Luftwaffe FlaK units on all fronts.

Plates 666-667. 3.7cm FlaK36 auf Fgst Zgkw 5t; right, with gun shield, and lowered sides to permit full traverse of the gun.

668

670

Plate 18 (Page 8). 2cm Flakvierling 38 auf Fgst 2g Kw 8t (Sd Kfz 7/1).
Plate 668. 2cm Flakvierling 38 auf Fgst Zgkw 8t (Sd Kfz 7/1).
Plate 669. A late version Sd Kfz 7/1 with armoured cab and modified gun shield.
Plates 670-671. 3.7cm FlaK36 auf Fgst Zgkw 8t (Sd Kfz 7/2); below, with armoured cab.
Plate 1035 (Page 268). Sd Kfz 7/2 with armoured cab and gun.
Plate 1036 (Page 268). Sd Kfz 7/1 firing.

669

671

2cm Flakvierling 38 auf Fahrgestell Zugkraftwagen 8t (Sd Kfz 7/1)
3.7cm FlaK36 auf Fahrgestell Zugkraftwagen 8t (Sd Kfz 7/2)

Other designations: KMm11, HLm11, Saurer 11
Type: Self-propelled anti-aircraft gun on medium semi-tracked vehicle

Chassis Nos.: 1320001–
319 2cm FV38 produced until October 1944
123 3.7cm FlaK36 produced until February 1945

Crew: 10	Engine: Maybach HL62TUK
Weight (tons): 11.55	Gearbox: 4 × 2 forward,
Length (metres): 6.85	1 × 2 reverse
Width (metres): 2.4	Speed (km/hr): 50
Height (metres): 2.62	Range (km): 250

Armament: One 2cm Flakvierling		One 3.7cm FlaK36 L/98
38 1/112.6 or		
Traverse: 360° (hand)		360° (hand)
Elevation: −10° +100°		−8° +85°
Sight: Flakvisier 40		Flakvisier 40

Armour (mm):	Front	Side	Rear	Top
Driver's cab (from 1943):	8	8	8	8

History: The basic Zgkw 8t was built by Krauss-Maffei, Borgward and, from 1943, by Saurer. The FlaK vehicle was built with a special superstructure which formed an adequate platform for all-round traverse if the sides were folded down. Ammunition was carried in a special single-axle trailer. The 3.7cm FlaK36 was mounted on the Zgkw 8t from 1943, after production of the 5t Zgkw ceased.

Specific features: From late 1943, the driver's cab and engine compartment of some vehicles were lightly armoured. Vehicles mounting the FV38 towed a Sonder Anhänger (special trailer) 56 to hold the 2cm ammunition, and for the 3.7cm FlaK, the trailer was the Sd Anh 57. The FlaK36 was given an anti-tank capability when it was equipped with a muzzle-loading 15cm, hollow charge, 3 cm Stielgranate 41.

Combat service: Issued to the FlaK units of the Luftwaffe.

Plate 672. 5cm FlaK41 (Sf) auf Zgkw 8t.

5cm FlaK41 (SF) auf Zugkraftwagen 8t

Type: Self-propelled anti-aircraft gun

History: Photographic evidence shows that a Zgkw 8t was fitted with stabilizers and used to mount the 5cm FlaK41. Since only a preproduction series of these 5cm FlaK41 were built in 1942, it is not known if more were mounted on the Zgkw 8t. Another mount for the 5cm FlaK41 was the Mercedes-Benz L4500A heavy truck.

Feuerleitpanzerfahrzeug für V-2 Raketen auf Zugkraftwagen 8t

Type: Control post for missile launching group

History: The V-2 missiles were launched from various sites to avoid attack by superior Allied airpower. The V-2 launch group was, therefore, highly mobile and capable of movement off the road. A number of semi-track vehicles were converted to armoured command-control posts by the fitting of a special superstructure.

Plates 673-674. Feürleitpanzerfahrzeug für V-2 Raketen auf Zgkw 8t; left, in travelling order, towing the 'Bodenplatte' (launching-pad base plate); right, in position for a launch, with the armoured rear section as the control point.

Gepanzerte Zugkraftwagen 8t (Sd Kfz 7)

Type: Armoured gun tractor

History: In 1939 the schwere Panzerjägerabteilungen equipped with the FlaK18 were provided with Zgkw 8t, which were specially fitted with armoured superstructures to accommodate the crew and driver.

Plate 675. Gep Zgkw 8t (Sd Kfz 7) towing an early 8.8cm FlaK18.

8.8cm FlaK18(Sfl) auf Zugkraftwagen 12t (Sd Kfz 8) und Zugkraftwagen 18t (Sd Kfz 9)

Other designations: 12t-DB10, 12t-Krupp m10, 18t-FAMO F3
Type: Self-propelled anti-aircraft gun on heavy semi-tracked vehicle

Manufacturer: Krupp, FAMO
Chassis Nos.: 45001–
10 produced in 1939 and 15 in 1940
Crew: 9

Weight (tons): 20(12t)
               25(18t)
Length (metres): 7.35(12t)
               9.32(18t)
Width (metres): 2.5 (12t)
               2.65(18t)
Height (metres): 2.8(12t)
               3.67(18t)

Engine: Maybach HL85TUKRM (12t)
        Maybach HL108TUKRM
        (18t)
Gearbox: 4×2 forward,
         1×2 reverse
Speed (km/hr): 50
Range (km): 260

Armament: One 8.8cm FlaK18 L/56
Traverse: 360° (hand)
Elevation: −3° +85°
Sight: FlaK
Ammunition: 40

Armour (mm/angle):	Front	Side	Rear	Top
Superstructure:	14.5/	14.5/	8/	open
Hull:	14.5/	14.5/	8/	none
Gun shield:	10/10°			

History: In 1939, the Waffenamt ordered 10 8.8cm FlaK18 mounted on the chassis of the Daimler-Benz DB10 Zgkw 12t. These were to act as heavy anti-tank vehicles which would also be capable of destroying fortified positions. In 1940 a further series was built on the Famo F3 Zgkw 18t which were also intended for an anti-aircraft role. In 1942, an order was placed for 112 8.8cm FlaK37 auf Zgkw 18t to be built for the Luftwaffe and Army, with the first 14 to be delivered in June and July 1943. However, interest in these vehicles was insufficient and the order was dropped.

Specific features: The Zgkw 12t conversion had a low armoured cab replacing the normal one, and a small armoured cupola for the driver so that generally, targets could be engaged from straight ahead. The 18t vehicles had an armoured version of the normal cab, limiting engagement of ground targets to the sides. In this case the vehicle was provided with stabilizers and fold-down sides which gave an adequate platform for 360° traverse at high elevations.

Combat service: The Zgkw 12t were issued to the 8th schwere Panzerjägerabteilung, and were used in action in Poland and France.

Plates 676-677. 8.8cm FlaK18(Sf) auf Zgkw 12t (Sd Kfz 8). The vehicle in Plate 676 is covered in wire netting for the attachment of camouflage material, Plate 677 shows a vehicle in action in France, 1940.
Plates 678-679. 8.8cm FlaK18(Sf) auf Zgkw 18t (Sd Kfz 9). In Plate 678, the sides are down and the stabilizers in position.

676

677

678

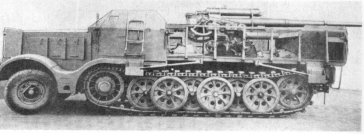

679

Plates 680-681. 7.5cm Sf L/40.8 Modell 1. **Plates 682-683.** 7.5cm Sf L/40.8 Modell 2.

7.5cm Selbstfahrlafette L/40.8 Modell 1

Other designation: Büssing-NAG BN10H
Type: Self-propelled anti-tank gun

History: In 1934, the Waffenamt ordered a powerful anti-tank gun from Rheinmetall-Borsig. This was to be mounted on an armoured Büssing-NAG half-track chassis. Three prototypes were built during the following years, each of which varied in height, width and length. The chassis numbers were 2006-2008. A crew of four was carried in this 6.08 ton vehicle which had armour from 20mm to 8mm. The 7.5cm L/40.8 was in a fully-rotating turret, and had a depression of 9° and elevation of 20°. A speed of 60km/hr could be achieved. An improved gun, 7.5cm L/40.8 Modell 2, was ordered in 1936 and this featured a muzzle-brake among other developments.

Panzer Selbstfahrlafette II auf Fahrgestell m Zugkraftwagen 5t

Other designation: Büssing-NAG HKp 902
Type: Self-propelled gun

History: This vehicle was a further development of the BN10H vehicles tested between 1934 and 1940. The HKp 902 used the chassis of the Zgkw 5t, but had its engine at the rear. A low armoured superstructure similar to that of contemporary Pz Kpfw was used. The armament was a 7.5cm L/40.8 Modell 2 which was mounted on two of the four prototypes built (chassis Nos 2009–2012). The motor was a Maybach HL45 which gave a speed of 50km/hr. The two armed vehicles were sent to North Africa and used in action. One of the remaining prototypes was found at the end of the war with an armoured command-post body for controlling V-2 missile launching. The 5cm FlaK41 was supposed to be mounted on the fourth vehicle. All HKp 902 weighed approximately 11 tons.

Plates 684-686. Pz Sf II auf Fgst m Zgkw 5t. Plate 685 shows a vehicle captured in North Africa; that in Plate 686 has been converted as an armoured command post for V-2 rocket launching.

3.7cm Selbstfahrlafette L/70

Other designation: HL K1 3(H)
Type: Self-propelled anti-tank gun

History: Early in 1935, the Waffenamt ordered Rheinmetall-Borsig to develop a 3.7cm L/70 self-propelled anti-tank gun. The armoured superstructure for this vehicle was designed on a Hansa-Loyd-Goliath Zgkw 3t. A fully-rotating turret mounted the 3.7cm L/70 and a ball-mounted MG, while a ring was provided on the top of the open turret for a second MG for anti-aircraft defence. The single prototype was available in late 1936, and was extensively tested by cavalry units.

Plates 687-688. 3.7cm Sf L/70.

Schwere Wehrmachtschlepper (Gepanzerte Ausführung)

Other designations: sWS, Gerät 71
Type: Heavy semi-tracked carrier

Manufacturer: Büssing-NAG, Ringhoffer-Tatra
Chassis Nos.: 150001–
825 produced from December 1943 to March 1945

Crew: 2	Engine: Maybach HL42TRKMS
Weight (tons): 13.5	Gearbox: 2×4 forward,
Length (metres): 6.92	2×1 reverse
Width (metres): 2.5	Speed (km/hr): 28
Height (metres): 2.07	Range (km): 300

Armament:	One 3.7cm FlaK43 L/89 or	One 15cm Nebelwerfer 42	One 7.92mm MG42
Traverse:	360°	270°	loose
Elevation:	−6° +90°	−5° +45°	loose
Sight:	Flakvisier 3×8°	RA35	direct
Ammunition:		50 Wurfgranate	2,000

Armour (mm/angle):	Front	Side		Rear	Top/Bottom
Turret (Nebelwerfer):	10/45°	10/40°		10/40°	10/90°
Superstructure:	15/30°	12/8°	+15°	8/30°	6/87°
Hull:	15/15°	12/15°		8/0°	6/90°
Gun shield (FlaK):	10/30°				

Plate 689. SWS load carrier.
Plate 690. 3.7cm FlaK auf sWS.

History: On 7 May 1942, Hitler issued an order that simple low-speed semi-track load-carrying vehicles be developed for use in the East. Büssing-NAG were entrusted with the development of a Zgkw 5t neuer Art which would replace both the 5t and 3t tractors. The first prototypes appeared in the spring of 1943, and production was ordered at a rate of 150 units per month. Only five sWS were delivered in 1943, and 825 of the total order for 7,484 had been completed by March 1945. Most sWS were completed with a lorry type cab, but from mid 1944, an armoured cab was introduced and used for a proportion of the load-carriers and weapon-carriers. A FlaK vehicle was created by mounting a 3.7cm FlaK43 with a 9mm armour shield and fold-down sides, permitting all-round traverse. The weight of the FlaK sWS was 15 tons. A 15cm Panzerwerfer 42 auf sWS (armoured (rocket) launcher) was the replacement for the Maultier based Panzerwerfer. The main advantage of the sWS was increased rocket storage capacity and improved cross-country performance. These units were in action from late 1944. After the war, Tatra in Czechoslovakia built a new version of the sWS known as the Tatra T809.

Specific features: The sWS differed from other German semi-tracks in having wide dry pin tracks. The suspension layout was similar to that of the Panther tank.

Combat service: Used on all major fronts from mid 1944.

691

692

Plate 691. 3.7cm FlaK auf sWS.
Plate 692. 15cm Panzerwerfer 42 (Zehnling) auf sWS.

Plate 693. LeWS second prototype.
Plate 694. HKp 602/603.
Plate 695. HKp 606.

693

694

695

Leichte Wehrmachschlepper

Other designation: Adler leWS
Type: Light semi-tracked carrier prototype

History: In May 1942, Hitler ordered a simplified semi-track tractor which would replace both the armoured and unarmoured vehicles in the same class. Employing dry pin tracks, they were to be powered by the Maybach HL42 100PS motor. From the beginning, they were built with an armoured cab and engine compartment. However, during 1943 it was decided to concentrate on the Sd Kfz 250 and RSO (tracked tractor, East). A total of three prototypes were built by Adler.

HKp 602/603

Type: Semi-tracked carrier prototype

History: In 1940 and 1941, Demag and Hanomag attempted to create a better version of the Sd Kfz 251. Improvements to the running gear and transmission, and the more powerful Maybach HL45Z 120PS motor were the main features.

HKp 605/606

Type: Semi-tracked carrier prototype

History: Demag and Hanomag continued in their endeavours to develop a more modern and simple medium armoured semi-track. The HKp 605 appeared in 1941, and the HKp 606, in 1942. Again, a more powerful engine, the Maybach HL50, was used, and a pre-selective gearbox was introduced. Only prototypes were built because it was decided to concentrate on the production of the Sd Kfz 251, but, some of the features of the simplified armoured body were used in the design of the Sd Kfz 251 Ausf D.

Armoured cars and wheeled armoured vehicles

Maschinengewehrkraftwagen (Kfz 13) / Funkkraftwagen (Kfz 14)

Type: Armoured reconnaissance car / radio car

Manufacturer: Daimler-Benz
147 Kfz 13 and 40 Kfz 14 produced from 1932 to 1934 on chassis
  supplied by Adlerwerke

Crew: 2(3)	Engine: Adler Standard 6 2.91lit
Weight (tons): 2.1	60PS at 3,200rpm
Length (metres): 4.2	Gearbox: 4 forward, 1 reverse
Width (metres): 1.7	Speed (km/hr): 70
Height (metres): 1.46	Range (km): 300

Armament: One 7.92mm MG13 (Kfz 13)
Traverse: 360° (hand)
Elevation: −35° +65°
Sight: direct
Ammunition: 1,000

Armour (mm/angle):	Front	Side	Rear	Top/Bottom
Hull (upper):	8/40°	8/15°	8/22°	open
(lower):	8/22°	8/5°	8/22°	none
MG shield:	8/35°			

History: The Kfz 13 and 14 were developed in 1929–1932 as reconnaissance vehicles for the developing motorized forces of the German Army.

Specific features: The Kfz 13 and 14 consisted of a Standard 4x4 passenger car chassis mounting an armoured body. The front-mounted engine was protected by a louvred grill in front of the radiator, but no armour protected the engine sides. The Kfz 13 had a crew of two, with the commander manning a pedestal-mounted MG13. The Kfz 14 had a crew of three whose only armament was their personal weapons. A long-range radio and a frame antenna were fitted to the Kfz 14 to provide mobile communications capability.

Combat service: The Kfz 13 and 14 were issued to motorized Aufklärungs detachments from 1932. In 1935 they were supplemented by, and in 1938 had been fully replaced by the Sd Kfz 221 and 223, and were then relegated to the reconnaissance units of non-motorized divisions. Many were used during the campaign in Poland and several were still in service in France, but they had been withdrawn from service by 1941.

697

698

Plates 696-697. Armoured reconnaissance car MG-Kw (Kfz 13).
Plate 698. Radio car Fu-kw (Kfz 14).
Plate 699. Kfz 13 and 14 on manoeuvres.

696

699

Leichte Panzerspähwagen (MG) (Sd Kfz 221)

Other designation: Gerät 80
Type: Light armoured car

Manufacturer: Weserhütte
Chassis Nos.: 810001–810800
339 produced from 1935 to May 1940

Crew: 2	Engine: Horch 3.5
Weight (tons): 4	Gearbox: 5 forward, 1 reverse
Length (metres): 4.8	Speed (km/hr): 90
Width (metres): 1.95	Range (km): 320
Height (metres): 1.7	Radio: FuG Spr Ger 'a'

Armament: One 7.92mm MG34, later: One 2.8cm sPZB41
Traverse: 360° (hand)
Elevation: $-5°$ $+45°$
Sight: direct
Ammunition: 1,050 Patr sS & SmK

Armour (mm/angle):	Front	Side	Rear	Top/Bottom
Turret:	8/35°	8/35°	8/35°	open
Superstructure:	8/37°	8/35°	5/65°	5/90° & open
Hull:	8/36°	8/35°	5/31°	none
Gun shield:	8/10°			

History: In 1934, the Sd Kfz 221 was developed as a light armoured car for reconnaissance and exploitation. The design was basically an armoured body and turret mounted on the German standard, four-wheeled, heavy, passenger-car chassis. Two series of the Sd Kfz 221 were ordered and completed before production ceased in favour of the other light armoured cars of the series.

Specific features: The sPkw I Horch 801 chassis for the Sd Kfz 221 featured a rear-mounted engine, independent coil-spring suspension, four-wheel drive, and front-wheel steering. The armoured body and turret consisted of rolled armour plates welded together at an angle which could withstand rounds fired from 8mm or .30 calibre machine-guns. The single machine-gun was mounted in the turret, which had an open top covered by anti-grenade screening. The first 143 had complicated vision ports cut from rolled plate. These were replaced by cast vision ports for the rest of the production series.

Combat service: The Sd Kfz 221 was issued to Panzerspähwagen squadrons of the Aufklärungs detachments of light, Panzer and motorized infantry divisions. In action, it was usually accompanied by armoured cars mounting the 2cm gun, and by armoured cars with radio equipment of longer range. From 1942, the 2.8cm sPzB41 was mounted in the modified turret, and this extended the service life of the Sd Kfz 221 until the end of the war.

Plates 700-702. Le Pz Sp Wg (MG) Sd Kfz 221.
Plates 703-704. Le Pz Sp Wg (Sd Kfz 221) mit 2.8cm sPzB41. (Note the cut-away turret.)
Plate 1034 (Page 268). Le Pz Sp Wg (Sd Kfz 221) mit 2.8cm sPzB41 in action.

701

702

703

704

700

Kleine Panzerfunkwagen (Sd Kfz 260/261)

Other designations: Gerät 83, Gerät 84
Type: Light armoured radio car

Plate 705. Kl Pz Fu Wg (Sd Kfz 260).
Plates 706-707. Kl Pz Fu Wg (Sd Kfz 261). Plate 706 shows the frame antenna in the raised position.

Manufacturer: Weserhütte, Ritscher
Chassis Nos.: 810001–811000, 8101001–8101424, 8110001–8111000
493 produced from November 1940 to April 1943

Crew: 4	Engine: Horch 3.5 or 3.8
Weight (tons): 4.3	Gearbox: 5 forward, 1 reverse
Length (metres): 4.83	Speed (km/hr): 85
Width (metres): 1.99	Range (km): 310
Height (metres): 1.78	

Radio: Sd Kfz 260 mit Funktrupp c : FuG7 + FuG Spr Ger 'a'
       Sd Kfz 261 mit Funktrupp d : FuG12 + FuG Spr Ger 'a'

Armour (mm/angle):	Front	Side	Rear	Top/Bottom
Superstructure:	8/35°	8/35°	8/30°	5/90° & open
Hull:	8/35°	8/35°	5/30°	none

History: The Sd Kfz 260 and 261 were a further development of the light, four-wheeled armoured car series. They were designed to provide mobility and armour protection for signals units, allowing swift and reliable communication even under enemy fire. The Sd Kfz 260 and 261 were produced in four series before being replaced by half-tracked radio-carriers.

Specific features: The Sd Kfz 260 and 261 had the same chassis and armoured body design as the rest of the light, four-wheeled armoured car series. Neither of these versions had a turret or armament other than the smallarms carried by the crew. The Sd Kfz 260 had a medium-range radio set with a rod antenna, and the Sd Kfz 261 had a long-range radio set with a frame antenna.

Combat service: The Sd Kfz 260 and 261 were issued to the signals troops at headquarters level of the regiments, brigades and divisions of the 'Panzer-Truppen' (Armoured Troops) plus the Panzerfunk companies of Nachrichten battalions. Coming into field service with the campaigns of the spring of 1941, the Sd Kfz 260 and 261 remained in service on all fronts until the end of the war.

706

705

707

Leichte Panzerspähwagen (2cm) (Sd Kfz 222)

Other designation: Gerät 81
Type: Light armoured car

Plates 708-711 (opposite page). Le Pz Sp Wg (2cm) Sd Kfz 222. Plate 708 shows a vehicle in Norway; Plates 710-711 show late versions.

Manufacturer: Weserhütte, Schichau, MNH, Büssing–NAG
Chassis Nos.: 810001–811000, 8101001–8101424, 8110001–8111000
989 produced from 1936 to June 1943

Crew: 3	Engine: Horch 3.5 or 3.8
Weight (tons): 4.8	Gearbox: 5 forward, 1 reverse
Length (metres): 4.8	Speed (km/hr): 85
Width (metres): 1.95	Range (km): 300
Height (metres): 2	Radio: FuG Spr Ger 'a'

Armament: One 2cm KwK30 or 38 L/55   One 7.92mm MG34
Traverse: 360° (hand)
Elevation: −4° +87°
Sight: TZF3a
Ammunition: 180   1,050

Armour (mm/angle):	Front	Side	Rear	Top/Bottom
Turret:	8/35°	8/35°	8/35°	open
Superstructure:	8/37°	8/35°	8/31°	5/90° & open
Hull:	8/36°	8/35°	5/31°	none
Gun shield:	8/35°			

History: The Sd Kfz 222 design was a modified version of the Sd Kfz 221, with a larger turret designed to carry an automatic gun.

Seven series were ordered and completed, each entailing minor modifications. Production ceased in mid 1943, but the proposed new four-wheel armoured car was not put into production because of changing requirements. It was felt that the heavy eight-wheel Sd Kfz 234 would be more suitable for reconaissance operations in the future.

Specific features: The first five series of the Sd Kfz 222 had the sPkw I Horch 801 chassis with the 3.5lit engine. In May 1942, an improved chassis, the sPkw I Type V, was introduced, incorporating hydraulic brakes and a 3.8lit engine. At the same time, the armour on the hull front was increased to 30mm, but the rest of the armour plate thicknesses remained unchanged. The 2cm automatic gun was mounted coaxially with a machine-gun in the turret, and could be elevated to an almost vertical position for engaging enemy air-craft.

Combat service: The Sd Kfz 222 was issued to the Panzerspähwagen squadrons of the Aufklärungs battalions. With only a short-range radio, it accompanied the armoured cars with long-range sets, in order to provide covering fire and engage enemy armoured reconnaissance vehicles. The Sd Kfz 222 served in all campaigns on all fronts from 1939 until the end of the war.

708 / 709

710 / 711

Leichte Panzerspähwagen (Fu) (Sd Kfz 223)

Other designation: Gerät 82
Type: Light armoured car (radio version)

Manufacturer: Weserhütte, MNH, Büssing-NAG
Chassis Nos.: 810001–811000, 8101001–8101424, 8110001–8111000
550 produced from 1935 to January 1944

Crew: 3	Engine: Horch 3.5 or 3.8
Weight (tons): 4.4	Gearbox: 5 forward, 1 reverse
Length (metres): 4.8	Speed (km/hr): 85
Width (metres): 1.95	Range (km): 300
Height (metres): 1.75	Radio: FuG10 + FuG Spr Ger 'a'

Armament: One 7.92mm MG34
Traverse: 360° (hand)
Sight: direct
Ammunition: 1,050

Armour (mm/angle):	Front	Side	Rear	Top/Bottom
Turret:	8/35°	8/35°	8/35°	open
Superstructure:	8/37°	8/35°	8/31°	5/90°/open
Hull:	8/36°	8/35°	5/31°	none
Gun shield:	8/35°			

712

Plates 712-714. Le Pz Sp Wg (Fu) Sd Kfz 223. Note that the frame aerial is raised in Plate 714, lowered in Plate 712.

713/714

History: In order to provide a light armoured car with a long-range radio set, the Sd Kfz 221 design was slightly modified and became the Sd Kfz 223. Six series were produced up to early 1944 when production ceased in favour of semi-track radio vehicles.

Specific features: In May 1942, the Sd Kfz 223 also changed to the new chassis with its larger motor and hydraulic brakes. As on the Sd Kfz 222, the armour on the front hull was increased to 30mm. The turret, with a single machine-gun, was mounted farther to the rear than in the Sd Kfz 221, allowing room for the large radio and its operator. The Sd Kfz 223 can be easily identified by the rectangular frame antenna, or the star antenna used with the long-range radio.

Combat service: The Sd Kfz 223 provided long-range communication links for the far-ranging groups of light armoured cars. Issued to the Panzerspähwagen squadrons of light, Panzer and motorized infantry divisions, it was utilized on all fronts throughout the war.

Leichte Panzerspähwagen (4-Rad) Büssing-NAG

Type: Armoured car prototype

History: In July 1941, the Waffenamt placed an order for the development of a new four wheel armoured car which was to replace the Sd Kfz 222 during 1943. In July 1942, 2 prototypes were under construction, and emphasis was placed on using the components of the s Pz Sp Wg 8-Rad TP which was later produced as the Sd Kfz 234. The new vehicle was to weigh 7 tons, with frontal armour of 30mm. A Tatra 6-cylinder air-cooled diesel drove the vehicle at 85km/hr. Proposed armament was the 5cm KwK39/1 and MG42. The prototypes were to be delivered early in 1942, and a preliminary order for 1,000 was placed, with 5 to be delivered in October 1943 and production rising to 80 per month. With the change in requirements for reconnaissance vehicles which came about as a result of the events of 1942, the order for these vehicles was cancelled.

Panzerspähwagen Schildkröte

Type: Experimental amphibious armoured car

History: From 1941, Trippel-Werke worked to produce an amphibious armoured car based on their existing amphibious passenger cars. Two prototypes were built on the basis of the SG6 in 1942. A third prototype was ordered in late 1942, and on this basis, the so-called E3 (Einheits = standard) series was built in 1943 and 1944. These cars were to have an MG armament, but the Schildkröte III had a 2cm MG151. This latter vehicle was the first to be powered with a Tatra V–8 air-cooled engine of 70PS. The E3 was built during 1944, and the three units included a E3M turretless ammunition-carrier. Armour of the latter type was between 5.5mm and 14.5mm. Overall length was 5.18m and the width, 1.9m. After testing in October 1944, the Waffenamt indicated that there was no requirement for an amphibious Pz Sp Wg at that time.

715

717

Plates 715-716. Pz Sp Wg Schildkröte on trials.
Plate 717. The amphibious E3M turretless munitions carrier.

Krupp gepanzerte Radfahrzeug

Type: Armoured car

History: Starting in 1936, Krupp designed an armoured car body which could be fitted on their 6 x 4 light truck type L2H 143. Several were sold to the Dutch East Indies Army. The original version had a single MG in a small, but high turret. The production vehicles had an MG in the front and rear of the hull and a third MG in a broad, low turret. Power was provided by a 3.3lit Boxer air-cooled engine. Length 5.07m, width 2.2m and height 2.30m. One of the production cars was destroyed in the grounds of the Reichstag building in Berlin in 1945.

Plate 718. Krupp gep Radfahrzeug.

Schwere Panzerspähwagen (Sd Kfz 231) 6-Rad / Schwerer Panzer-spähwagen (Fu) (Sd Kfz 232) 6-Rad / Panzerfunkwagen (Sd Kfz 263) 6-Rad

Type: Heavy armoured car / radio car

Manufacturer: Daimler-Benz, Büssing-NAG, Magirus
Chassis Nos.: 30001– , 40001– , 50001–
123 Sd Kfz 231/232 (6-Rad), 28 Sd Kfz 263 (6-Rad) produced from
1932 to 1937

Crew: 4
Weight (tons): 5.35–6
Length (metres): 5.57
Width (metres): 1.82
Height (metres): 2.25

Engine: Büssing-NAG G, Daimler-Benz MO9, Magirus s88
Gearbox: 4 forward, 1 reverse
Speed (km/hr): 70
Range (km): 300
Radio: FuG Spr Ger 'a'

Armament: One 2cm KwK30 L/55   One 7.92mm MG13
Traverse: 360° (hand)
Elevation: −12° +20°
Ammunition: 200   1,500

719

Armour (mm/angle):	Front	Side	Rear	Top/Bottom
Turret:	8/0°	8/30°	8/30°	5/75°–90°
Superstructure:	8/25°	8/37°	8/30°	5/80°–90°
Hull:	8/25–35°	8/35°	8/25°–42°	none
Gun mantlet:	8/0°			

History: The development of an armoured car based on the chassis of a 6 x 4 truck was ordered in 1929. The three companies involved in the manufacture of the trucks were given contracts to modify their truck chassis to adapt them to a six-wheeled armoured car. Thus, these early armoured cars were basically an armoured body fitted to a slightly modified truck chassis.

Specific features: The engine was still mounted in the front as in normal trucks. The chassis was strengthened to take the additional weight, and a second steering control was added at the rear. The Sd Kfz 232 was the same model as the Sd Kfz 231 except for the additional long-range radio and its large frame antenna. The Sd Kfz 263 had a fixed turret with a single MG13, a long-range radio set and a large frame antenna together with a telescoping mast antenna. The engines ranged from 3.6lit to 4.5lit and developed between 60PS and 70PS at 2,000rpm.

Combat service: The Sd Kfz 231 and 232 were issued to the motorized Aufklärungs detachments of the developing motorized forces in the German Army. The Sd Kfz 263 was issued to the motorized Nachrichten (signals) units. Taking part in the marches into Austria and Czechoslovakia and the campaigns in Poland and France, the six-wheeled Panzerspähwagen were withdrawn from front-line service in 1940 because of their very limited mobility off the road.

720

722

723

Plates 719, 720 and 722. S Pz Sp Wg (Sd Kfz 231) 6-Rad. Plate 720 shows a vehicle in France during the 1940 campaign.
Plates 721 and 724. S Pz Sp Wg (Fu) (Sd Kfz 232) 6-Rad. Plate 721 Büssing-NAG.
Plate 723. Pz Fu Wg (Sd Kfz 263) 6-Rad. (Magirus).

Mannschaftstransportwagen I

Other designations: DB-ARW, BN-ZRW, M-ARW
Type: Heavy cross-country armoured car

Manufacturer: Daimler-Benz, Büssing-NAG, Magirus
6 prototypes built from 1928 to 1930

Crew: 5
Weight (tons): 7.8
Length (metres): 5.45
Width (metres): 2.28
Height (metres): 2.14

Engine: Daimler-Benz M36 6cyl
7.8lit 100PS at 2,000rpm
Gearbox: 5 forward, 5 reverse
Speed (km/hr): 65
Range (km): 250

Armament: One 3.7cm KwKL/45   One 7.92mm MG
Traverse: 360° (hand)
Elevation: −10° +70°
Ammunition: 66

Armour (mm):	Front	Side	Rear
Turret:	13.5	13.5	13.5
Hull:	13.5/	13.5/	13.5/

History: In 1927, an order for six experimental reconnaissance vehicles was placed with three firms. Daimler-Benz and Magirus developed similar 8-Rad vehicles which were powered by 6cylinder 100PS engines. Magirus used a Maybach engine in their prototypes. Büssing-NAG developed a larger 10-Rad vehicle powered by a 150PS V-8 motor. All vehicles were tested in both Germany and in Kazan in Russia. All vehicles were designed to swim and had a propeller at the rear. Some difficulties were experienced with steering the ZRW, but in most respects, trials were a success. Rheinmetall-Borsig were ordered to develop a suitable turret in 1928, and one prototype was built in 1929. In March 1930, it was decided that these MTW would not be produced as they were too expensive, in view of the requirements of the German Army at that time. However, in 1934, these designs were used as the basis for an order which lead to the development of the Sd Kfz 231 (8-Rad).

Plates 725-728. ARW/MTW I: the Daimler-Benz prototype (Plate 725); a wooden model with hemispherical turret (Plate 726); a cork-bodied prototype for water trials (Plate 727); and the Magirus prototype (Plate 728). See also Plate 35, page 13.

725/726

727/728

Schwere Panzerspähwagen (Sd Kfz 231) 8-Rad / Schwere Panzerspähwagen (Fu) (Sd Kfz 232) 8-Rad

Other designations: Vs Kfz 623/624, Sd Kfz 233/234, Gerät 85/86
Type: Heavy cross-country armoured car

Manufacturer: Deutsche Werke, Schichau
Chassis Nos.: 59902–87267
607 produced from 1936 to September 1943

Crew: 4
Weight (tons): 8.3
Length (metres): 5.85
Width (metres): 2.2
Height (metres): 2.35

Engine: Büssing-NAG L8V
Gearbox: 6 forward, 6 reverse
Speed (km/hr): 85
Range (km): 300
Radio: FuG Spr Ger 'a' (Sd Kfz 231)
FuG12 & FuG Spr Ger 'a' (Sd Kfz 232)

Armament: One 2cm KwK30 or 38   One 7.92mm MG34
Traverse: 360° (hand)
Elevation: −10° +26°
Sight: TZF6
Ammunition: 180
2,100 (Sd Kfz 231)
1,050 (Sd Kfz 232 Fu)

Armour (mm/angle):	Front	Side	Rear	Top/Bottom
Turret:	15/20°	8/30°	8/30°	6/80°−90°
Superstructure:	15/28°	8/35°	8/35°	6/84°−90°
Hull:	8+10/35°	8/35°	10/25°	5/90°/none
Gun mantlet:	15/20°			

History: The development of a schwerer Panzerspähwagen with improved cross-country mobility was ordered in 1934. Designated Versuchskraftfahrzeug (experimental vehicle) 623 and 624, an eight-wheeled chassis was developed to carry the armoured body and turret. The designation changed to Sd Kfz 233 and 234 in mid 1937 and, finally, to Sd Kfz 231 and 232 (8-Rad) in October 1939. Only the Sd Kfz 232 version was produced after May 1942. Sd Kfz 232 production ceased in September 1942 to be replaced by the Sd Kfz 234 series.
Specific features: All chassis were produced by Büssing-NAG, and featured steering and drive for all eight road wheels. Double controls

were installed to allow rapid manoeuvring, advancing and retiring. The engine was located in the rear, which gave adequate protection together with adequate cooling. Early in 1940, an 8mm armour shield (Pakschütz) was added to the front of many of the Sd Kfz 231/232 already produced, and this practice continued until early 1942. From May 1942, this temporary solution was eliminated from production vehicles, since the hull and turret frontal armour thickness was increased to 30mm. The weight then increased to 9.1 tons.

Combat service: Six Sd Kfz 231 and 232 were issued to the heavy platoon of the Panzerspähwagen squadron of each motorized Aufklärungs detachment. The entire platoon was not usually employed together, but was split up to accompany and give support to the smaller, four-wheeled armoured cars. The Sd Kfz 231 and 232 were employed in all campaigns throughout the war.

732

729

Plate 19 (Page 9). S Pz Sp Wg (Sd Kfz 231) 8-Rad late production vehicle.
Plates 729-731. S Pz Sp Wg (Sd Kfz 231) 8-Rad, early, middle and late production vehicles respectively. In Plate 731, note the armoured shield on the front of the vehicle, the space behind which was used as a storage bin.
Plates 732-733. S Pz Sp Wg (Fu) (Sd Kfz 232) 8-Rad.
Plates 734-735. Late version radio vehicles, with star aerial attached to the rear of the hull. In Plate 735, note the armoured cover over the rear air louvres.

733

730

734

731

735

ARMOURED CARS AND WHEELED ARMOURED VEHICLES 199

Schwere Panzerspähwagen (7.5cm) (Sd Kfz 233)

Other designation: Gerät 87
Type: Heavy cross-country armoured car—support version

Manufacturer: Schichau
Chassis Nos.: 85615–87267
109 produced from December 1942 to October 1943
10 converted from Sd Kfz 231/232 chassis in October 1942

Crew: 3	Engine: Büssing-NAG L8V
Weight (tons): 8.7	Gearbox: 6 forward, 6 reverse
Length (metres): 5.85	Speed (km/hr): 80
Width (metres): 2.2	Range (km): 300
Height (metres): 2.25	Radio: FuG Spr Ger 'a'

Armament: One 7.5cm StuK37 L/24	One 7.92mm MG42
Traverse: 12° left 12° right (hand)	loose
Elevation: −10° +12°	loose
Sight: SflZF1	direct
Ammunition: 32	1,500

Armour (mm/angle):	Front	Side	Rear	Top/Bottom
Superstructure:	15/30°	8/35°	8/35°	6/84° + open
Hull:	30/35°	8/35°	10/25°	5/90° + none
Gun shield:	15/30°			

736

History: The Sd Kfz 233 was developed to give the armoured reconnaissance squadron a weapon capable of engaging enemy armour and area targets. The order was issued to build 115 Sd Kfz 233, completing the Sd Kfz 263 order.

Specific features: The Sd Kfz 233 was an altered Sd Kfz 231 design, with the turret removed, the superstructure roof open and the right side of the superstructure front cut away to mount the StuK37.

Combat service: Issued as a platoon of six Sd Kfz 233 to the Panzerspähwagen squadrons of the Aufklärungs battalions detachments. Well liked by the reconnaissance troops, the Sd Kfz 233 saw service on all major fronts until the end of the war.

737

738

Plates 736-739. S Pz Sp Wg (7.5cm) (Sd Kfz 233). Plate 736 shows a vehicle in Russia, fitted with an MG42 for anti-aircraft defence; Plate 738 shows a later model Sd Kfz 233, with raised superstructure around the fighting compartment.

739

Panzerfunkwagen (Sd Kfz 263) 8-Rad

Other designation: Gerät 95
Type: Heavy cross-country radio car

Manufacturer: Deutsche Werke, Schichau
Chassis Nos.: 59902–87267
240 produced from April 1938 to April 1943

Crew: 5	Engine: Büssing-NAG L8V
Weight (tons): 8.1	Gearbox: 6 forward, 6 reverse
Length (metres): 5.85	Speed (km/hr): 100
Width (metres): 2.2	Range (km): 300
Height (metres): 2.9	Radio: 1 Sätz Funkgerät für (m)
	Pz Funktrupp b

Armament: One 7.92mm MG34
Traverse: hand
Ammunition: 1,050

Armour (mm/angle):	Front	Side	Rear	Top/Bottom
Superstructure:	18/17°	8/35°	10/35°	6/90°
Hull:	8/30°–35°	8/35°	10/31°	5/90° + none

History: The Sd Kfz 263 (8-Rad) was developed from 1934 to 1938 alongside the Sd Kfz 231/232 (8-Rad), and utilized the same chassis.
Specific features: In place of the turret on the Sd Kfz 231/232 (8-Rad), the Sd Kfz 263 (8-Rad) had the superstructure sides extended higher to form a large crew compartment. The only armament was an MG34 mounted in the superstructure front. A large frame antenna and a telescoping mast antenna were provided for the long-range radio set.
Combat service: The Sd Kfz 263 was issued to the Nachrichten detachments of motorized and Panzer divisions, as well as Korps and Army headquarters. It was not meant to be a fighting vehicle, but was to be employed as a mobile base for a highly-effective communications network.

Plates 740-742. Pz Fu Wg (Sd Kfz 263) 8-Rad, showing the star aerial open (Plate 740), the mast telescoped down (Plate 741) and the MG34 (Plate 742).

740

741

742

Ballistik-Messfahrzeug auf schwere Panzerspähwagen (8-Rad)

Type: Ballistics Measuring vehicle

History: A fully armoured observation vehicle based on the chassis of the 8-Rad armoured car (Sd Kfz 231). An example of this vehicle was found on the Artillery proving ground at Hillersleben in 1945.

Plates 743-744. Ballistik-Messfahrzeug auf s Pz Sp Wg (8-Rad).

743

744

Schwere Panzerspähwagen (2cm) (Sd Kfz 234/1)

Other designation: Gerät 95
Type: Heavy armoured car

Manufacturer: Büssing-NAG
Chassis Nos.: 3001–
200 produced from June 1944 to January 1945

Crew: 4	Engine: Tatra 103
Weight (tons): 11.5	Gearbox: 6 forward, 6 reverse
Length (metres): 6	Speed (km/hr): 80
Width (metres): 2.4	Range (km): 900
Height (metres): 2.1	Radio: FuG Spr Ger 'a' & FuG12

Armament: One 2cm KwK38 L/55   One 7.92mm MG42
Traverse: 360° (hand)
Elevation: −4° +70°
Sight: TZF3a
Ammunition: 480   2,400

Armour (mm/angle):	Front	Side	Rear	Top/Bottom
Turret:	30/40°	8/40°	8/38°	open
Superstructure:	30/40°	8/35°	10/38°	6/87°–90°
Hull:	30/35°+50°	8/35°	10/31°+46°	5/90°
Gun shield:	10/40°			

History: In September 1943, an order was given that fifty per cent of the Sd Kfz 234 production was to mount the 2cm KwK38 following the completion of the 100 Sd Kfz 234/2. In June 1944, this was increased to 75 per cent to be produced in conjunction with the Sd Kfz 234/2 and later Sd Kfz 234/4. The Gerät number 95 was that formerly allocated to the Sd Kfz 263 (8-Rad) which was no longer available by June 1944.

Specific features: The Sd Kfz 234/1 had the same hull as the Sd Kfz 234/2, but mounted a different turret. The turret for the Sd Kfz 234/1 resembled the short, open-topped turret mounted on the Sd Kfz 222, but was of simpler, six-sided construction with thicker frontal armour. The designation for this turret was 2cm Hängelafette (swinging mount) 38.

Combat service: Nineteen Sd Kfz 234/1 were included in the organization of the Panzerspähwagen company (d) of the Panzer Aufklärungs battalions. Issued to the Panzer and Panzergrenadier divisions, the Sd Kfz 234/1 saw action on the collapsing fronts in the East and in the West, from July 1944 until the end of the war.

745

Plates 745-746. S Pz Sp Wg (2cm) (Sd Kfz 234/1). Plate 745 shows the 2cm KwK38 L/55 mounted in the open turret; in Plate 746, the turret is traversed and the gun points to the rear of the vehicle.

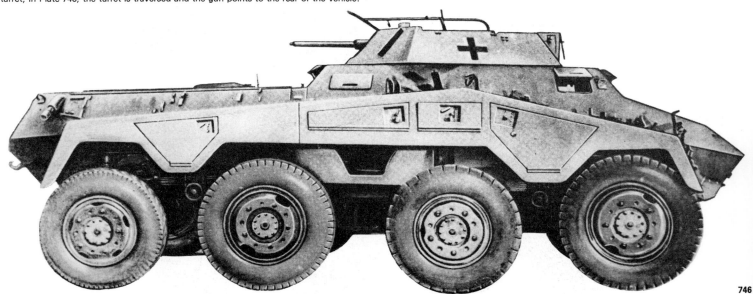

746

Schwere Panzerspähwagen (5cm) (Sd Kfz 234/2)

Other designations: Puma, Gerät 93
Type: Heavy armoured car

Manufacturer: Büssing-NAG
Chassis Nos.: 3001–
101 produced from September 1943 to September 1944

Crew: 4
Weight (tons): 11.74
Length (metres): 6.8
Width (metres): 2.4
Height (metres): 2.28

Engine: Tatra 103
Gearbox: 6 forward, 6 reverse
Speed (km/hr): 80
Range (km): 900
Radio: Fug Spr Ger a + FuG12

Armament: One 5cm KwK 39/1
L/60
Traverse: 360° (hand)
Elevation: −10° +20°
Sight: TZF4b
Ammunition: 55

One 7.92mm MG42

1,050

Armour (mm/angle):	Front	Side	Rear	Top/Bottom
Turret:	30/20°	10/25°	10/25°	10/90°
Superstructure:	30/35°	8/30°	10/22°	6/87°-90°
Hull:	30/30° +55°	8/30°	10/40°	5/90°
Gun mantlet:	Saukopfblende			

History: On 5 August 1940, the order was given to design an eight-wheeled armoured car similar in design to the Sd Kfz 231. Instead of the previous design, where the armoured body was bolted to a chassis, the Sd Kfz 234 armoured hull was to serve as the chassis. This s Pz Sp Wg 8–Rad Tp (Tropen = tropical) was to have heavier armour and a 12-cylinder air-cooled diesel engine designed to operate in the hot climate of North Africa, and in the Steppes of Russia. Two trial vehicles were built and an initial order for 500 was later increased to 1.500. The initial order was for a vehicle carrying the 5cm KwK 39/1 which was given the designation Sd Kfz 234/2. In January 1944, the order was cut to limit the Puma production to 100 vehicles and to continue the series by mounting the 2cm KwK and 7.5cm KwK.

Specific features: The hull design, similar to that of the Sd Kfz 231, had better frontal protection, provided by thicker plates laid at a greater angle. A large, fully-enclosed turret with curved side plates was provided to mount the 5cm KwK 39/1 and the coaxial MG42 in the 'Saukopf' (sow's head) gun mantlet.

Plates 747-750. The Puma heavy armoured car. In Plate 747, the turret aerial is in the raised position; note the 'Saukopf' gun mantlet.

Combat service: Each Panzerspähwagen company (a) consisted of 25 Pumas. These units were assigned to four Panzer divisions which fought on both the Eastern and Western fronts.

747

748

749

750

Schwere Panzerspähwagen (7.5cm KwK) (Sd Kfz 234/3)
Schwere Panzerspähwagen (7.5cm PaK40) (Sd Kfz 234/4)

Other designation: Gerät 94 / Gerät 96
Type: Heavy armoured car—support versions

Manufacturer: Büssing-NAG
Chassis Nos.: 3001–
88 Sd Kfz 234/3 produced from June to December 1944
89 Sd Kfz 234/4 produced from December 1944 to March 1945

Crew: 4	Engine: Tatra 103
Weight (tons): 11.5	Gearbox: 6 forward, 6 reverse
Length (metres): 6	Speed (km/hr): 80
Width (metres): 2.4	Range (km): 900
Height (metres): 2.21	Radio: FuG Spr Ger "a"

752

Armament:
One 7.5cm KwK51 L/24
(Sd Kfz 234/3)
One 7.5cm PaK40 L/46
(Sd Kfz 234/4)

Traverse: 12° left 12° right	loose
Elevation: −10° +12° (Sd Kfz 234/3)	loose
−3° +22° (Sd Kfz 234/4)	
Sight: Sfl ZF1b (Sd Kfz 234/3)	direct
ZF3×8° (Sd Kfz 234/4)	
Ammunition: 50 (Sd Kfz 234/3)	1,950
12 (Sd Kfz 234/4)	

One 7.92mm MG34 or 42

Armour (mm/angle):	Front	Side	Rear	Top/Bottom
Superstructure:	30/35°	8/30°	10/22°	6/88°
Hull:	30/30° & 55°	8/30°	10/40°	5/90°
Gun shield:	15/40°	15/0°	15/38°	open

753

History: In September 1943, 50 per cent of the Sd Kfz 234 production was ordered to mount the 7.5cm KwK (H24). This was decreased to 25 per cent in June 1944, reflecting an organizational change by the reconnaissance troops. In late November 1944, Hitler ordered that, from December 1944, the 7.5cm PaK40 be mounted on the Sd Kfz 234. Therefore, production of the Sd Kfz 234/3 ceased in December 1944, but production of the Sd Kfz 234/4 continued until March 1945. A further model was to mount the 7.5cm L/48 AK 7B84 which was basically the KwK 40 in a mount similar to that of the Sd Kfz 234/3.

Specific features: The Sd Kfz 234/3 and 234/4 both consisted of the basic Sd Kfz 234 hull without a turret. The superstructure roof was open, with the 7.5cm KwK51 in a gun shield at the front of the superstructure, and the 7.5cm PaK40 mounted with its original gun shield and carriage on a pedestal mount.

Combat service: Six Sd 234/3 made up a platoon of the Panzer-spähwagen company (d) to support the nineteen Sd Kfz 234/1. They were also issued to the armoured reconnaissance companies during the closing months of the war, to give anti-tank support to the other armoured cars.

751

754

Plates 751-753. S Pz Sp Wg (7.5cm) (Sd Kfz 234/3).
Plates 754. S Pz Sp Wg (7.5cm PaK40) (Sd Kfz 234/4).

Plates 755-756. S Pz Sp Wg (7.5cm PaK40) (Sd Kfz 234/4).

Schwere geländegängige gepanzerte Personenkraftwagen (Sd Kfz 247)

Other designation: s gl gep PKW Typ 1c
Type: Heavy wheeled armoured personnel carrier

Manufacturer: Daimler-Benz
Chassis Nos.: 140001–140058
58 produced from July 1941 to January 1942
Crew: 6
Weight (tons): 4.46
Length (metres): 5
Width (metres): 2
Height (metres): 1.8

Engine: Horch 3.5
Gearbox: 5 forward, 1 reverse
Speed (km/hr): 80
Range (km): 400

Armour (mm/angle):	Front	Side	Rear	Top/Bottom
Hull (upper):	8/38°	8/35°	8/30°	6/90°/open
(lower):	8/35°	8/35°	8/35°	none

History: The Sd Kfz 247 was developed as an armoured staff car for commanders of reconnaissance detachments. Ten of an early Sd Kfz 247 series designed on a Krupp L2H143 6 x 4 chassis had been produced in 1937. Although the weight was 5.2 tons it was slightly smaller all round. The Krupp M305 57PS motor gave a speed of 70km/hr and a range of 350km.

Specific features: The Sd Kfz 247 consisted of an armoured body mounted on a 4 x 4 heavy passenger car chassis. The engine was mounted in the front, with cooling air supplied through armoured louvres. No radio or armament was provided for the crew of six who rode in this open-topped vehicle.

Combat service: One issued to the commander of each Aufklärungs battalion of the Panzer and other motorized divisions.

757

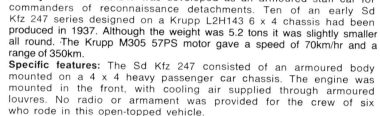

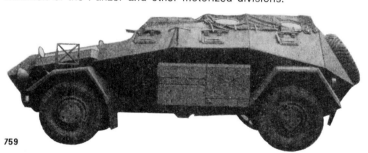

759

Plates 757-758. S gl gep PKW (Sd Kfz 247) Ausf A.
Plates 759-760. S gl gep PKW (Sd Kfz 247) Ausf B, based on the 4 x 4 chassis with frontal armour shield and star aerial (Plate 760).

758

760

Polizei-Panzerkampfwagen ADGZ

Other designation: M35 mittlere Panzerwagen
Type: Heavy armoured car

Manufacturer: Steyr-Daimler-Puch AG
Chassis Nos.: GZ 1-GZ 27
25 produced in early 1942
27 received from Austrian Army in 1938

Crew: 6	Engine: Austro-Daimler M612
Weight (tons): 12	6cyl 12lit 150PS at 1,800rpm
Length (metres): 6.26	Gearbox: 3 × 2 forward,
Width (metres): 2.16	3 × 2 reverse
Height (metres): 2.56	Speed (km/hr): 70
	Range (km): 450

Armament: One 2cm   One 7.92mm MG34   Two 7.92mm MG34
  KwK35 L/45
Traverse: 360° (hand)   15° left 15° right
  +10° left 10° right   (hand)
Elevation: −12° +18°   −15° +45°
Ammunition: 100   2,500

Armour (mm/angle):	Front	Side	Rear	Top/Bottom
Turret:	11/0°	11/0°	11/0°	11/65°−75°
Superstructure:	11/5°−45°	11/18°	11/25°−68°	11/90°
Hull:	11/30°	11/15°	11/10°	11/90°
Gun mantlet:	11/round			

History: Developed as a heavy armoured car for the Austrian Army from 1934 and delivered between 1935 and 1937. Series production was under consideration, but the events of 1938 precluded the completion of this possibility. In 1941, Steyr received an order from the Reichsführer-SS to complete a further 25 new ADGZ for the SS. These were delivered during 1942.

Combat service: The original fourteen ADGZ served with police detachments in Danzig in September 1939. The ADGZ delivered in 1942 were used by the SS to fight partisans in the East.

762

763

761

Plates 761-763. Police armoured cars: ADGZ (Plates 761-762), and a Strassenpanzerwagen (Plate 763). The latter was one of a number of commercial vehicles armoured for use by SS police patrols and armed with the Maxim MG08 machine-gun.

Leichte Truppenluftschütz Kraftwagen (Kfz 4)

Other designation: Gerät 220
Type: Self-propelled anti-aircraft gun

History: To provide air protection for motorized units, a FlaK vehicle was created by mounting the Zwillingslafette (dual mount) 36 in the passenger compartment of the le gl Einheits PKW (light standard cross-country car). The Zwillingslafette 36 consisted of two 7.92mm MG34 on a special pedestal mount with an anti-aircraft sight and 360° traverse. The le gl Einh PKW were of course the standard light passenger cars (4 x 4) used by the German Army. They were built by Stoewer from 1937 to 1942 and by BMW and Hanomag from 1937 to 1940. Photographic evidence clearly shows that many other types of PKW and LKW were used to carry the Zwillingslafette 36 in action.

Plate 764. Le Truppenluftschütz Kraftwagen (Kfz 4), based on the Stoewer le gl Einh PKW 4 x 4.

Plate 765. Kfz 4 based on the BMW le gl Einh PKW 4 x 4.
Plate 766. The Zwillingslafette 36 mounted on a medium truck.

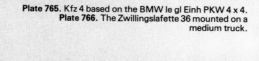

765

766

2cm FlaK30 oder 38 (Sf) auf schwere geländegängiger Einheits PKW

Type: Self-propelled anti-aircraft gun

History: A limited number of the heavy 4 x 4 Horch s gl Einh PKW were specially converted to FlaK vehicles. Like the 2cm FlaK on the Zgkw 1t, the sides of the vehicle could be lowered to provide a wide platform for all-round traverse. Subsequent conversions had the 2cm FlaK38 mounted in the standard passenger body. 800 rounds of 2cm ammunition and a seven-man crew were carried.

767

Plate 767. 2cm FlaK38(Sf) auf LKW (Opel Blitz)—a converted medium truck, with armoured front and drop sides.
Plate 768. 2cm FlaK30(Sf) auf s gl Einh PKW.
Plate 769. 2cm FlaK38(Sf) mounted in the standard passenger body.

768

769

770

774

771

775

772 / 773

776 / 777

2cm FlaK30 oder 38 (Sf) auf Lastkraftwagen

Type: Self-propelled anti-aircraft gun

History: The need of air-defence for mobile units led to the mounting of the 2cm FlaK30 and, later, the FlaK38 on normal load-carrying trucks. Many varieties of light and medium trucks and Maultier vehicles were used for this purpose.

Schwerer Geländegängiger Lastkraftwagen 4.5t für FlaK (Sf)

Other designation: Mercedes-Benz L4500A
Type: Self-propelled anti-aircraft gun

History: From 1943 until late 1944, when the Mercedes-Benz L4500 A went out of production, the Luftwaffe received a considerable number of specially designed armoured FlaK vehicles based on this chassis. The driver's cab was lightly armoured, and a protective plate was placed in front of the radiator. The sides of the load platform, on which was mounted a 3.7cm FlaK36, could be folded down to a horizontal position to increase the platform size. Four stabilizer legs could be lowered to provide a rigid mount for 360 degree traverse. These vehicles were powered by a diesel engine of 112PS and had four-wheel drive. The overall dimensions were 7.86m length, and 2.35m width. Photographic evidence also shows that the 5cm FlaK41 was mounted on this armoured vehicle, but since only 44 of these guns were available in 1944, it is presumed that this was an experimental mounting.

Schwere Geländegängiger Lastkraftwagen 4.5t Mercedes-Benz L4500A als Flakwagen für 3.7cm FlaK 36.

Type: Self-propelled anti-aircraft gun.

History: These heavy four-wheel drive trucks were fitted with an armoured cab and a protective plate in front of the radiator, and were provided with a special load platform having sides which folded down to increase the platform size. The Mercedes-Benz and Büssing-NAG had slightly different cab configurations. Both vehicles were primarily used to mount the 2cm Flakvierling 38, but after the Mercedes-Benz L4500A production ended, the Büssing-NAG vehicle was used to mount the 3.7cm FlaK36. The Büssing vehicle was powered by a diesel engine delivering 105PS.

3.7cm PaK35/36 auf Leichter Geländegängiger Lastkraftwagen 1t

Other designation: Krupp Protze L2H143
Type: Self-propelled anti-tank gun

Schweres Minenräumfahrzeug

Other designation: Krupp Räumer-S
Type: Mine destroyer vehicle

History: The Krupp Protze (Krupp Limber) 6 x 4 light truck was the main wheeled tractor for the 3.7cm PaK. To provide greater mobility, a considerable number of these 3.7cm PaK were mounted on the rear of the trucks to make a simple self-propelled gun.

History: In 1944, Krupp built a prototype of this super heavy mine-clearing vehicle. The 130t vehicle was articulated in the centre, and was suspended on 2.7m diameter steel wheels. These were set on different track widths at front and rear, so as to sweep a wider path. Each section of the Räumer was powered by a Maybach HL90 motor.

778

Plate 22 (Page 10). 2cm FlaK 38 mounted on 6 × 4 truck.
Plate 30 (Page 12). 2cm KwK 30 mounted on a steyr 1500 truck.

Opposite page.
Plate 770. 2cm FlaK30 on a standard medium 4 x 4 truck.
Plate 771. 2cm FlaK38 on a Kruppe Protze light 6 x 4 truck.
Plates 772-773. 2cm Flak-vierling 38 auf s gl LKW 4.5t: Mercedes-Benz L4500A (Plate 772) and Büssing-NAG (Plate 773).
Plate 774. 3.7cm FlaK43 auf s gl LKW 4.5t (Mercedes-Benz L4500A). Note the folded stabilizers.
Plate 775. 5cm FlaK41 auf s gl LKW 4.5t (Mercedes-Benz L4500A) with stabilizers extended.
Plate 776. 3.7cm FlaK36 on an Opel Blitz standard heavy 4 x 4 truck.
Plate 777. 3.7cm PaK35/36 auf le gl LKW 1t.
Plate 778. S Minenräum-fahrzeug.

French AFVs in German service

7.5cm PaK40/1 auf Geschützwagen (GW) Lorraine Schlepper (f) (Sd Kfz 135)

Type: Self-propelled anti-tank gun on captured tracked carrier chassis

Manufacturer: Alfred Becker
Chassis Nos.: 731001–
170 converted in July and August 1942
Crew: 5
Weight (tons): 8

Engine: DelaHaye 103TT
  6cyl 3.55lit 70PS at 2,800rpm
Gearbox: 5 forward, 1 reverse
Speed (km/hr): 34
Range (km): 135
Radio: FuG5

Armament: One 7.5cm PaK40/1
  L/46
Traverse: 32° left 32° right
Elevation: −5° +22°
Sight: ZF3 × 8

One 7.92mm MG34

loose
loose
direct

Armour (mm/angle):	Front	Side	Rear	Top/Bottom
Turret:	10/33°	9/20°	7/28°	open
Superstructure:	9/35°	9/45°	9/35°	6/90°
Hull:	12/round	9/0°	9/36°	5/90°
Gun shield:	10/33°			

History: With adequate supplies of the Russian 7.62cm PaK36(r) available for mounting on the existing series of Panzerjäger, using the Pz Kpfw 38(t) and Pz Kpfw II Ausf D/E chassis, it was decided in May 1942 to mount the German 7.5cm PaK40 on the Lorraine Schlepper (f). Of a total of 387 of these French 'Tracteur Blindé 37L', built by the Société Lorraine between 1937 and May 1940, more than 300 were in the German stockpile. The initial order was for 160 Lorraine Schlepper (f) to be converted to 60 Panzerjäger, 60 leFH18 and 40 sFH13. By July, a further 78 were made available, of which, 24 were for Panzerjäger. Likewise, 48 of the chassis scheduled for the 10.5cm leFH18 were, instead, used for the same purpose. The total number converted was 170. Photographic evidence indicates the existence of a Panzerjäger vehicle armed with the French 4.7cm PaK181(f) on an open pedestal mount—it is not clear if this was a German or a French development. Together with the

Panzerjäger, 39 Beobachtungswagen auf Lorraine Schlepper (f) were converted in 1942. In 1942, 315 Lorraine chassis were converted by the Germans. The remaining serviceable units were issued as Munitionstransportkraftwagen auf Lorraine Schlepper (f).
Specific features: The basic Lorraine tractor was unmodified except for the replacement of its load platform by the new superstructure to protect the gun and its crew. Hinged side shields fitted to the PaK40 gave protection during traverse.
Combat service: The Sd Kfz 135 was issued to the Panzerjäger detachments (SP), mainly to units operating in France. At the beginning of 1944, there were still 131 in service on the Western Front.

779

Plates 779-780. The basic Lorraine Schlepper (f), or 'Tracteur Blindé 37L'.

Plates 781-788 (opposite page).
Plates 781-783. 7.5cm PaK40/1 auf GW Lorraine Schlepper (f) (Sd Kfz 135).
Plates 784-785. 10.5cm leFH18 auf GW Lorraine Schlepper (f). See also overleaf.
Plate 786. 4.7cm PaK181(f) auf Pz Jäg Lorraine Schlepper (f).
Plates 787-788. Beobachtungswagen auf Lorraine Schlepper (f).

780

781

782

783

784

785

786

787

788

15cm sFH13/1(Sf) auf Geschützwagen Lorraine Schlepper (f) (Sd Kfz 135/1)
10.5cm leFH18(Sf) auf Geschützwagen Lorraine Schlepper (f)

Type: Self-propelled field howitzer on captured tracked carrier chassis

Manufacturer: Alfred Becker
Chassis Nos.: 731001–
94 15cm converted in July 1942
12 10.5cm converted in 1942

Crew: 4	Engine: DelaHaye 103TT 6cyl
Weight (tons): 8.49	3.55lit 70PS at 2,800rpm
Length (metres): 5.31	Gearbox: 5 forward, 1 reverse
Width (metres): 1.83	Speed (km/hr): 34
Height (metres): 2.23	Range (km): 135
	Radio: FuG Spr f

Armament: One 15cm sFH13/1   One 10.5cm leFH18/40 L/28
    (L/17) or
Traverse: 5° left 5° right
Elevation: −0° +40°
Sight: Rblf36
Ammunition: 8   20

Armour (mm/angle):	Front	Side	Rear	Top/Bottom
Turret:	10/8°	9/12°	7/12°	open
Superstructure:	9/35°	9/10° & 35°	9/11°	6/90°
Hull:	12/round	9/0°	9/36°	5/90°
Gun shield:	10/8°			

History: During the early months of 1942, many decisions were taken in an effort to get self-propelled anti-tank guns to the front line as soon as possible. More than 300 French 'Tracteur Blindé 37L' had been captured and stockpiled after the campaign in the West in 1940. It was intended to use these only for the Panzerjäger, but in May 1942, Hitler ordered that 40 be used to mount a 15cm sFH which was needed for special operations under Rommel in North Africa. The superstructures came from Alkett, and assembly took place in Paris. In July, a further 78 Lorraine Schlepper were made available, and Keitel decided that 30 were to be immediately fitted with 15cm SFH at Krefeld, while the remainder be divided between Panzerjäger and 15cm sFH, and were to be assembled in Paris. In May 1942, sixty 10.5cm leFH18/4 were ordered to be mounted on the Lorraine Schlepper, but, only 12 were completed. One such vehicle, refitted with a Russian 122mm howitzer, was part of an armoured train captured in Burgundy in September 1944.

Specific features: The original Tracteur Blindé 37L was unmodified except for slight strengthening of the suspension units. Overhauled vehicles, encountered in 1944, featured a lengthened recoil spade, which, like the gun travel rest, could be operated from within the fighting compartment.

Combat service: First issued to the Panzerartillerie Abteilung of the 21st Panzer Division in North Africa. At the beginning of 1944, there were still fifty-four 15cm sFH in service on the Western Front.

789

790

791

Plates 789-790. 15cm sFH13/1(Sf) auf GW Lorraine Schlepper (f) (Sd Kfz 135/1). Plate 790 shows the large recoil spade.
Plate 791. GW Lorraine Schlepper rearmed with the Russian 122mm Field Howitzer Model 1938.
Plate 792. 15cm sFH13/1(Sf) auf GW Lorraine Schlepper (f) in North Africa.

792

793

795

Plates 793-795. Pz Kpfw B-2 740(f); Plate 794 shows the Schulfahrzeug (training) vehicle.

Panzerkampfwagen B-2 740(f)

Other designation: Char B-1 bis
Type: Captured medium tank

Manufacturer: Renault
Captured from French Army in 1940

Crew: 4	Engine: Renault 6cyl 16.5lit
Weight (tons): 32	300PS at 1,900rpm
Length (metres): 6.52	Gearbox: 5 forward, 1 reverse
Width (metres): 2.52	Speed (km/hr): 28
Height (metres): 2.88	Range (km): 150
	Radio: FuG5

Armament:	One 7.5cm KwK35(f) L/17	One 4.7cm KwK35(f) L/34	One 7.5mm MG(f)
Traverse:	none	360° (electric)	10° left 10° right
Elevation:	−15° +25°	−18° +18°	
Ammunition:	74	50	

Armour (mm/angle):	Front	Side	Rear	Top/Bottom
Turret:	56/0°	46/22½°	46/22½°	30/72½° & 90°
Superstructure:	60/20°	60/0°	55/0°	25/80° & 90°
Hull:	60/45°	60/0°	55/43°	20/90°
Gun mantlet:	56/round			

History: The Char B-1 bis was the principal medium tank of the French Army in 1940, some 365 having been built before the collapse in June. In addition, there were a number of vehicles on the production lines, including 35 of the Char B-1, which had 40mm rather than 60mm armour. A considerable number of these were captured in a serviceable condition, but because of limitations of the one-man turret, and performance, they were not immediately issued to German units. From 1942, they were refitted with a German radio set and issued to second-line units, mainly in the West. Some were converted to driver instruction vehicles by removing the turret. The designation was Pz Kpfw B-2 als Schulfahrzeug training vehicle.

Specific features: Vehicles issued to the German forces were generally unmodified, but could be identified by the 2 metre rod aerial to the left behind the turret. Some tanks were fitted with additional armour to the right of the turret front to protect the turret ring, and others had a modified cupola with an opening hatch.

Combat service: Issued to Heeres Panzer detachments in France from 1941, and used for occupation duties in Jersey and Guernsey. Also issued to the 14th and 21st Panzer Divisions when they were being reformed in 1943. The only specimens moved out of France were those with the 223rd Panzerkompanie which took four B-2 to Russia, the seven which the SS Division Prinz Eugen took to the Balkans and those mentioned above in Jersey and Guernsey.

Flammwagen auf Panzerkampfwagen B-2(f)

Type: Flame-thrower on captured heavy tank

60 converted from November 1941 to June 1942

Crew: 4

Weight (tons): 34
Length (metres): 6.86
Width (metres): 2.52
Height (metres): 2.88

Engine: Renault 6cyl 16.5lit 300PS at 1,900rpm
Gearbox: 5 forward, 1 reverse
Speed (km/hr): 28
Range (km): 150
Radio: FuG5

Armament:	One Flammen-werfer	One 4.7cm KwK35(f) L/34	One 7.5mm MG(f)
Traverse:	10° left 10° right	360° (electric)	10° left 10° right
Elevation:	−2° +10°	−18° +18°	
Ammunition:		50	

Armour (mm/angle):	Front	Side	Rear	Top/Bottom
Turret:	56/0°	46/22½°	46/22½°	30/72½° & 90°
Superstructure:	60/20°	60/0°	30/20°	25/80° & 90°
Hull:	60/45°	60/0°	30/43°	20/90°
Gun mantlet:	56/round			

History: In March 1941, an order was placed for a series of 25 flame-thrower assault tanks to be built on the basis of the captured Char B-1 bis. Production rate was supposed to be five in November and ten in December and January, depending upon the availability of serviceable tanks. The total order was increased to include a second series of 35. The flame-thrower was supplied by Koebe and was powered by a two-stroke motorcycle engine.

Specific features: The tanks converted to Flammwagen had the 7.5 cm hull gun removed and replaced by the flame-thrower mounted in a special ball mount. A new housing, with a Fahrersehklappe 50 driver's visor, was provided for the operator above the flame weapon. The flame fuel was carried in a large 30mm armoured tank fitted to the rear of the vehicle. The 2 metre rod aerial was mounted to the right of the flame weapon. Some vehicles had the commander's cupola removed.

Combat service: The 213th schwere Panzerabteilung, formed in late 1941, for occupation duties in Jersey and Guernsey, was given one platoon of Fl Wg B-2 in each of the two companies of normal Pz Kpfw B-2. The only unit to take the Fl Wg B-2 away from the Western Front was the 223rd schwere Panzerkompanie, which took twelve to the Crimea in the summer of 1942, and the 7th SS Freiwilligen Gebirgs Division Prinz Eugen, which operated in the

Plate 26 (Page 12). Vehicle in action.

796

Plates 796-797. Flammwagen auf Pz Kpfw B-2(f). Plate 796 shows the flame-projector that replaced the 75mm gun in the front of the hull; Plate 797 shows the armoured fuel tank for the flame-projector, built on to the rear of the vehicle.

797

Balkans. Nine Fl Wg B-2 were still in service with the 223rd schwere Panzerkompanie on 30 December 1944. While reforming in France during 1943, the 14th and 21st Panzer Divisions had been issued with them, but these were returned to depot before seeing action.

10.5cm leFH18/3 (Sf) auf Geschützwagen B-2(f)

Type: Self-propelled light field howitzer on captured heavy tank chassis

Manufacturer: Rheinmetall-Borsig

16 converted in 1942

Crew: 4

Weight (tons): 32.5
Length (metres): 7.5
Width (metres): 2.52
Height (metres): 3.05

Engine: Renault 6cyl 16.5lit 300PS at 1,900rpm
Gearbox: 5 forward, 1 reverse
Speed (km/hr): 28
Range (km): 150
Radio: FuG Spr f

Armament: One 10.5cm leFH18/3
Traverse: 15° left 15° right
Elevation: −4° +20°
Sight: Rblf36
Ammunition: 42

Armour (mm/angle):	Front	Side	Rear	Top/Bottom
Turret:	20/8°	20/15°	20/8°	open
Superstructure:	60/20°	60/0°	55/0°	25/80° & 90°
Hull:	60/45°	60/0°	55/43°	20/90°
Gun shield:	20/8°			

History: When the first 25 flame-thrower vehicles based on the Char B-1 bis were ordered in March 1941, it was planned to introduce artillery support for the units to which they were to be issued. As a result, in the same month an order for 16 10.5cm leFH18/3 (Sf) auf GW B-2 (f) were ordered, but, because of the slow delivery of serviceable tank chassis, the production of both the flame-thrower and the supporting self-propelled howitzer were delayed until late in 1941, and the 16 howitzer vehicles were not delivered until 1942.

Specific features: Unmodified Char B-1 bis chassis with turret replaced by a new fixed superstructure housing the 10.5cm leFH18.

Combat service: Issued to Panzerartillerie detachments serving in France in 1942.

Plate 798. 10.5cm leFH18/3(Sf) auf GW B-2(f), showing the modified hull front.

Plate 799. 10.5cm leFH18/3(Sf) auf GW B-2(f).
Plate 800. Geschützwagen B-2 vehicles on rail flats.

799

800

Panzerkampfwagen 35-S 739(f)

Other designation: Somua S—35
Type: Captured medium tank

Manufacturer: Somua
Captured from the French Army in 1940

Crew: 3	Engine: Somua V—8 190PS at 2,000rpm
Weight (tons): 20	
Length (metres): 5.46	Gearbox: 5 forward, 1 reverse
Width (metres): 2.11	Speed (km/hr): 37
Height (metres): 2.62	Range (km): 257
	Radio: FuG5

Armament: One 4.7cm KwK35(f) L/34   One 7.5mm MG31(f)

Traverse: 360° (electric)   10° left 10° right
Elevation: −18° +18°
Ammunition: 118   1,250

Armour (mm/angle):	Front	Side	Rear	Top/Bottom
Turret:	56/0°	46/22½°	46/22½°	30/72½° & 90°
Superstructure:	36/22°	35/22°	25/30°	20/82° & 90°
Hull:	36/round	10+25/0°	35/0° & 25/30°	20/90°

Gun mantlet: 56/round

History: About 400 Somua S—35 medium tanks were available to the French Army in 1940. Despite the limitation of the one-man turret, this tank was considered the best tank opposing the Germans. By mid 1941, a number had already been issued to units of the German Army. From 1941 until 1944, the 35-S was used to equip tank units in training. Because of losses during 1941 and 1942, a large number of 35-S were issued to units in secondary theatres and to those engaged against partisans. Some 35-S 'ohne Aufbau' (without superstructures) were issued as Fahrschulefahrzeug (driver-training vehicles).

Specific features: German-used Somua can be identified by the modified cupola with opening hatch, and the 2 meter aerial on the right-hand side behind the turret.

Combat service: The Pz Kpfw 35-S were issued to the same Panzer detachments as the 38H. Typical organization called for four 38H in each platoon, with the 35-S issued to the platoon commander. The 35-S was also issued to company and battalion commanders. The first unit to use them in action was the 211th Panzerabteilung which served in Finland in June 1941. Reforming units, such as the 21st and 25th Panzer Divisions, were issued with these tanks for a period during 1943. There were still twelve 35-S in service on 30 December 1944.

801

Plates 801-802. Pz Kpfw 35-S 739(f)—converted, in Plate 801, to Schulfahrzeug.
(Back Dust Jacket). Pz Kpfw 35-S 739(f) in action.

802

Panzerkampfwagen 38H 735(f)

Other designations: Hotchkiss H-35, H-38 and H-39
Type: Captured light tank

Manufacturer: Hotchkiss
Captured from the French Army in 1940

Crew: 2	Engine: Hotchkiss 6cyl 6lit
Weight (tons): 12	120PS at 2,800rpm
Length (metres): 4.22	Gearbox: 5 forward, 1 reverse
Width (metres): 2.14	Speed (km/hr): 36
Height (metres): 1.85	Range (km): 150
	Radio: FuG5

Armament: One 3.7cm KwK18(f) L/21 or   One 7.5mm MG31(f)
One 3.7cm KwK38(f) L/33
Traverse: 360° (hand)
Ammunition: 100   2,400

Armour (mm/angle):

	Front	Side	Rear	Top/Bottom
Turret:	45/0° & 25°	40/30°	40/30°	12/90°
Superstructure:	34/7° & round	34/20°	34/25°	22/88° & 90°
Hull:	29–34/30°	34/0°	22/30°	12/90°
Gun mantlet:	25/round			

History: The Hotchkiss was the French Army Cavalry tank which had been ordered in 1936. Although slightly larger than the Renault R–35, it had the same fighting ability and performance. The turret was also of the APXR type. Neither the French nor the Germans differentiated between the three different versions in manuals or organization reports. The original, so-called, 35H had a 3.48lit 75PS motor, and the L/21 gun. The 38H was similarly armed, but had the 120PS motor, while the 39H was armed with the longer L/33 gun. In May 1940, the French had more than 800 38H in service, and large numbers fell into German hands. Many of these, after some modification were issued to German units from 1941. Turretless 38H were also issued in large numbers as 'Artillerie Schlepper 38H(f)' and were also used as Munitionspanzer. In 1943, some 38H were fitted with various types of launcher for the 28cm Wurfgerät 40, to increase offensive power.

Specific features: All the Hotchkiss tanks taken into German service had the commander's observation cupola replaced by an opening split hatch. German radio sets were fitted, with a 2 meter rod aerial mounted on a tripod on the front right-hand mudguard.

Combat service: From 1941, the Pz Kpfw 38H was issued to newly-formed units and to units being reformed in France after destruction in earlier actions. The 211th Panzerabteilung with its 38H, attacked across Finland in the summer of 1941, and was the first German unit to see action with French equipment. Other units with 38H were also sent to Norway and the Balkans from 1941 to 1943, including 10 independent platoons to fight partisans in the Balkans. Twenty-nine 38H were still in service on 30 December 1944.

803

804

Plate 803. Pz Kpfw 38H with short gun in Russia.
Plate 804. Pz Kpfw 38H with long gun on operations against Yugoslav partisans in 1944.
Plate 805. Pz Kpfw 38H with the short gun being used as a training vehicle.

805

Plate 806. Pz Kpfw 39H.

Plate 807. Munitionsschlepper 38H.

Plate 808. 28/32cm Wurfrahmen auf Pz Kpfw 35H, consisting of a frame with two metal projectors bolted to movable plates, one frame being attached to each side of the vehicle as permanent fittings. Elevations of the launchers was achieved with the plates, the rockets being aimed by manoeuvering the vehicle.

Plate 809. Generalfeldmarschall Erwin Rommel inspecting a Pz Kpfw 39H fitted with schweres Wurfrahmen 40 rocket-launching frames. This device was similar to that fitted on the Sd Kfz 251/1 (page 170). Three racks were attached to each side of the vehicle, and they were designed to act both as container and launcher for the rockets. The pivoting plates within the sWR40 frames were adjustable for elevations from 5° to 45°, and the rockets were aimed by manoeuvering the vehicle.

Plate 810. Pz Kpfw 35H(f) mit 28/32cm Wurfrahmen launching a rocket. The vehicle to the left is a UE Chenillette carrying the crated rockets.

7.5cm PaK40(Sf) auf Geschützwagen 39H(f)
10.5cm leFH18(Sf) auf Geschützwagen 39H(f)

Type: Self-propelled anti-tank gun / light field howitzer on captured light tank chassis

24 converted to carry the 7.5cm PaK40 in 1942
48 converted to carry the 10.5cm leFH18

Crew: 4

Weight (tons): 12.5

Engine: Hotchkiss 6cyl 6lit
   120PS at 2,800rpm
Gearbox: 5 forward, 1 reverse
Speed (km/hr): 36
Range (km): 150
Radio: FuG Spr d

Armament: One 7.5cm One 10.5cm leFH18 One 7.92mm MG34
  PaK40 L/46 or   L/28
Traverse: 30° left   loose
  30° right
Elevation: −5° +22°   loose
Sight: ZF3×8   Rblf36   direct

Armour (mm/angle):	Front	Side	Rear	Top/Bottom
Turret:	20/30°	20/10°	10/25°	open
Superstructure:	20/30°	20/40°	10/20°	
Hull:	29–34/30°	34/0°	22/30°	12/90°
Gun shield:	20/30°			

History: These self-propelled guns were built to the same specifications as the Sd Kfz 135 Lorraine Schlepper, but were fitted with an armoured superstructure of greater thickness. The leFH18 and the Panzerjäger conversion were unusual, in that the engine was left at the rear in the same way as the 7.5cm PaK40/2 auf Fgst Pz Kpfw II (Sf). The complete superstructure and engine cover were removed, and a new plate for the driver was fitted as part of the new self-propelled gun conversion. Photographic evidence also shows that some vehicles were fitted with the older 10.5cm leFH16.

Specific features: Extensive conversion, using just the hull pan and nose armour of the original Hotchkiss tank. Photographic evidence indicates components of the older 35H on at least one Panzerjäger.

Combat service: The leFH18 were issued to the 8th Panzerartillerie Abteilung serving in France, and were in action during 1944. The Panzerjäger were also issued to units in France.

813

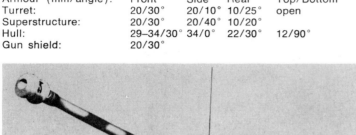

811

814

812

815

Plates 811-812. 7.5cm PaK40(Sf) auf GW 39H(f).
Plates 813-814. 10.5cm leFH18(Sf) auf GW 39H(f).
Plate 815. 10.5cm leFH16(Sf) auf GW 39H(f).

10.5cm leFH16(Sf) auf Geschützwagen FCM(f)
7.5cm PaK40(Sf) auf Geschützwagen FCM(f)

Type: Self-propelled anti-tank gun / light field howitzer on captured light tank chassis

12 converted to 10.5cm leFH16 in 1942
10 converted to 7.5cm PaK40 in 1943

Crew: 4
Weight (tons): 12.8
Length (metres): 4.77
Width (metres): 2.1
Height (metres): 2.23

Engine: Berliet MDP diesel
  4cyl 83PS
Gearbox: 4 forward, 1 reverse
Speed (km/hr): 24
Range (km): 225
Radio: FuG Spr d

Armament: One 7.5cm PaK40
  L/46 or
Sight: ZF3 × 8

One 10.5cm leFH16 L/22

Rblf36

Armour (mm/angle):	Front	Side	Rear	Top/Bottom
Turret:	20/10°	20/25°	10/	open
Superstructure:	20/10°	20/45° & 10°	20/65°	20/90°
Hull:	40/20°	20+20/0° & 20°	40/	12/90°
Gun shield:	20/10°			

History: The FCM36 tank was a light infantry support vehicle similar to the Renault R35, but its high purchase price caused the French Army to reduce its order to 100 vehicles. These equipped two battalions near Sedan in May 1940. The conversion of the first 12 of these tanks took place in 1942 and, like the 15cm sFH13 on the Lorraine Schlepper, the 10.5cm leFH16 was an old Krupp weapon which had been replaced by the Rheinmetall leFH18 from 1935. The conversion of the diesel FCM was complex, and production was limited to re-equipping Panzer Brigade West.

Specific features: Armoured superstructure mounted in the middle of the tank chassis, the engine rear deck remaining uncovered to the rear. The frontal armour layout of the Panzerjäger was made up of two armour plates.

Combat service: Served in France.

Plate 816. 7.5cm PaK40(Sf) auf GW FCM(f).
Plate 817. 10.5cm leFH(Sf) auf GW FCM(f).

816

817

Panzerkampfwagen 35R 731(f)

Other designation: Renault R35
Type: Captured light tank

Manufacturer: Renault
Captured from French Army in 1940

Crew: 2
Weight (tons): 10
Length (metres): 4.02
Width (metres): 1.87
Height (metres): 1.94

Engine: Renault 4cyl 5.8lit
  80PS at 2,200rpm
Gearbox: 4 forward, 1 reverse
Speed (km/hr): 20
Range (km): 140
Radio: FuG5

Armament: One 3.7cm KwK18(f)
  L/21
Traverse: 360° (hand)
Ammunition: 58

One 7.5mm MG31(f)

360° (hand)
2,400

Armour (mm/angle):	Front	Side	Rear	Top/Bottom
Turret:	45/0° & 25°	40/30°	40/30°	12/90°
Superstructure:	32/15° & round	40/10°	40/11°	13/90°
Hull:	32/round	40/0°	40/35°	14/90°
Gun mantlet:	45/round			

History: The Renault R35 was the main infantry tank of the French Army, and was issued to the independent tank battalions which supported the infantry divisions. First ordered in January 1935, there were 870 available in May 1940. Despite heavy losses, a considerable number were captured intact. They were modified to German requirements, and a number were issued to troops operating in secondary theatres or against partisans. A considerable number had their turrets removed and were issued as 'Artillerie Schlepper 35R(f)' or 'Munitionsschlepper 35R(f)' Their other main use was as the basis of a self-propelled anti-tank gun, and some were exported to Italy in 1941.

Specific features: The tanks issued to German units had the turret observation dome removed and replaced by an opening hatch. A radio set was fitted with its aerial mounted on the front left-hand mudguard. The Artillerie Schlepper/Munitionsschlepper were turretless and unarmed, though some were fitted with a small shield for an MG34.

Combat service: Pz Kpfw 35R were issued to only one regular unit of the Panzer troops, the reforming 100th Panzerbrigade of the 21st Panzer Division (New), in 1943. These returned to the depot after a few months. Six platoons of 35R were sent to the Channel Islands in 1941 and, also in 1941, twenty-six 35R were issued as Command-vehicles to the Panzerjäger detachments equipped with 4.7cm PaK(t) auf Pz Kpfw 35R(f). A number of other 35R were scattered among infantry divisions garrisoned in France.

Plate 818. Pz Kpfw 35R(f).

(Continued overleaf.)

4.7cm PaK(t) auf Panzerkampfwagen 35R(f) ohne Turm

Type: Self-propelled anti-tank gun on captured tank chassis

Plate 822. 4.7cm PaK(t) auf Pz Kpfw 35R.

Manufacturer: Alkett
174 converted from May 1941 to October 1941

Crew: 3	Engine: Renault 4cyl 5.8lit
Weight (tons): 10.5	80PS at 2,200rpm
Length (metres): 4.3	Gearbox: 4 forward, 1 reverse
Width (metres): 1.87	Speed (km/hr): 19
Height (metres): 2.11	Range (km): 140
	Radio: FuG Spr d

Armament: One 4.7cm PaK(t) L/43.4
Traverse: $17\frac{1}{2}°$ left $17\frac{1}{2}°$ right (hand)
Elevation: $-8°$ $+12°$
Sight: ZF2×30

Armour (mm/angle):	Front	Side	Rear	Top/Bottom
Turret:	20/30°	10/10°	10/0°	open
Superstructure:	32/15° & 40/10° round		40/11°	15/90°
Hull:	32/round	40/0°	40/35°	14/90°
Gun shield:	20/30°			

History: On 25 December 1940, the Renault R35 was ordered to replace the Pz Kpfw I as the chassis to carry the 4.7cm PaK(t) when the conversion of those vehicles would cease in February 1941. Like the Pz Kpfw I, the R35 was a two-man tank of limited fighting potential. A mild steel prototype was delivered on 8 February 1941.

The first order was for 130 units, but this was continued in July 1941 by a further 70. This was Germany's second Panzerjäger (Sf) and protection was improved over and above the Panzerjäger I, by having a fully-enclosed, but open-topped superstructure. Twenty-six normal Pz Kpfw 35R were issued as Command vehicles alongside the Sf.

Specific features: Large open-topped fixed superstructure replaced the turret, and storage space was increased by extending this over the engine compartment. The 4.7cm PaK(t) was the Czech anti-tank gun which had been introduced in 1938, before the incorporation of Bohemia and Moravia into the Reich.

Combat service: 174 4.7cm PaK(t) auf Pz Kpfw 35R and 26 command vehicles were issued to the Panzerjäger detachments stationed in secondary theatres. By May 1942, 183 were in service, the remainder having been re-converted to Artillerie Schlepper. At the start of 1944, 110 units were in service, mainly in France, with a few in the Channel Islands.

Plates 823-824. 4.7cm PaK(t) auf Pz Kpfw 35R. Note how the rear of the superstructure is built over the engine compartment. Plate 824 shows a vehicle in France, during 1944.

823

824

8cm schwere Granatwerfer 34 auf Panzerspähwagen AMR35(f)

Other designation: Renault ZT
Type: Self-propelled mortar on captured tracked reconnaissance vehicle

Crew: 4
Weight (tons): 9
Length (metres): 4.3
Width (metres): 1.8
Height (metres): 1.8

Engine: Renault 4cyl 5.8lit
82PS at 2,200rpm
Gearbox: 4 forward, 1 reverse
Speed (km/hr): 50
Range (km): 200
Radio: FuG Spr a

Armament: One 8cm sGrW34
Traverse: hand
Elevation:
Sight: RA35

One 7.92mm MG34
loose
loose
direct

Armour (mm/angle):	Front	Side	Rear	Top/Bottom
Turret:	13/15°	13/40°	10/10°	open
Superstructure:	10/20°	10/32°	10/10°	
Hull:	13/8°	10/0°	10/0°	6/90°

History: This was the first conversion based on a French chassis. The Renault ZT was the French Army's tracked reconnaissance vehicle or AMR35. In May 1940, 200 units were in service. The conversion involved the removal of the entire fighting compartment and engine superstructure, and its replacement by an open-topped superstructure which was wider and higher.

Specific features: Bolted superstructure with large opening door in rear. The mortar was mounted in the turret ring, with the ammunition in the former fighting compartment of the tank.

Combat service: Served with units in France.

Plates 825-826. 8cm s GrW 34 auf Pz Sp Wg AMR35(f).
Plate 827. A modified version of the AMR35(f) mortar vehicle, with a cupola atop the superstructure and a small armoured cab at the rear.

825

826

827

Infanterie Schlepper UE 630(f)

Other designation: Renault UE/AMX UE
Type: Captured tracked infantry carrier

Manufacturer: Renault
Captured from the French Army in 1940

Crew: 2
Weight (tons): 2
Length (metres): 2.7
Width (metres): 1.7
Height (metres): 1.03

Engine: Renault 85 4cyl
Gearbox: 3 forward, 1 reverse
Speed (km/hr): 30
Range (km): 180
Radio: none

Armament: One 3.7cm PaK35/36 or 4 × 28/32cm Wurfrahmen 40
Traverse: 30° left 30° right (hand) 360° (vehicle tracks)
Elevation: −8° +25°
Sight: ZF1 × 11   RA35
Ammunition: 4 Wurfgranate

Armour (mm/angle):	Front	Side	Rear	Top/Bottom
Superstructure:	7/	7/	4/	7/
Hull:	7/	7/	4/	4/90°

829

History: More than 6,000 UE tractors were in service in the French Army in May 1940—production having started as early as 1931 at Renault, and 1936, at AMX. The German Army used the UE as a Munitionsschlepper or le Schlepper from 1941. It was then used for a vast variety of miscellaneous tasks. Armoured conversions were carried out, to mount a 7.92mm MG34 for police and airfield security duties, and in 1941 it was the basis of a light Panzerjäger mounting the 3.7cm PaK. In 1943, a considerable number of UE were fitted with four Wurfrahmen 40 so as to give increased bombardment potential to the German forces in France. The Wurfrahmen 40 were mounted either on each side of the vehicle like the Sd Kfz 251, or in a rack of four over the load tray at the rear.

Specific features: Very light armoured supply vehicle. The crew sat to either side of the engine and transmission, and the load was carried in an open tray to the rear.

Combat service: While Panzerjäger PaK34/36 served with infantry units, the bulk of UE served with Security Units. The Wurfrahmen were issued to Panzerpionier companies in France in 1943/44.

830

831

Plate 828. Infanterie Schlepper UE.
Plates 829-830. Armoured conversions of the UE, mounting one MG34 machine-gun (Plate 829) and two MG34s (Plate 830).
Plate 831. Mun Schl UE(f) für RW (fitted with Wurfrahmen 40 frames).
Plate 832. Mun Schl UE towing a trailer on the Eastern Front.

828

832

833

834

Plates 833-834. Infanterie Schlepper UE(f) mit 28/32cm Wurfrahmen. This version of the rocket-launching UE carried the crated rockets on a raised platform, which could be raised or lowered for elevation, at the rear of the vehicle. Note the sighting vane on the front of the vehicle.

Plate 835. The UE(f) as a mobile mount for a dummy wooden tank.

Plates 836-837. 3.7cm PaK35/36 auf Infanterie Schlepper UE(f).

Plates 838-839. UE converted to an armoured light gun tractor.

837

838

835

836

839

FRENCH AFVS IN GERMAN SERVICE   223

Leichte Schützenpanzerwagen U304(f)

Other designation: Unic Kegresse P107
Type: Semi-tracked light armoured personnel carrier on captured chassis

Converted in 1943 and 1944
Crew: 2
Weight (tons): 5
Length (metres): 4.85
Width (metres): 1.8

Engine: Unic P39 4cyl 3.4lit
   60PS at 2,800rpm
Gearbox: 4 × 2 forward,
      1 × 2 reverse
Speed (km/hr): 45
Range (km): 400
Radio: FuG Spr d

Armour (mm/angle):	Front	Side	Rear	Top/Bottom
Superstructure:	10/30°	8/20°	8/10°	open
Hull:	10/20°	8/20°	8/10°	8/90°

History: The leichter Zgkw 37 Unic(f), or leichter Zgkw U304(f), was in service with the Wehrmacht from 1941 as an artillery tractor for anti-tank guns including the 7.5cm PaK40, and artillery pieces such as the 10.5cm leFH18. Initially, an armoured superstructure was fitted behind the driver's cab, but in 1943, many of the tractors were fully armoured with a body similar to that of the Sd Kfz 250. Later conversions had a simplified armour body. These vehicles were used as ambulances and personnel carriers.
Specific features: Kegresse trackwork similar to the larger Somua S307(f), but with an anti-ditching roller under the front nose armour.
Combat service: Issued to armoured infantry units serving in France.

840

Plates 840-842. Le SPW U304(f); the vehicle in Plate 840 has been converted to an armoured ambulance.

841

842

Mittlere Gepanzerter Zugkraftwagen S303(f)
Mittlere Schützenpanzerwagen S307(f)

Other designation: Somua MCG/Somua MCL
Type: Semi-tracked medium armoured personnel carrier on captured chassis

Plate 843. Mittlerer Schützenpanzerwagen S307(f).

SPW converted in 1943
Reihenwerfer converted in 1943
Sixteen 7.5cm PaK40(Sf) converted in 1944
Crew: 3/4
Weight (tons): 8.5
Length (metres): 5.76
Width (metres): 2.1
Height (metres): 2.04

Engine: Somua 4cyl 4.7lit
   60PS at 2,000rpm
Gearbox: 5 forward, 1 reverse
Speed (km/hr): 36
Range (km): 170
Radio: FuG Spr d

Armament:	16 × 8.1cm GrW(f) or	One 7.5cm PaK40	One 7.92mm MG34 or 42
Traverse:	360° (hand)	hand	loose
Elevation:	−40° +85°		loose
Sight:	RA35	ZF3 × 8	direct
		L/46	

Armour (mm/ angle):	Front	Side	Rear	Top/Bottom
Superstructure:	10/23°	10/0°	10/20°	
Hull:	10/30°	10/0°		6/90°
Gun shield:	20/30°	10/10°	open	open

History: From late 1940, the German Army used the captured French Somua MCG, as the 'Le Zgkw S307(f)', to tow artillery pieces. From 1943, in an effort to increase the armoured equipment available to the forces stationed in France, a considerable number of the Somua were converted with an armoured body to 'm SPW S307(f)'. At the

844

same time, a self-propelled multiple mortar was created by mounting 16 French 81mm mortars in two rows at the rear of the m SPW. The mortars could be preloaded for simultaneous automatic firing. In 1944, 16 vehicles were converted to Panzerjäger by mounting the 7.5cm PaK40 (Sf). The PaK40 was mounted to the rear over the trackwork, with the driver ahead of the gun shield, so the appearance of these units was different from the basic m SPW. After the war, a French experimental establishment showed an armoured Somua mounting the 15cm Panzerwerfer 42, similar to the Maultier. A similar armoured vehicle was created from the Somua MCL—m Zgkw S303(f). The MCL was a more powerful tractor with a 6-cylinder 105PS engine. At Rouen in May 1944, versions with the 8cm R-Vielfachwerfer (multiple rocket launcher) and Reihenwerfer (tiered launcher) were demonstrated. The R-Vielfachwerfer was the launcher for 24 fin-stabilized rockets adopted by the Waffen SS. The Rheinwerfer on the S303 was fitted with 20 mortars.

Combat service: Served in France during 1944.

Plates 844–845. Mittlere Schützenpanzerwagen S307(f) mit Reihenwerfer multiple mortars.
Plates 846-847. 7.5cm PaK40 L/46 auf m SPW S307(f).
Plates 848-849. 8cm R-Vielfachwerfer auf m gep Zgkw S303(f).
Plate 850. 15cm Panzerwerfer 42 auf gepanzerter MTW Somua.

848

845

849

846

847

850

Panzerspähwagen Panhard 178-P204(f)

Other designation: Panhard P-178
Type: Captured armoured car

Manufacturer: Panhard
Captured from the French Army in 1940

Crew: 4	Engine: Panhard SK 4cyl 6.33lit
Weight (tons): 8.5	105PS at 2,000rpm
Length (metres): 4.79	Gearbox: 4 forward, 4 reverse
Width (metres): 2.01	Speed (km/hr): 72
Height (metres): 2.31	Range (km): 300
	Radio: FuG Spr Ger 'a'

Armament: One 2.5cm KwK(f)   One 7.5mm MG31(f)
L/73
Traverse: 360° (hand)   10° left
Elevation: −12° +14°   −12° +15°
Ammunition: 150   3,750

Armour (mm/angle):	Front	Side	Rear	Top/Bottom
Turret:	26/24°	15/26°	15/30°	7/82°
Superstructure:	20/21°	15/0°	15/3°	7/87°
Hull:	20/0°	15/0°	15/41°	7/90°
Gun mantlet:	26/round			

History: The Panhard P-178 was the most advanced medium armoured car of the French Army when the German forces invaded France. In 1940, 360 units were already in service, and a large number of these were captured by the Wehrmacht in a serviceable condition. Before the start of Operation Barbarossa in June 1941, 190 Panhard cars were issued un-modified to German units. In addition to the standard Pz Sp Wg, there was the radio-vehicle which served in small numbers as Pz Sp Wg (Fu). Forty-three cars were converted as railway-protection vehicles, fitted with rail wheels, and additional radio equipment which necessitated a frame aerial. The final development was the conversion in 1943 of some cars to a self-propelled gun, by removing the turret and replacing it by an armoured superstructure mounting the German 5cm KwK L/42, which was available in numbers following the up-gunning of the Pz Kpfw III.

Specific features: Four-wheel drive chassis, specially designed for use as an armoured car. The large wheels gave good off road performance.

Combat service: Issued to reconnaissance companies from 1941, 107 lost in action during 1941.

Plate 851. The original French Panhard P-178 command vehicle in service with the Waffen SS.
Plate 852. Pz Sp Wg Panhard 178-P204(f). Note that this particular vehicle mounts two machine-guns.
Plates 853-854. Pz Sp Wg (Fu) Panhard 178-P204(f). The vehicles in Plate 853 have been modified to German standard, with frame aerial and spaced armour, while that in Plate 854 has been adapted to run on railway lines.
Plate 855. 5cm KwK L/42 auf Pz Sp Wg 178-P204(f).

852

853

854

851

855

Panzerkampfwagen FT-17/18 730(f)

Other designation: Renault FT17 and FT18
Type: Captured light tank

History: Large numbers of these old tanks, dating from the First World War, were captured by the German Army during the advance into France. Because of the general shortage of equipment after the Invasion of Russia, a considerable number of the FT17/18 were issued for security and police duties. Carried aboard railway wagons, they provided protection from partisans.

856

857

858

Plates 858-859. 19.4cm Kanone 485(f) GPF, a French First World War design produced in the mid-thirties. It consisted of a 194mm gun on a self-propelled mounting, and was designated by the French 'Canon de 194 mle GPF sur Chenilles'. A number of these were taken into service by the German Army, and Plate 859 shows one of them on the Eastern Front.

859

Plate 860. Pouche de La Rochelle 7.5cm PaK40(Sf), a German field improvization that appeared during the siege of La Rochelle in France. It consisted of a 7.5cm PaK40 mounted on an armoured tractor.

860

Italian AFVs in German service

Panzerkampfwagen M13/40 735(i) und M14/41 736(i)

Other designation: Carro Armato M13/40 and M14/41
Type: Captured medium tank

Manufacturer: FIAT-Ansaldo
22 Pz Kpfw M13/40 and 1 Pz Kpfw M14/41

Crew: 4	Engine: 8 T V–8 diesel
Weight (tons): 14.3	125PS at 1,800rpm
Length (metres): 4.92	Gearbox: 4 forward, 1 reverse
Width (metres): 2.23	Speed (km/hr): 32
Height (metres): 2.39	Range (km): 200
	Radio: RF 1 CA

Armament: One 4.7cm   One 8mm MG38(i)   Two 8mm MG38(i)
 KwK47/32(i) L/32
Traverse: 360° (hand)   28° (hand)
Elevation: −15° +25°   −15° +23°
Ammunition: 87   2,592

Armour (mm/angle):	Front	Side	Rear	Top/Bottom
Turret:	37/16°	25/22°	25/22°	14/85°
Superstructure:	30/11°	25/9°	25/0°	14/90°
Hull:	30/round	25/0°	25/20°	6/90°
Gun mantlet:	37/round			

History: The M13/40 was ordered for the Italian Army in January 1940, and was in service by the second half of that year. A total of 785 were built and these were followed by 895 of the improved model M14/41 from mid 1941 until early 1943. The M14/41 differed little from the M13/40 except for the 15 TM41 motor, which developed 145PS at 1,800 rpm. After the German occupation of Italy in September 1943, a small number of the surviving tanks of this type were confiscated for use by the German Army. The remainder served with the R.S.I. armoured units.

Combat service: These tanks were issued to two SS Sturmgeschütz detachments and also to Panzerabteilung Adria. On 30 December 1944, there were 68 tanks of the M13/40, M14/41 and M15/42 still in service with German units.

Plate 861. Carro Armato M13/40.

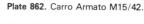

Plate 862. Carro Armato M15/42.

Panzerkampfwagen M15/42 738(i)

Other designation: Carro Armato M15/42
Type: Captured medium tank

Manufacturer: FIAT-Ansaldo
28 produced in 1944
92 confiscated from Italian Army in September 1943

Crew: 4	Engine: 15TB V–8 petrol
Weight (tons): 14.7	185PS at 2,400rpm
Length (metres): 5.04	Gearbox: 5 forward, 1 reverse
Width (metres): 2.23	Speed (km/hr): 38
Height (metres): 2.39	Range (km): 180
	Radio: RF 1 CA

Armament: One 4.7cm   One 8mm MG38(i)   Two 8mm MG38(i)
 KwK 47/40(i) L/40
Traverse: 360° (electric)   28° (hand)
Elevation: −15° +25°   −15° +25°
Ammunition: 111   3,048

Armour (mm/angle):	Front	Side	Rear	Top/Bottom
Turret:	12+37/16°	25/22°	25/22°	14/85°
Superstructure:	12+30/11°	25/9°	25/0°	14/90°
Hull:	30/round	25/0°	25/20°	6/90°
Gun mantlet:	37/round			

History: In 1943, the Italian Army received an updated model of their medium tank. Designated M15/42, it featured slightly heavier frontal armour, a longer gun and a new, more powerful motor. The motor was now petrol-driven because of a shortage of diesel fuel in Italy. Italian sources indicate that only 82 had been delivered to the Italian Army before September 1943, and these were used in the defence of Rome against the Germans. A further 30 new vehicles were available, and the German Army was thus able to take over 92 tanks.

Specific features: Heavier frontal armour achieved by the addition of a 12mm plate. The gun was increased in length to L/40 from L/32, and performance was substantially improved. To accommodate the larger petrol engine, the hull length was increased, and to support it, the suspension bogies were moved apart. The M15/42 is clearly distinguished from the earlier M13/40 and M14/41 by the location of the access door on the right-hand side of the superstructure.

Panzerkampfwagen P40 737(i)

Other designation: Carro Pesante P26/40
Type: Captured medium tank

Manufacturer: FIAT-Ansaldo
5 pre-series vehicles confiscated from Italian Army in September 1943.
100 built in 1943 and 1944

Crew: 4	Engine: SPA V–12 diesel 25lit
Weight (tons): 26	330PS at 2,100rpm
Length (metres): 5.8	Gearbox: 5 forward, 1 reverse
Width (metres): 2.8	Speed (km/hr): 42
Height (metres): 2.5	Range (km): 275
	Radio: RF 1 CA

Armament: One 7.5cm One 8mm MG38(i)   One 8mm MG38(i)
         75/34

Traverse: 360° (electric)			loose	
Elevation: −10° +23°			loose	
Sight:			direct	
Ammunition: 65	576			

Armour (mm/angle):	Front	Side	Rear	Top/Bottom
Turret:	60/15°	45/25°	40/25°	20/82° & 90°
Superstructure:	50/45°	45/35°	40/10°	20/83° & 90°
Hull:	50/55°	40/0°	40/40°	15/90°
Gun mantlet:	60/round			

History: The Italian Army had been developing this heavy tank since 1940. By early 1943, 500 P40 armed with the 75/34 gun had been ordered. FIAT had proposed to improve production models by fitting a new 420PS petrol engine, while the Italian Army wished to fit the German Maybach HL120. In September 1943, five pre-series vehicles fell into German hands together with the materials to complete more than 200 tanks. At a conference with Hitler on 23 September 1943, it was pointed out that the armour of this tank was the best of any captured vehicle and the gun had moderate performance. Because of the unsatisfactory engine, it was proposed to fit the Maybach

Combat service: The Pz Kpfw M15/42 were issued to three Heeres Panzer Detachments and to the Volunteer Cavalry Division of the 22nd SS 'Maria Theresa' which was formed with Hungarian volunteers in April 1944. By 30 December 1944, there were still 68 Italian medium tanks M13/40, M14/41 and M15/42 still in service with the German forces.

Plate 863. Carro Armato P40.

as quickly as possible with a view to using these tanks as the equipment for four Panzerartillerie regiments, 36 tanks for each. An order for 75 P40 was immediately placed and again, on 5 October, another 75 were ordered. But the engine problems were never satisfactorily resolved. Out of the 100 P40 built up to 30 March 1945, only 60 could be supplied with the original diesel engine. However, a number of the P40 without engines were pressed into service as static fortifications at Anzio and on the Gustav line. A German report indicates that 100 P40 turrets were available for use in fortifications, but it is not clear if these were additional to the tanks which had been completed without engines.

Combat service: The 5 pre-series vehicles were issued to the Panzer Ausbildung Abteilung South—the training unit of Army Group C.

Panzerbefehlswagen M41 771(i) / Panzerbefehlswagen M42 772(i)

Other designation: Carro Commando M41/M42
Type: Captured tracked armoured command vehicle

Manufacturer: FIAT-Ansaldo
41 produced from 1943 to 1945
16 confiscated from Italian Army in September 1943

Crew: 4	Engine: 15 TB V–8
Weight (tons): 13.3	185PS at 2,400rpm
Length (metres): 5.04	Gearbox: 5 forward, 1 reverse
Width (metres): 2.23	Speed (km/hr): 40
Height (metres): 1.82	Range (km): 200
	Radio: RF 1 CA & RF 2 CA
	or RF 3M2

Armament: One 13.2mm MG31(i)   One 8mm MG38(i)

Traverse: 13° left 13° right (hand)		loose	
Elevation: −8° +20°		loose	
Sight:		direct	
Ammunition: 420		1,560	

Armour (mm/angle):	Front	Side	Rear	Top/Bottom
Superstructure:	30/11°	25/9°	25/0°	15/90°
Hull:	30/round	25/0°	25/9°	15/90°

History: The Italian Carro Commando was a command-vehicle for controlling Semovente units. Basically, the initial model was a furretless M13/40 tank. The M41 and M42 were the models which fell into German hands. The M41 was a turretless M14/41 tank fitted with a heavy MG. It weighed 12.5 tonnes, had a shorter chassis (4.92m) and was powered by the 145PS diesel engine. Late in 1942, the M42 was introduced, based on the chassis of the M15/42 tank. In addition to the 16 vehicles confiscated, material was available to build a further 89. Italian sources claim that production continued under German control and that Pz Bef Wg M42 were supplied both to German and R.S.I. units.

Plate 864. Carro Commando Semovente M42.

Specific features: Turretless tank chassis with additional radio equipment. The RF 1 CA was the standard Italian inter-tank radio, the RF 2 CA was for Command group communications, and the RF 3M2, when fitted, was for ground-to-air control. Their conspicuous silhouette and poor visibility, made these Pz Bef Wg unpopular with their crews.
Combat service: Served in Italy and the Balkans in 1944.

Plate 865. Carro Commando Semovente M41.
Plate 866. Pz Kpfw P40 captured during the advance into Austria.

Sturmgeschütz M42 mit 75/18 850(i) / Sturmgeschütz M42 mit 75/34 851(i)

Other designations: Semovente DA 75/18, Semovente DA 75/34
Type: Captured assault gun

Manufacturer: FIAT-Ansaldo
123 StuGM42 mit 75/18 confiscated from Italian Army in September 1943
55 produced in 1943 and 1944
36 StuGM42 mit 75/34 confiscated and 80 produced in 1943 and 1944

Crew: 3
Weight (tons): 15
Length (metres): 5.04
  5.69 (with 75/34 gun)
Width (metres): 2.23
Height (metres): 1.85

Engine: 15 TB V–8 petrol
  185PS at 2,400rpm
Gearbox: 5 forward, 1 reverse
Speed (km/hr): 38
Range (km): 230
Radio: RF 1 CA

Armament:	One 7.5cm StuK 75/18(i) L/18 or	One 7.5cm StuK75/34 (i) L/34	One 8mm MG38(i)
Traverse:	20° left 20° right (hand)	16° left 18° right (hand)	loose
Elevation:	−12° +22°		
Ammunition:	44	42	loose 1,104

Armour (mm/angle):	Front	Side	Rear	Top/Bottom
Superstructure:	25+25/5°	25/9°	25/0°	10/84° & 90°
Hull:	30/round	25/0°	25/20°	15/90°
Gun mantlet:	50/round			

History: This series was a continuation of the successful Italian Semovente M40 and M41. The Sturmgeschütz M42 was developed early in 1943 on the basis of the Pz Kpfw M15/42 chassis for the 75/34 gun, but as this weapon was still under test in March 1943, the M42 was fitted with the short 75/18, and 200 such vehicles were ordered. Satisfactory trials with the 75/34 led to a further order for 500 equipped with the long gun. Many of those built for the Italian Army were confiscated for immediate use by the German Army in September 1943. At the Ansaldo Factory, material was available to build many more of each series, and the Germans continued production at a somewhat slower rate.

Specific features: Same chassis and power plant as for the M15/42 tank. The short 75/18 had already equipped previous Italian Semovente. On the M42 chassis, the suspension bogies were spaced

Plate 867. Semovente M42 DA 75/34, German designation StuG M42 mit 75/34.

Plates 868-870 (opposite page, top).
Plate 868. StuG M40 in service with the Afrika Korps.
Plate 869. Semovente M40/M41, designated StuG M40 und M41 mit 75/18 850(i) in German service.
Plate 870. StuG M42 captured by the Allies during the campaign in Italy.

867

further apart, and grills were fitted in the forward engine-cover hatches.

Combat service: A total of 294 StuG M42 were issued to German units in 1943 and 1944. On 31 December 1943, 191 were in service with six infantry divisions, two Panzer divisions, three Panzergrenadier divisions and one Jäger division, of Army Groups C and F, in Italy and the Balkans. By 30 December 1944, despite new deliveries, that number had been reduced to 93 as a result of battle losses.

868

869

870

Sturmgeschütz M43 mit 105/25 853(i)

Other designation: Semovente DA 105/25
Type: Captured assault howitzer

Manufacturer: FIAT-Ansaldo
91 produced in 1943 and 1944
26 confiscated from Italian Army in September 1943

Crew: 3	Engine: 15 TB V–8
Weight (tons): 15.7	185PS at 2,400rpm
Length (metres): 5.52	Gearbox: 5 forward, 1 reverse
Width (metres): 2.42	Speed (km/hr): 38
Height (metres): 1.74	Range (km): 180
	Radio: RF 1 CA

Plates 871-872. StuG M43 mit 105/25 853(i).

Armament: One 10.5cm StuK105/25(i) L/25 — One 8mm MG38(i)

Traverse: 18° left 18° right (hand)	loose	
Elevation: −10° +16°	loose	
Ammunition: 48	864	

Armour (mm/angle):	Front	Side	Rear	Top/Bottom
Superstructure:	75/0°	45/15°	25/0°	15/86° & 90°
(Late production):	25/20°+75/0°	15/0°+45/15°	25/0°	15/86°+90°
Hull:	50/55°	25/0°	25/13½°	15/90°
Gun mantlet:	50/round			

History: In 1942, the Italian Army considered mounting a 10.5cm gun on the chassis of their proposed medium tank P40. Delays to the P40, caused an alternative chassis, based on the M15/42 tank, to be ordered. To accommodate the 10.5cm, this chassis had to be widened and, therefore, became known as M43. In February 1943, 30 units were ordered, in April, a further 100 and by June, a total of 454 had been ordered. Only 26 of the first order fell into German hands, but material existed to manufacture many more, and German records indicate that it was intended to fit 80 with the 7.5cm 75/34 gun. On 5 October 1943, the Germans ordered sixty 105/25. Later, more were ordered and some of these were fitted with additional spaced armour on the superstructure front and sides.

Specific features: Same performance and components as the M15/42 tank, but the chassis was wider, with a new nose armour layout.

Combat service: On 31 December 1943, twenty-seven StuG M43 mit 105/25 were in service with the 336th Infantry Division and the 26th Panzer Division, in Italy. By 30 December 1944, 66 were still in service with Army Groups C and F in Italy and the Balkans.

Sturmgeschütz M43 mit 75/34 851(i)/Sturmgeschütz M43 mit 75/46 852(i)

Type: Captured assault gun / tank destroyer

29 StuG M43 mit 75/34 and 11 StuG M43 mit 75/34 produced in 1944 and 1945

Crew: 3	Engine: 15 TB V–8	
Weight (tons): 16	185PS at 2,400rpm	
Length (metres): 5.97	Gearbox: 5 forward, 1 reverse	
Width (metres): 2.45	Speed (km/hr): 38	
Height (metres): 1.74	Range (km): 180	
	Radio: RF 1 CA	

Armament: One 7.5cm StuK75/34(i) L/34 or	One 7.5cm StuK 75/46(i) L/46	One 8mm MG38(i)
Traverse: 18° left 18° right (hand)		loose
Elevation: −10° +20°		loose
Ammunition: 43		864

Armour (mm/angle):	Front	Side	Rear	Top/Bottom
Superstructure:	25/20° + 75/0°	15/0° + 45/15°	25/0°	15/86° & 90°
Hull:	50/55°	15 + 25/0°	25/13½°	15/90°
Gun mantlet:	50/round			

History: The Semovente 105/25 was the best Italian vehicle at the time of the German occupation, and the Germans ordered production to continue using the material already earmarked for the large Italian orders. By December 1943, tests had been carried out which indicated that the Sturmgeschütz M43 could be improved without loss of performance by the addition of spaced armour. Additionally, it was decided that the Italian 75/46 anti-aircraft gun was to be modified to have the characteristics and ammunition of the German PaK40. After the initial production of sixty 105/25 and eighty 75/34 on the M43, all these were to be rebuilt with the heavier armour and the 75/46 gun. However, production proceeded at a slower rate, because of the difficulties created by the Occupation, and additional M43 were fitted with the heavier armour and the 105/25, while a small number appeared with the 75/34 and the remainder were produced with the 75/46. Italian sources indicate that the total production of M43 in 1945 was 22. It was also intended to rebuild all StuG M42 with the 75/18, and later those with the 75/34, and to fit the 75/46 gun. The shorter superstructure of the M42 was to be modified, and a muzzle brake was to be added to the gun.

Combat service: Used in Italy in late 1944 and early 1945.

Plate 873. Semovente M43 DA 75/46, German designation StuG M43 mit 75/46 852(i).

Panzerspähwagen AB41 201(i)

Other designation: Autoblinda AB41
Type: Captured armoured car

Manufacturer: Ansaldo
37 confiscated from Italian Army in September 1943 with a further 20 in production
Total of 120 so-called AB41/43 produced from 1943 to 1945

Crew: 4	Engine: SPA Abm 1 6cyl petrol 5lit
Weight (tons): 7.5	88PS at 2,700rpm
Length (metres): 5.2	AB41/43 Abm 6cyl 5lit
Width (metres): 1.92	108PS at 2,800rpm
Height (metres): 2.48	Gearbox: 6 forward, 4 reverse
	Speed (km/hr): 78
	81 (AB41/43)
	Range (km): 400
	350 (AB41/43)
	Radio: RF 3 M

Plates 874-875. Pz Sp Wg AB41 201(i).

874

Armament: One 2cm M35(i) L/65	One 8mm MG38(i)	One 8mm MG38(i)
Traverse: 360° (hand)		14° left 14° right (hand)
Elevation: −10° +20°		−7° +14°
Ammunition: 456	1,992	

Armour (mm/angle):	Front	Side	Rear	Top/Bottom
Turret:	18/16°	9/20°	9/16°	6/90°
Superstructure:	9/23°	9/30°	9/20°	6/90°
Hull:	9/45°	9/0°	9/40°	6/90°
Gun mantlet:	18/round			

History: From 1941, the AB41 was the standard Italian heavy armoured car, succeeding the AB40 which was armed with MG only. The 2cm gun turret was very similar to that on the L6/40 tank. Before the German Occupation, a new AB43 had been tested. It had a 108PS motor and a new, wider superstructure to accommodate a larger turret with the 4.7cm 47/40 gun. Some sources claim that ten pre-series AB43 were built. All cars built after the Occupation were fitted with the new 100PS motor and were designated AB41/43. These vehicles had a new turret which could be fitted with either the 2cm M35 or a 5cm KwK.

Specific features: Driving positions at front and rear, with all-wheel drive and steering.

Combat service: Used by German Forces in Italy and the Balkans. A considerable number were issued to R.S.I. units.

875

Plates 876-877. Carro Armato L6/40, adopted by the Germans as Pz Kpfw L6/40 733(i).
Plate 878. Carro Commando Compagnia Semovente DA 47/32, German designation Pz Bef Wg 47/32 770(i).
Plates 879-880. Carro Veloce 35, German designation Pz Kpfw CV35 731(i).
Plate 881. Autocannone DA 75/27 CK su Ceirano 50 CMA, an Italian 75mm mobile anti-aircraft gun, a small number of which were taken over by the Germans during the fighting in the Western Desert.

Panzerkampfwagen L6/40 733(i)

Other designation: Carro Armato L6/40
Type: Light tank

History: This light tank was produced for the Italian Army from 1941 to February 1943. 283 were built and many were confiscated from the Italian Army in September 1943. Armed with a 2cm M35 and an 8mm MG, it was protected by armour of 40mm for frontal plates. The engine was a Spa18D 70PS. These tanks were issued to the Panzerabteilung Adria and to Police units. The remainder were exported to Croatia.

Sturmgeschütz L6 mit 47/32 770(i)

Other designation: Semovente L/40 DA47/32
Type: Light assault gun

History: About 300 of this light assault gun were built for the Italian Army from 1941 to 1943. 78 were confiscated by the Germans. The gun was the 4.7cm 47/32 and the mounting allowed traverse of 27° and −12°+20° elevation. Seventy rounds of 4.7cm ammunition was carried with a crew of 3. Sixteen of these StuG L6 were issued to the Pz Kp z b V12 (Armoured Company for Special Employment), and in 1944, many of the remainder were exported to the Croatian Army.

Panzerkampfwagen CV35 731(i)

Other designation: Carro Veloce 35
Type: Tankette

History: Since over 2,000 CV33 and CV35 had been built for the Italian Army, there were still considerable numbers available after the Germans had taken over in September 1943. Panzerabteilung Adria had some CV35 as late as 30 December 1944, but these CV were also used by Police and Organisation Todt units.

876

877

878

879

880

881

Captured enemy vehicles in German service

French and Italian armoured vehicles were included in the OKH lists because these occupied countries provided large numbers of armoured vehicles which could be maintained from existing stocks of spare parts. Furthermore, factories within the occupied territories were manufacturing both components and full vehicles for the German Army.

Armoured vehicles captured from other enemies were generally used by the front-line units which had captured them, and, with a few exceptions, were not converted or listed officially by the OKH. The major problem with any enemy vehicle was maintenance. In the case of a tracked vehicle, maintenance was the most important activity. Without spare parts and support, it was impossible to keep any tracked vehicle running for more than a short period. Unless large numbers of a particular type of vehicle were captured, it was not worthwhile attempting to establish any maintenance system. For this reason, even the French and Italian vehicles were generally kept in France and Italy.

Foreign vehicle designations were usually accompanied by Fremdgerät Numbers, which are explained and listed on page 267. Generally, this number was only retained if the vehicle remained unmodified when issued to German troops.

Great Britain

In North Africa, a small number of British vehicles were captured from time to time. These were used by DAK (Deutsches Afrika Korps) until they were lost. Matilda tanks could only be lost through lack of maintenance, because no British gun was capable of destroying them.

On the Atlantic Wall in France and The Low Countries during 1942 and 1943, a small number of British armoured vehicles were converted to self-propelled guns. These vehicles came from the stockpiles remaining since Dunkirk in 1940. They were used only by local garrison units in the areas of these stockpile dumps. Again, after the Invasion in July 1944, a small number of British vehicles were used by the German units which captured them.

5cm KwK L/42 (Sf) auf Infanterie Panzerkampfwagen Mk II 748(e)

Other designation: 5cm KwK auf Matilda (e)
Type: Self-propelled gun

History: When the 5cm KwK L/42 was replaced by the L/60 in the Pz Kpfw III, the older guns were made available mounted on a Sockellafette (pivoting mount). This was a pedestal mount for fixed fortifications. In the West, on the so-called Atlantic Wall in 1943, there was a great shortage of armour, and a number of old Matilda tanks were stripped of their turrets and converted to self-propelled guns by mounting the 5cm KwK.

10.5cm leFH16 (Sf) auf Leichte Panzerkampfwagen Mk IV 736(e)

Type: Self-propelled howitzer

History: A small number of these 5t vehicles were converted to self-propelled mounts for the old leFH16, without muzzle brake, L/22. Elevation was −18°+41°. A crew of four was carried. With the engine alongside the driver in the front, this chassis provided an easy conversion.

Gepanzerter Maschinengewehr Träger Bren 731(e)

Other designation: Bren-gun carrier / Universal Carrier
Type: Tracked carrier

History: The Germans utilized captured carriers for many purposes, as tractors and ammunition carriers. A small number were made into light Panzerjägers by mounting the 3.7cm PaK L/45 on a pedestal above the engine. Photographs of the 3rd Panzergrenadier Division show a number of carriers converted to light fighting units with three 8.8cm Raketenpanzerbüchse (anti-tank rocket launcher) 54 mounted over the engine.

Plates 882-888 (opposite page).
Plate 882. A number of Infantry Tanks Mk II (Matilda) were captured in the Western Desert and used by the German Army. The German designation was: Infanterie Panzerkampfwagen Mk II 748(e).
Plate 883. 5cm KwK L/42 (Sf) auf Inf Pz Kpfw Mk II 748(e).
Plate 884. Infantry Tank Mk III (Valentine), captured and used by the Germans in North Africa, under the designation Infanterie Panzerkampfwagen Mk III 749(e).
Plates 885-886. 10.5cm leFH16(Sf) auf le Pz Kpfw Mk IV 736(e). In Plate 886, note the folded recoil spade at the rear of the vehicle.
Plate 887. Gep MG Träger Br 732(e) — captured British carriers in use by the Germans on the Eastern Front.
Plate 888. Gep MG Träger Br 731(e) armed with a Maxim MG08 machine-gun on a pedestal mount. These vehicles were used by the Luftwaffe for airfield defence.

882

883

884 / 885

886

887 / 888

889

892

890

893

891

894

Plate 889. Schneeschaufel auf Bren (e)—a carrier converted into a snow-plough by removing the superstructure and fitting a small plough at the front.
Plate 890. 2cm FlaK38 auf Fahrgestell Bren (e). A number of carriers were modified for the 2cm FlaK38, with the gun and shield mounted on the engine compartment.
Plates 891-893. 3.7cm PaK auf Fahrgestell Bren (e). In Plate 892, the vehicle has a wooden superstructure.
Plate 894. Panzerjäger Bren—the carrier modified as a tank-hunter and equipped with three 8.8cm Raketenpanzerbüchse 43 or 54 rocket-launchers mounted on the engine compartment. Also carried were a number of Panzerfaust, Models 30 or 60, for use by the crew.

895

897

898

896 / 899

Plate 895. A line up of Panzerjäger Brens; the Panzerfaust rocket-launchers can be seen stored upright in the vehicles.
Plate 896. A Humber Mk II armoured car captured and used in the Western Desert.
Plate 897. An AEC armoured command vehicle in service with the DAK in the Western Desert.
Plate 898. A Marmon-Herrington armoured car captured by the German Army in North Africa and used as an armoured rail unit.
Plate 899. A Canadian 3ton Ford GS 4 x 4 truck captured in North Africa and utilized as a mobile mount for a 2cm FlaK30.

U.S.S.R.

During the four years of war in Russia, a great deal of Russian Army equipment fell into German hands. During the early period, most armoured vehicles were inferior obsolete designs which were discarded by the advancing German forces. In the defensive battles of the following years, the Russian armoured vehicles were generally put to good use by the units which captured them until, inevitably, they broke down and could not be repaired. Photographs clearly show the use to which Russian armour was put when captured by individual units. The official OKH lists show how insignificant they were in the overall picture.

902

	31 May 1943 (Before Kursk)	30 December 1944
Pz Kpfw T–26(r)	1	2
Pz Kpfw T–70(r)	4	2
Pz Kpfw KVI(r)	2	–
Pz Kpfw KVII(r)	1	–
Pz Kpfw T–34(r)	50	39 +

Of the fifty T–34 officially listed as available on 31 May 1943, only 17 were serviceable. Twenty-five of the fifty were allocated to the SS Division Das Reich. Of the 39 listed at the end of December 1944, twenty-nine were allocated to the 100 Ski Jäger Division.

Plate 900. Gepanzerter Artillerie Schlepper 630(r) (Russian artillery tractor STZ Komsomolets) used by the Germans to tow light field or PaK guns.
Plate 901. 3.7cm PaK auf gep Artillerie Schlepper 630(r), a field improvization that consisted of the 3.7cm PaK mounted on the STZ tractor.
Plates 902-903. Pz Kpfw T–26C 740(r).
Plate 904. 7.5cm PaK97/98 auf Beute Panzer T-26, an experimental equipment built in 1943 and consisting of a French 75mm gun Model 1897 on a Russian T-26 chassis.
Plate 905. Pz Kpfw BT 742(r)—a Russian BT 7 in German service.
Plates 906-908. Pz Kpfw T-34 747(r); that in Plate 907 is a late (1943) version, with German commander's cupola.
Plate 1033 (Page 268). Pz Kpfw T-34 747(r).
Plates 909-910. Jgd Pz SU 85(r), a Russian self-propelled 85mm anti-tank gun. A similar equipment used by the German Army in limited numbers was the SU 100; both vehicles were based on the T-34 chassis.
Plate 911. Pz Kpfw KV la 753(r) on view at a German ordnance store for captured equipment.
Plates 912-913. StuG SU 122(r)—basically the same vehicle as the SU 85, but armed with a 122mm howitzer. A few were used by the German Army.

903

900

904

901

905

906

910

907

911

908

912

909

913

914

918

915

919

916

920

Plate 914. Stu Pz KW II(r), the assault version of the KV I, armed with a 152mm howitzer M1938/40 L/20.

Plate 915. Stu Pz SU 152, the Model 1937 152mm howitzer based on the KV chassis. (The gun was also mounted on the IS chassis.)

Plate 916. Russian light tank T-70, German designation Pz Kpfw T-70(r).

Plate 917. Gep Art Schl T-70(r) towing a 7.5cm PaK40.

Plate 918. Mun Schl T-70(r).

Plate 919. Russian 4-wheeled light armoured car BA 20 adapted to run on railway lines, in use by the Germans as a railway protection unit. The German designation for this series was Pz Sp Wg BA 20 2(r) (Bronieford).

Plates 920-921. Pz Sp Wg BAF 203(r), the German designation given to all models of the Russian 6-wheeled armoured cars. The vehicle in these two plates is the BA 10 Model 1932—that in Plate 920 has a 37mm gun, while the car in Plate 921 has, before its recapture by the Russians, had its turret replaced by a heavy machine-gun with an armoured shield.

Plates 922-923. Pz Sp Wg BAF 203(r): BA 10 Model 1935, mounting a 45mm gun. The large turret was similar to that fitted on the T-26B tank.

Plates 924-925. Pz Sp Wg BAF 203(r): BA 10 Model 1937.

Plate 926. Sowjetischer Raketenwerfer (Katjuscha)—or 'Stalinorgel'—were multiple rocket-launchers mounted on trucks and tractors; the rockets ranged in calibre from 8cm to 30cm. This plate shows the M-13 launcher in action with German troops.

Plate 927. Sixteen 132mm rockets on an M-13 launcher.

917

921

924

922

925

923

926

927

Miscellaneous captured vehicles

Plate 928. Pz Sp Wg DAF 201(h), one of a number of Dutch Van Doorne armoured cars that the Germans used for police duty.
Plate 929. Polish 7 TP light tanks in service with the German Army.
Plates 930-931. Art Schl VA 601(b), the Vickers-Armstrong Utility Tractor built under licence in Belgium. Two versions were built, with and without rear seats: in Plate 930, the vehicle has rear seats and is towing a 5cm PaK38; in Plate 931, the rear seats are folded to carry mail.
Plate 932. An American M8 armoured car in German service.
Plate 933. Another Art Schl VA 601(b).

934

936

935

937

Plate 934. An American M5 light tank recaptured by the American Army.
Plates 935-936. The M4 Sherman, German designation Pz Kpfw M4 748(a); Plate 936 shows a 76mm-gunned M4 that has been knocked out.
Plate 937. An American M3 semi-tracked vehicle knocked out while in German service.
Plate 938. A Sherman Firefly VC, armed with a 17-pounder gun.

938

Appendices

I. German tank armament

The development of German tank armament from 1935 to 1945 featured continuous increases in calibre, weight of projectile and barrel length (and consequently muzzle velocity). In general, the main armament consisted of a high-velocity anti-tank gun with a coaxial 7.92mm machine-gun. An auxiliary machine-gun was usually ball-mounted in the front vertical (or glacis) plate.

The Pz Kpfw I, being a light tank, was armed with two turret-mounted, coaxial 7.92mm MG 13. In the Pz Kpfw II, the left-hand machine-gun was increased in calibre to 2cm (2cm KwK30 or 38). These 2cm guns were adaptations of the 2cm FlaK30 and 38 respectively. Apart from the mounting, neither of them differed materially from its prototype. Both were automatic magazine-loaded weapons, and although the KwK38 was intended to replace the KwK30, both remained in use. The performance of the KwK30 was similar to that of the KwK38, but the latter had a higher rate of fire. These guns were also mounted in the principal 4-, 6- and 8-wheeled armoured cars.

The early Ausf A to G of the Pz Kpfw III mounted a 3.7cm KwK with two coaxial 7.92mm MG34 in the turret, and one MG34 in a gimbal mounting on the offside of the front vertical plate. This was replaced in Ausf E, F, G, H and some Ausf J by the 5cm KwK L/42 and one coaxial MG34. The 5cm KwK L/42 was a relatively short anti-tank weapon, specially designed for mounting in tanks, generally known as the short-barrelled 5cm, the barrel having a length of 42 cals as opposed to the 60 cals of the latter KwK39. Late models of the Pz Kpfw III received the 5cm KwK39 L/60. This weapon was introduced as an anti-tank gun in 1941, to replace the 3.7cm anti-tank gun. It was evolved merely by substituting a longer barrel in the 42 calibre gun. Hence the breech rings and mountings were identical. The longer barrel had a lengthened chamber to take the 5cm PaK38 cartridge

case. It was almost identical with the 5cm PaK, but the muzzle brake was removed, an electrical firing system was incorporated, and the carriage was modified to suit it for tank mounting. A modified version of the 5cm KwK39/I L/60 with muzzle brake, was mounted in the 8-wheeled armoured car Sd Kfz 234/2 'Puma'. Final development of the Pz Kpfw III main armament came with the Ausf N, which mounted the short, low-velocity 7.5cm KwK L/24 which had been rendered superfluous by the up-gunning of the late models of the Pz Kpfw IV.

The early models of the Pz Kpfw IV, mounted a 7.5cm KwK L/24, together with a coaxial MG34 and, in case of Ausf A, D, E and F, an auxiliary hull-mounted MG34. The 7.5cm KwK L/24 was primarily a close-support weapon intended mainly for firing high explosive. The ammunition scale comprised only 25 per cent AP against 10 per cent smoke and 65 per cent HE shells. Its armour-piercing performance was relatively poor because of the low muzzle velocity. It was electrically fired, and the breach action was semi-automatic. Versions of the 7.5cm KwK L/24 were also mounted in the following vehicles:

StuG III	Sd Kfz 142
8-Wheeled armoured car	Sd Kfz 233
8-Wheeled armoured car	Sd Kfz 234/3
semi-tracked vehicle	Sd Kfz 250/8
semi-tracked vehicle	Sd Kfz 251/9

With the introduction of Pz Kpfw IV, Ausf F2 and G, the length of the 7.5cm KwK gun was increased to 43 calibres (7.5cm KwK40 L/43). This was a new weapon intended both as an anti-tank and HE-firing weapon. None of the parts were interchangeable with those of the short gun. Like the 7.5cm KwK L/24, it was electrically fired and had semi-automatic breech action. It was always fitted with a muzzle brake, of which there were at least four types. From 1943, Ausf G and then Ausf H

Plates 941-942. The Pz Kpfw III Ausf L machine-gunner and wireless operator positions; note the stowage of machine-gun belt bags and radio.

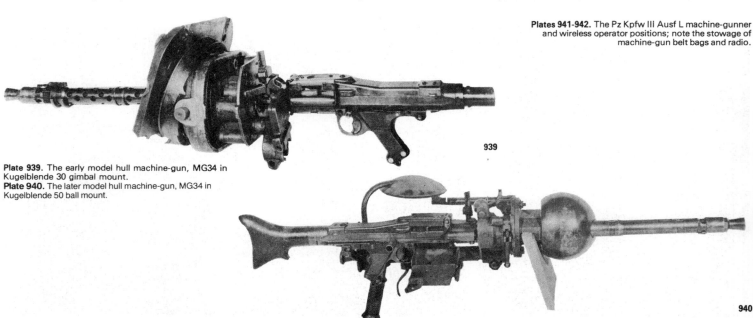

Plate 939. The early model hull machine-gun, MG34 in Kugelblende 30 gimbal mount.
Plate 940. The later model hull machine-gun, MG34 in Kugelblende 50 ball mount.

939

940

Weapon	Ammunition	Weight (kg)	Muzzle Velocity (m/s)	100m	500m	1,000m	1,500m	2,000m
				Penetration of Homogeneous Armour Plate at 30° from Vertical (mm):				
7.92mm MP44	Patr SmK Kurz		650					
7.92mm MG13, 34 & 42	Patr SmK	0.0115	785	8	3			
2cm KwK30 & 38 L/55 and	2cm Pzgr	0.148	780	20	14	9		
2cm FlaK30 & 38 L/112.5	2cm Pzgr40	0.100	1,050	49	20			
2.8cm sPzB41	2.8cm Pzgr41	0.121	1,430	60	40	19		
3.7cm PaK35/36 L/45	3.7cm Pzgr	0.685	745	34	29	22	19	
and 3.7cm KwK L/46.5	3.7cm Pzgr40	0.368	1,020	64	34			
3.7cm KwK34(t)(A3) L/40	3.7cm Pzgr	0.815	690	37	31	26	22	
3.7cm KwK38(t)(A7) L/47.8	3.7cm Pzgr	0.815	750	41	35	29	24	
	3.7cm Pzgr40	0.368	1,040	64	34			
3.7cm FlaK43 L/89	3.7cm Pzgr18	0.685	770	35	28	21	17	
4.7cm PaK(t) L/43.4	Pzgr36(t)	1.65	782	54	48	41	35	
	Pzgr40	0.825	1,080	100	59			
5cm KwK38 L/42	Pzgr39	2.06	685	54	46	36	28	22
	Pzgr40	0.925	1,060	96	58			
5cm KwK39 L/60	Pzgr39	2.06	835	67	57	44	34	26
	Pzgr40	0.925	1,180	130	72	38		
5cm PaK38 L/60	Pzgr39	2.06	835	69	59	48	38	29
	Pzgr40	0.925	1,180	130	72	38		
7.5cm KwK37 L/24 and	K Gr rot Pz	6.80	385	41	39	35	33	30
7.5cm StuK37 L/24	Gr38 H1/A	4.40	450	70	=	=	=	
	Gr38 H1/B	4.57	450	75	=	=	=	
	Gr38 H1/C	4.80	450	100	=	=	=	
7.5cm KwK40 L/43 and	Pzgr39	6.80	740	98	91	82	72	63
7.5cm StuK40 L/43	Pzgr40	4.10	920	126	108	87	69	
7.5cm KwK40 L/48,	Pzgr39	6.80	790	106	96	85	74	64
7.5cm StuK40 L/48, 7.5cm PaK40 L/46 and 7.5cm PaK39 L/48	Pzgr40	4.10	990	143	120	97	77	
7.5cm KwK42 L/70 and	Pzgr39/42	6.80	925	138	124	111	99	89
7.5cm StuK42 L/70	Pzgr40/42	4.75	1,120	194	174	149	127	106
7.62cm PaK36(r) L/51.5	Pzgr39	7.60	720	98	90	82	73	65
	Pzgr40	4.15	960	135	116	94	75	58
8.8cm FlaK18 & 37 L/56	Pzgr	9.50	810	97	93	87	80	72
8.8cm KwK36 L/56	Pzgr39	10.2	800	127	117	106	97	88
	Pzgr39	10.2	773	120	110	100	91	84
8.8cm PaK43 L/71 and	Pzgr40	7.3	930	171	156	138	123	110
8.8cm KwK43 L/71	Pzgr39-1	10.2	1,000	203	185	165	148	132
10cm K18	Pzgr40/43	7.3	1,130	237	217	193	171	153
10.5cm leFH18 L/28 and	Pzgr rot	15.6	805	164	149	133	119	109
10.5cm StuH42 L/28	Pzgr	14.0	470	63	59	54	50	46
	Gr39 H1/A	12.3	495	80	=	=	=	
	Gr39 H1/B	12.1	495	90	=	=	=	
	Gr39 H1/C	12.35	495	100	=	=	=	
12.8cm K40 L/61	Pzgr	26.4	880	201	176	150	132	120
12.8cm PaK44 L/55	Pzgr	26.4	860	189	166	143	127	117
	Pzgr43	28.3	845	187	178	167	157	148
15cm sIG33 L/11 and	Gr39 H1/A	25.0	280	160	=	=	=	
15cm StuH43 L/12								
15cm sFH13 L/17	Gr39 H1/A	25.0	460	160	=	=	=	=
15cm sFH18 L/29.6	Gr39 H1/A	25.0	465	160	=	=	=	=

and J of the Pz Kpfw IV, appeared, mounting a gun with an even longer barrel, the 7.5cm KwK40 L/48. This fired the same ammunition as the 43 calibre gun, but had a barrel 5 calibres longer. At the time of its introduction, the breech mechanism was slightly modified to simplify production. However, except for a few small parts, barrel and breech rings of 43 and 48 calibre guns were completely interchange-able. The following vehicles mounted a version of the 7.5cm KwK40 L/48:

StuG III (7.5cm StuK40) Sd Kfz 142/1   7.5cm Kan40 L/48
Pz Jäg 38 (7.5cm le StuG38(t))   7.5cm PaK39 L/48
Pz Jäg IV (StuG IV für 7.5cm StuK40 Sd Kfz 162) 7.5cm PaK39 L/48
The 7.5cm PaK39 was not usually provided with a muzzle brake

although on earlier models the muzzle had been prepared for one. The Pz Kpfw V Panther was designed to replace the Pz Kpfw III and IV in the Panzer divisions, and although heavier than its predecessors, it retained the calibre of 7.5cm for its main armament, 7.5cm KwK42 L/70. The length of the gun (70 calibres) however, was considerably greater than that which could be mounted in the latest Pz Kpfw IV models. A coaxial 7.92mm MG34 was also provided in all models, but the hull machine-gun ball mount was unavailable for fitting in the early Ausf D. The 7.5cm L/70 gun originally fired the same projectiles as the 43 and 48 calibre guns, which had single 17mm driving bands. However, new projectiles with two 17mm bands, about 4mm apart, were introduced. An assault-gun version of the 7.5cm KwK42, known as the 7.5cm StuK42 L/70 was mounted in the Jagdpanzer IV Sd Kfz 162/1. With the introduction of the slower, heavy tank, Pz Kpfw VI Tiger Ausf E, a change was made, from 7.5cm to 8.8cm, for the calibre of the main armament, with the mounting of the 8.8cm KwK36 L/56, while the subsidiary armament again consisted of one coaxial 7.92mm M34 plus a similar MG in a ball mounting in the front vertical plate. The 8.8cm KwK36 was a version of the FlaK36, but, unlike the FlaK36, the KwK36 was fitted with a double baffle muzzle brake. It was electrically fired and had a different recoil gear, to enable it to be fitted in a tank-type mounting. It fired the same ammunition as the 8.8cm FlaK18, 36 and 37. The breech mechanism was based on that of the 7.5cm 43 and 48 calibre tank guns. The Tiger E was the only vehicle to be armed with this weapon.

The 8.8cm main and subsidiary armament was retained in the Tiger Ausf E's successor, the Tiger Ausf B, but in the latter vehicle, the calibre length of the 8.8cm gun was increased to 71 (8.8cm KwK43 L/71). The 71 calibre gun fired the same ammunition as the 8.8cm PaK 43/1 and 43/41. The projectiles, but not the cartridge cases, were the same as those for the 8.8cm FlaK41. The breech mechanism was of the simplified type as for the 48 calibre 7.5cm and 56 calibre 8.8cm.
This gun represented the largest calibre and calibre length to be employed operationally in a tank mounting.

The Pz Kpfw Maus, Löwe and E.100 were, however, to have mounted the 12.8cm KwK82 L/55 or 15cm KwK44 L/38 and a coaxial 7.5cm KwK44 L/36, while 7.5cm, 8.8cm, 10.5cm and even 15cm guns, with calibre lengths of up to 100, were in various stages of design, construction or trials.

The 8.8cm of 71 calibres was also used in the following vehicles:
8.8cm PaK43/1 (L/71) auf Fgst Pz Kpfw III/IV (Sf) Hornisse
                                                 Sd Kfz 164
8.8cm PaK43/2 (L/71) Pz Jäg Tiger (P) Elefant   Sd Kfz 184
8.8cm PaK43/3 (L/71) Jagdpanther   Sd Kfz 173

All German tank guns had similar main features, such as electric primer firing, recoil gear consisting of hydraulic buffer and hydro-pneumatic recuperator, semi-automatic breech operation with spring opening and closing, and vertical sliding wedge breech blocks. All guns (except the 12.8cm KwK82 L/55) employed fixed QF ammunition of HE (fuzed DA or Graze) and APCBC shell types. Originally, in most cases, composite-rigid tungsten-carbide-cored projectiles were also provided, but, later in the war, the supply of these projectiles ceased because of shortage of tungsten-carbide. In the case of the lower velocity guns, hollow charge and smoke ammunition were also fired.

Muzzle brakes: On AFV guns, the muzzle brake was to shorten the recoil. It used the energy of the propellant gases, which leave the muzzle after the projectile, to apply a forward pull to the piece. Muzzle brakes usually consisted of two chambers, (one only on early 7.5cm KwK40) front (outer) and rear (inner). Each chamber had two side ports, and, at the front, a baffle with a hole in it for the projectile to pass through. The shape of the muzzle brake varied considerably; there were at least four patterns for the 7.5cm KwK40.

943   944

945

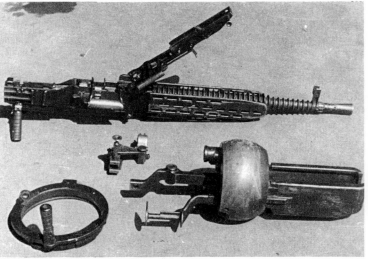

946

Plate 943. Fliegerbeschussgerät: this device for anti-aircraft defence consisted of a light tubular mounting for the machine-gun, which could be attached to the cupola by a clamp. The mounting was adjustable to suit the user. Maximum elevation was about 80°, and traverse was 30° each way. Additional traverse was obtainable by loosening the clamp and sliding the mount along. The device shown is mounted on the Pz Kpfw III Ausf L.
Plate 944. Panther, Königstiger and Tiger Ausf E with the new cupola were provided with a rail around it for attaching the Fliegerbeschussgerät.
Plate 945. The Fliegerbeschussgerät rail around the Panther Ausf G cupola.
Plates 946–947. The hull and turret machine-gun mountings on the Pz Kpfw 38(t) Ausf E.
Plate 948. Combination mount for two machine-guns, fitted in the turret of the early Pz Kpfw III Ausf A, B, C, D. A similar mount but with thicker armour was used on the Ausf E, F and G.
Plate 949. Interior view of Pz Kpfw III with internal gun mantlet, showing 3.7cm KwK L/46 and twin machine-guns.
Plate 950. 2cm KwK30 L/55 mounted in Pz Kpfw II Ausf C.
Plate 951. The breech of the 5cm KwK L/42 and coaxial machine-gun (Pz Kpfw III Ausf H).
Plate 952. 5cm KwK L/42 and coaxial machine-gun. Note the bag for spent shell cases. (Pz Kpfw III Ausf H.)
Plate 953. Interior view of a Jagdtiger, showing a Nähverteidigungswaffe installed in the roof as a smoke-projector and close-defence weapon.
Plate 954. Interior view of the Pz Kpfw III Ausf H.

947

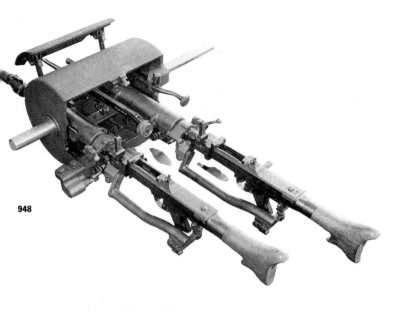

948

949

950

951

952

953

954

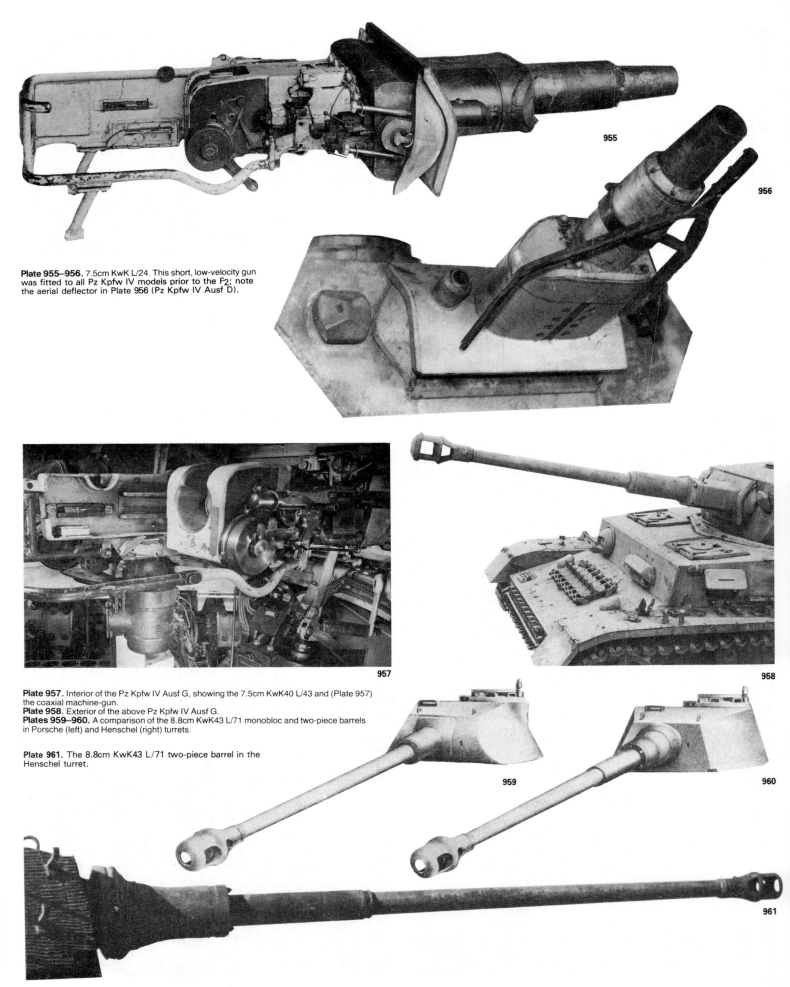

Plate 955–956. 7.5cm KwK L/24. This short, low-velocity gun was fitted to all Pz Kpfw IV models prior to the F2; note the aerial deflector in Plate 956 (Pz Kpfw IV Ausf D).

Plate 957. Interior of the Pz Kpfw IV Ausf G, showing the 7.5cm KwK40 L/43 and (Plate 957) the coaxial machine-gun.
Plate 958. Exterior of the above Pz Kpfw IV Ausf G.
Plates 959–960. A comparison of the 8.8cm KwK43 L/71 monobloc and two-piece barrels in Porsche (left) and Henschel (right) turrets.

Plate 961. The 8.8cm KwK43 L/71 two-piece barrel in the Henschel turret.

962

963

Plate 962. Interior view of the Panther Ausf D, showing the breech of the 7.5cm KwK42 L/70 and coaxial machine-gun. Note air blast gear on 7.5cm gun breech ring.
Plate 963. Interior view of the Tiger Ausf E, showing the massive breech-block of the 8.8cm KwK36.

Plate 964. 7.5cm KwK 42/I for the Panther Schmal turret (Pz Kpfw V Ausf F) on proof mounting.

964

Plates 965-967. Armament of the Jagdtiger—12.8cm PaK80 L/55. The interior views show the storage of the projectiles and cartridge cases.

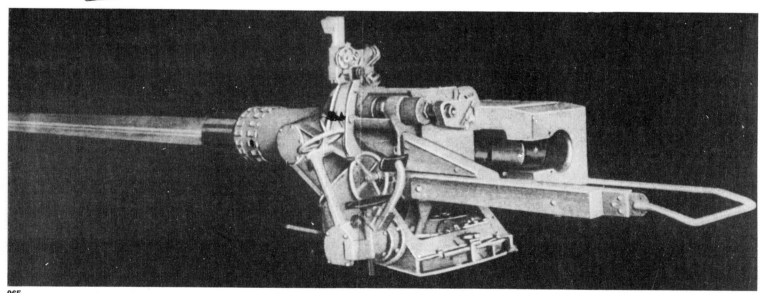

965

966

967

Plates 968–971. Armament for the Maus – a 12.8cm KwK82 L/55 with coaxial 7.5cm KwK44 L/36. Plate 968 shows the combination on the test rig; and Plate 969 is a close-up of the breech-blocks.
Plates 972–973. Pz Kpfw IV Ausf F2 mit 7.5cm KwK42 L/70, an experimental mock-up.

974

977

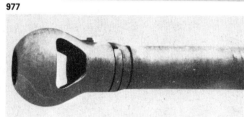

978

975

979

980

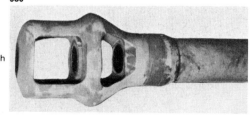

981

Plate 974. Experimental mounting of the 5cm KwK39 L/60 in the Pz Kpfw IV Ausf D.
Plates 975-976. Pz Kpfw III Ausf L and Pz Kpfw IV Ausf F mit Waffe 0725. This was an experimental gun based on the Gerlich principle, which involved the use of a tapered-bore barrel of 75/55mm, and a skirted projectile, the skirts of which were squeezed down as the projectile passed along the bore of the barrel, thereby increasing the velocity of the projectile. The rounds used had a core of tungsten-carbide, the shortage of which caused the discontinuance of the experiment.
Plates 977-983. Muzzle brakes for 2.8cm Panzerbüchse 41 (Plate 977); 7.5cm KwK40 first (Plate 978), second (Plate 979), third (Plate 980) and fourth types (Plate 981); 7.62cm PaK36(r) (Plate 982); and 8.8cm KwK36 (Plate 983).

976

982

983

II. Ammunition

The Germans were not content merely to increase the size of their tank guns, they also developed the ammunition. The main AP round (Pz gr) was an armour-piercing shell containing a small HE charge. All tanks were equipped with this type plus ordinary HE (Sp gr) ammunition. With the introduction of the 5cm gun, a capped AP shell (APC) was produced in order to improve performance against face-hardened armour. This was additional to the ordinary 5cm AP shell. For guns of 7.5cm calibre and over, a ballistic cap was fitted in addition to the armour-piercing cap (APCBC). This improved performance at long range, by giving the projectile a better ballistic shape. Since the AP cap was enclosed, it was possible to make it blunter and so improve performance at oblique attack without deterioration in its ballistic properties. For low-velocity guns, hollow charge ammunition was produced. The projectile penetrated armour plate by means of a concentrated forward blast, which meant that performance was independent of striking velocity and, therefore, to a large degree, independent of range. To give very high performance at short ranges, the Germans introduced the AP40 shot. This had a small, very hard tungsten-carbide core in a mild steel envelope. Only the core penetrated. This ammunition was even produced for the 8.8cm gun, although the projectile weighed only 16lb.

Armour piercing, capped: This consisted of a hard steel cap fitted to armour-piercing projectiles to assist penetration of face-hardened armour. A projectile so fitted was known as APC. All German AP projectiles of 5cm and over, had a piercing cap, and in calibres of 7.5cm and over, this was of a blunt shape making a ballistic cap necessary.

Ballistic cap: This was a long and pointed cap fitted to a projectile to reduce air resistance in flight. (Where both armour-piercing cap and ballistic cap were fitted, the projectile was designated APCBC.) In the case of normal AP projectiles, the presence of a ballistic cap, although in itself slightly impeding penetration, actually increased it at medium and long ranges, because of the reduced deceleration by air resistance, and consequent higher striking velocity.

AP40 (Pzgr 40): This was a special type of AP ammunition used with most German tank and anti-tank guns, in addition to the more conventional types of AP projectile. The AP40 consisted of a mild steel body, a light alloy or plastic ballistic cap, and a cemented tungsten-carbide core. The weight of this type of projectile was only 50–65 per cent of that of the normal AP shell. The MV was high, but the velocity dropped rapidly with increased range, so that increased penetration was obtained at short ranges only.

Hollow charge shell: This type of shell had a shaped cavity in the forward end of the HE filling. The effect on impact was to concentrate a very high temperature jet in a forward direction, the object being to pierce armour by chemical energy instead of the projectile forcing its way through the armour by its weight and striking velocity. The penetrative power of hollow charge AP projectiles was, therefore, independent of the striking velocity. Their use in low-velocity weapons, such as howitzers or infantry guns, gave these weapons an improved performance against tanks, within the limits of their accuracy.

984

Plate 984. Loading the 8.8cm PaK43/1 L/71 on a Hornisse.

Plates 985-998. Ammunition: 2cm armour-piercing round for KwK30 (Plate 985); the short 7.5cm KwK L/24 AP/HE round (Plate 986); 7.5cm KwK (Plate 987); 7.5cm KwK40 (Plate 988); 7.5cm KwK42 (Plate 989); 7.5cm KwK42 AP (Plate 990); 7.5cm KwK42 HE (Plate 991); 7.5cm PaK40 (Plate 992); 7.5cm KwK L/48 AP/HE (Plate 993); 8.8cm FlaK18, 36, 37 and KwK36 (Plate 994); 8.8cm FlaK41 (Plate 995); 8.8cm PaK43, 43/1, 43/2, 43/3 and KwK43 (Plate 996); and (Plates 997-998) a comparison of cartridge cases for 8.8cm KwK43 and 7.5cm KwK42.

985 986 987 988 989 990 991 992 993 994 995 996 997 998

Light Alloy or Plastic Ballistic Cap   Tungsten-Carbide Core   Mild Steel Body

Light Alloy Cap   Tungsten-Carbide Core   Mild Steel Skirts

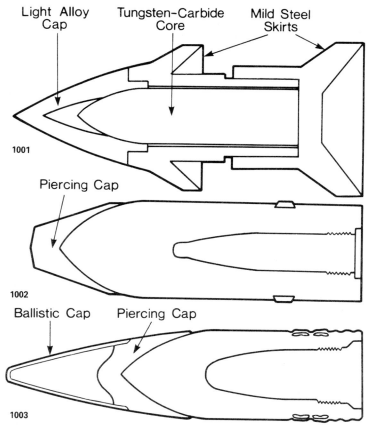

999

1001

Fuze   Cavity   Filling

Piercing Cap

1000

1002

Ballistic Cap   Piercing Cap

1003

Plates 999-1003. Cross-sections of armour-piercing projectiles: AP40 shot (Plate 999); and a hollow-charge shell (Plate 1000); Gerlich-type projectile (Plate 1001); AP shell with piercing cap (Plate 1002); AP shell with piercing cap and ballistic cap (Plate 1003).

Plates 1004-1007. 38cm Raketenwerfer 61 L/54 auf Stu Mrs Tiger (page 138). The development of this equipment in 1943 arose from a naval project for U-boat attacks on land targets. Although the Kriegsmarine dropped the project, it was developed by the Army and mounted on the chassis of the Tiger Ausf B as an assault mortar. Plates 1005 and 1006 show the interior of the Sturmmörser: note the collapsible loading tray and, to right and left of the breech, stowage racks for the projectiles, with locking straps to keep the rounds securely in place. Plate 1007 shows a 38cm projectile being attached to the wire of the hand-operated winch for loading it into the vehicle.

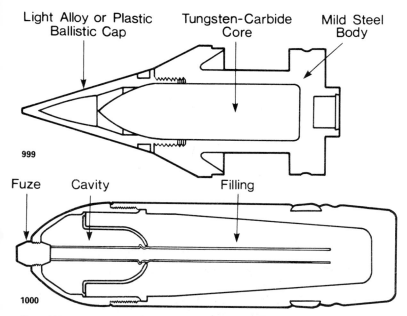

1004

1006

1005

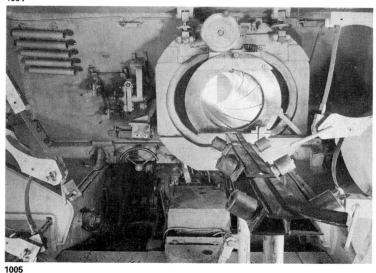

1007

Plates 1008-1009. The 60cm Gerät 040 was the largest calibre gun to be mounted on a fully-tracked chassis; Plate 1008 shows the enormous round being manoeuvred into the breech.

III. Radio equipment

Type	Set Description	Accessories	Frequency Band (Kc/s)	Aerial	Range (Km) WT	RT	Vehicle
FuG1	Pack receiver b	—	100-6,970	—			Listening set only—generally in HQ vehicles such as Sd Kfz 250/3
FuG2	USW receiver c1	EUa2	27,200-33,300	1.4 metre rod	4	2	Listening set only for all subordinate armoured vehicles
FuG4				2 metre star rod			Artillery control set—Pz Art Beob Wg
FuG5	10 watt transmitter c USW receiver c1	SE10u	27,200-33,300 27,200-33,300	2 metre rod	4	2	Standard tank set—all Pz Kpfw III-VI and supporting armoured vehicles
FuG6	20 watt transmitter c USW receiver c1, later e	SE20u	27,200-33,300	2 metre rod	8	6	Early Pz Bef Wg
FuG7	20 watt transmitter d USW receiver d1	SE20u	42,100-47,800 42,100-47,800	2 metre rod	50	50	Ground-to-air set—Pz Bef Wg, Sd Kfz 250/3, 251/3
FuG8	30 watt transmitter a MW receiver b, later MW receiver c	SE30	1,130-3,000 580-3,000 835-3,000	frame later 8 metre winch mast	40 50	10 10	Main Divisional link set—Pz Bef Wg Funkwagen
FuG10	30 watt transmitter Pack receiver b, later 30 watt transmitter a	SE30	950-1,670 100-6,970 1,120-3,000	frame	40	10	Reconnaissance vehicles—Sd Kfz 223
FuG11	100 watt transmitter Pack receiver b	SE100	200-1,200 100-6,970	frame later 9 metre winch mast p	50 200	10 70	Command link set—Sd Kfz 232(Fu)
FuG12	80 watt transmitter c MW receiver c	SE80	1,120-3,000 835-3,000	2 metre rod			Late reconnaissance vehicles—Luchs, Sd Kfz 234, etc.
FuG13	20 watt transmitter c USW receiver e USW receiver e	SE20u	27,200-33,300 27,200-33,300 27,200-33,300	2 metre rod	8	6	Command-vehicle set, similar to FuG6, but with two receivers
FuG15	USW receiver h		23,000-24,950	2 metre rod	4	2	Sturmartillerie—StuK, StuG Listening set for subordinate StuG
FuG16	10 watt transmitter h USW receiver h		23,000-24,950 23,000-24,950	2 metre rod	4	2	Sturmartillerie
FuG37(t)	10 watt transmitter/receiver			rod battle		1 5	Czech armoured vehicles
FuG Spr a to f/FuG Spr Ger a to f	USW transmitter/receiver			1.4 or 2 metre rod		1	Inter-vehicle communication—most armoured vehicles other than Pz Kpfw: range 3km when vehicle stationary
RF 1 CA	transmitter/receiver			1.8 metre rod			Italian standard APV set
RF 2 CA	transmitter/receiver			1.8 metre rod			Italian command group set
RF 3M or M2	transmitter/receiver			3 metre rod			Italian long-range set

IV. Optical equipment

Type	Weapon	Mag*	F**	Range in metres for MG	AP	AP40	HE	Indirect	Vehicle
Telescopes									
Kugel Zielfernrohr: (Ball Mounting Sighting Telescopes)									
KgZF1	MG13	mx1.8	18	200					All vehicles, auxiliary MG
KgZF2	MG34/MG42	mx1.75	18	200					
MGZF38(t)	MG37(t)	mx2.6	25	1,700					
Turmzielfernrohr: (Turret Sighting Telescopes)									
TZF2	MG13	mx2.5	28	800					Pz Kpfw I Ausf A/B
TZF3a	2cm KwK38	mx2.5	17	1,200	1,200		1,200		Sd Kfz 222, 234/1, 250/9, 251/23 Aufkl Pz 38(t)
TZF4/TZF4/38	2cm KwK30	mx2.5	25	1,200	1,200		1,200		Pz Kpfw II Ausf a, b, c/Ausf C, F
TZF4/36	2cm KwK30	mx2.5	25	800	800		800		Pz Kpfw II Ausf A, B
TZF4b	5cm KwK39/1	mx2.5							Sd Kfz 234/2
TZF38(t)	3.7cm KwK34(t)								Pz Kpfw 35(t)
	3.7cm KwK37(t)	mx2.6	25		2,000	400	2,000		Pz Kpfw 38(t)
TZF5a	3.7cm KwK	mx2.4	25	800	2,000		2,000		Pz Kpfw III Ausf A-G
TZF5averl	5cm KwK(L/42)	mx2.4	25	1,500	2,000		2,000		Pz Kpfw III Ausf E-G
TZF5b	7.5cm KwK(L/24)	mx2.4	25	800	2,000		2,000	6,500	Pz Kpfw IV Ausf A-F1
TZF5bvergr	7.5cm KwK(L/24)	mx2.4	25	1,200	2,000		2,000	6,500	Pz Kpfw III Ausf N
TZF5d	5cm KwK(L/42)	mx2.4	25	1,500	3,000		3,000		Pz Kpfw III Ausf F-J
TZF5e	5cm KwK39	mx2.4	25	1,200	3,000	1,500	3,000		Pz Kpfw III Ausf J-M Pz Bef Wg Ausf K
TZF5f	7.5cm KwK40(L/43)	mx2.4	25	1,200	2,500	1,500	3,300		Pz Kpfw IV Ausf F2-G
TZF5f/1+f/2	7.5cm KwK40(L/48)	mx2.4	25	1,200	3,000	1,500	4,000		Pz Kpfw IV Ausf G-H+Ausf J
TZF6	2cm KwK30	x2.4	22	1,200	1,200		1,200		Sd Kfz 231, 232
TZF6/38	2cm KwK38	x2.5	25	1,200	1,200		1,200		Pz Sp Wg II Ausf L
TZF8	MG34	bx							VK1801
TZF9	7.5cm KwK	bx							VK3001/VK3601
TZF9b	8.8cm KwK36	bx2.5	26	1,200	4,000		4,000	8,000	Pz Kpfw Tiger Ausf E (early)
TZF9c	8.8cm KwK36	mx2.5	25	1,200	4,000		4,000	8,000	Pz Kpfw Tiger Ausf E (late)
TZF9b/1	8.8cm KwK43	bx2.5	26	1,200	4,000		4,000		Pz Kpfw Ausf B (P-turm)
TZF9d	8.8cm KwK43	mx2.5	25	1,200	3,000		5,000		Pz Kpfw Tiger Ausf B
TZF10	EW141								VK601/VK901
TZF12	7.5cm KwK42	bx2.5	28	4,000	3,000	2,000	4,000		Pz Kpfw Panther Ausf D, A (early)
TZF12a	7.5cm KwK42	mx2.5	19	4,000	3,000	2,000	4,000		Pz Kpfw Panther Ausf A, G
		mx5.0	15						
TZF13	7.5cm KwK42								Pz Kpfw Panther Ausf F
Driver's Episcopes									
Kampfwagen Fahrer Fernrohr:									
KFF1		bx1.0	65						Pz Kpfw II Ausf A-B, Pz Kpfw III Ausf A-D
KFF2		bx1.0	63						Pz Kpfw II Ausf C-L, Pz Kpfw III Ausf E-M, Pz Kpfw IV Ausf A-G, Pz Kpfw Tiger Ausf E (early) StuK Ausf A-G (early)
Observation Periscopes									
TBF1		bx3.0	20	360° traverse through turret roof.					Pz Bef Wg Ausf D1-K
TBF2									Pz Art Beob Wg III/Panther
TBF3									Sd Kfz 234/2
TSR1		mx6.0	6	1.4 metre high.					Pz Bef Wg IV/Panther/Tiger Pz Art Beob Wg IV
Episcopic Periscopes/Telescopes									
SflZF	15cm StuH43		8						StuPz IV, sIG 33B
SflZF1/Rblf32	7.5cm StuK(L/24)	mx5.0	8		1,500		3,000	6,000	StuK Ausf A-E
	7.5cm K37(L/24)								Sd Kfz 233, 251/9 (early)
SflZF1a/Rblf36	7.5cm StuK40	mx5.0	8		2,000	1,500			StuG Ausf F-G, StuG IV
	7.5cm PaK39								Jagdpz IV, 38(t)
	7.5cm StuK42				3,000		5,000		PzIV/70(V), PzIV/70(A)
	10.5cm StuH42							12,325	StuH42
	8.8cm StuK43/1								Ferdinand
SflZF1b/Rblf36	7.5cm K51(L/24)	mx5.0	8						Sd Kfz 234/3, 250/8, 251/9 (late)
SflZF5	8.8cm StuK43	mx3.0	8		3,000		5,400	15,300	Jagdpanther (early)
WZF1/3	7.5cm PaK39/1	mx3.0	7						Jagdpz IV Starr
WZF1/4	8.8cm StuK43	mx10.0	7		4,000	2,400	3,400	15,300	Jagdpanther (late)
WZF2/2	7.5cm PaK39/1	mx3.0	16						Jagdpz 38(t) Starr
WZF2/7	12.8cm PaK44		8						Jagdtiger
ZF3x8	7.5cm PaK40(Sfl)	mx3.0	8		2,000	1,000		7,700	Sf auf Pz Kpfw II, 38(t), Lrs(f), etc.
	7.62cm PaK36(r)	mx3.0	8		1,800	1,100	2,800	10,000	Sf auf Pz Kpfw II, 38(t)
	2cm FlaK38								Flakpz 38(t), Zgkw Sd Kfz 251/17
	3.7cm FlaK36								Flakpz IV, Ostwind, Zgkw
ZF3x8/Rblf36	8.8cm PaK43	mx3.0	8					10,900	Hornisse
ZF1x11	3.7cm PaK	mx3.0	11						Sf auf UE(f)
ZF2x16	3.7cm PaK	mx2.0	16						Sd Kfz 250/10, 251/10, Zgkw, LKW
ZF2x30	4.7cm PaK(t)	mx2.0	30						Sf auf Pz Kpfw I, 35-R(f)
ZF20/Rblf32	8.8cm FlaK18/36								Sf auf gep Zgkw, Sd Fgst
Rblf36	15cm sIG33 (Sf)								Sf auf Pz Kpfw I, II, 38(t)
	10.5cm leFH18(Sf)								Sf auf Pz Kpfw II, Lrs(f), B-2(f)
Rblf37	15cm sFH18								Hummel
RA35	15cm PzW42								Maultier Pz W42

Mag* = (m) monocular/(b) binocular x magnification. F** = Field of view in degrees.

V. Engines

Type	Form	Cyls	Fuel	Coolant	Capacity litres	Power PS	Speed rpm	Vehicles
Maybach NL38TR	I	6	P	W	3.791	100	3,000	Pz Kpfw I, Zgkw 1t.
Maybach HL42TRKM	I	6	P	W	4.198	100	3,000	Sd Kfz 250, 2, 3, Zgkw 1t.
Maybach HL42TUKRM								Sd Kfz 251, 250 (late).
Maybach HL42TRKMS								sWS.
Maybach HL45P	I	6	P	W	4.678	150	3,800	VK601, 1601, 1801.
Maybach HL45Z								HKp602, 3
Maybach HL50P	I	6	P	W	4.995	180	4,000	HKp605, 6, Kätzchen.
Maybach HL54TUKRM	I	6	P	W	5.420	115	2,600	Zgkw5t.
Maybach HL57TR	I	6	P	W	5.698	130	2,600	Pz Kpfw IIa.
Maybach HL62TR/TRM	I	6	P	W	6.191	140	2,600	Pz Kpfw IIb-F.
Maybach HL62TUK								Zgkw 8t.
Maybach HL66P	I	6	P	W	6.754	180	2,800	Luchs, GW IVb VK901, 3
Maybach HL85TUKRM	V	12	P	W	8.520	185	2,500	Zgkw 12t.
Maybach HL90	V	12	P	W	9.990	360	3,600	Heuschrecke, GW III/IV, Sd Fgst Räumer-S.
Maybach HL108TR	V	12	P	W	10.838	250	3,000	Pz Kpfw IIIA-D, IV A.
Maybach HL108TUKRM								Zgkw 18t. Bef Wg D1, E.
Maybach HL116	I	6	P	W	11.048	300	3,300	VK3001(H), Sf 12.8cm.
Maybach HL120TR/TRM	V	12	P	W	11.867	300	3,000	Pz KpfwIII E-N, StuK, StuG, Bef Wg, Pz Kpfw IV B-H.
Maybach HL120TRM112						272	2,800	Pz KpfwIV J.
Maybach HL157P	V	12	P	W	15.580	550	3,500	VK1602.
Maybach HL174	V	12	P	W	19.144	550	3,000	VK3601.
Maybach HL210P45	V	12	P	W	21.353	650	3,000	Pz Kpfw Tiger E (early).
Maybach HL224	V	12	P	W	21.353	600	3,000	VK6501.
Maybach HL230P30	V	12	P	W	23.095	700	3,000	Panther, Tiger B.
Maybach HL230P45								Tiger E (late).
Maybach HL234	V	12	P	W	23.095	800	3,000	E-100.
Krupp M305	H	4	P	A	3.460	57	2,500	Pz Kpfw IA Sd Kfz 247.
Porsche 100	V	10	P	A	10.000	210	2,500	VK3001(P).
Porsche 101/1	V	10	P	A	15.060	320	2,500	VK4501(P).
Praga EPA	I	6	P	W	7.750	125	2,200	Pz Kpfw 38(t) A-G.
Praga EPA/2						140	2,500	Pz Kpfw 38(t) H.
Praga AC								GW 38(t) M.
Praga AC/2						160	2,800	Hetzer.
Skoda T11	I	4	P	W	8.520	120	1,800	Pz Kpfw 35(t).
Tatra 103	V	12	D	A	14.825	220	2,250	Sd Kfz 234, Jagdpz38 (d).
Büssing-NAG L8V	V	8	P	W	7.913	150	3,000	Sd Kfz 231, 2, 3, 263.
					8.363	180	3,000	Sd Kfz 231, 2, 3 (late).
Horch 3.5	V	8	P	W	3.5177	75	3,600	Sd Kfz 221, 2, 247.
Horch 3.8					3.823	90	3,600	Sd Kfz 222, 3, 260, 1.

VI. Supplementary armour

To obtain extra protection against armour-piercing shot, various methods were used. With the Panzerkampfwagen III Ausf H, extra 30mm armour plates w:ere bolted to the basic 30mm upper and lower nose plates, and an additional 20mm armour plate was attached to the front vertical plate. The Pz Kpfw IV Ausf E had additional 30mm armour plates on the front vertical plate, and 20mm plates on the sides of the hull. This modification was carried out during the production of these vehicles. Subsequent models of the Pz III and IV had the basic armour increased, but this still failed to give effective protection against the increasing size and power of armour-piercing shot. The next method resorted to, was the use of spaced armour. 20mm armour plates were attached to brackets, about 100mm-120mm in front of the vertical superstructure plate and gun mantlet. The plate in front of the vertical plate had two openings to accommodate the driver's visor and the hull machine-gun. These spaced plates were intended to take the first impact of an AP shot, which would then shatter against the basic armour plate behind.

In 1943, it became the standard German practice to secure thin (5mm) plates, by means of brackets, to the sides of the vehicle, and 8mm plates around the sides and rear of the turret. Hinged doors were fitted in the additional armour to permit the opening of the access doors in the turret sides. However, it was possible to escape via the turret without opening the doors in the spaced plates. These plates, called 'Schürzen' (skirts), were of mild steel boiler plating, lightly secured, either by spot welding or by hooks on rails, and were intended to protect the basic armour against hollow-charge projectiles. On the Pz Kpfw IV Ausf J, the mild steel plating was replaced by heavy gauge meshed wire.

German tanks were frequently provided with improvised additional protection in the form of sandbags, attached wherever possible, and lengths of track secured over vulnerable parts. It was common for sandbags to be arranged on the roof of the superstructure in front of the turret, so as to shield the turret joint and the space below the bottom of the gun mantlet. Others were fitted round the front and sides of the superstructure, care being taken not to obstruct the driver's vision, or the elevation and traverse of the hull machine-gun. Lengths of track were usually attached across the upper and lower nose plates. The track on the lower nose plate was generally held in position by means of a transverse bar welded to the plate at its ends, while that on the upper nose plate was attached by 'S' hooks to the air inlet cowls of the track brake cooling system. Tracks were also secured on the front of the superstructure between the driver's visor and the hull machine-gun, and draped over the top of the turret and gun mantlet.

To prevent the attachment of magnetic mines to tanks, they were sometimes coated with a substance called 'Zimmerit'. This was applied like plaster over red lead paint to form a coating about 4–5mm thick. Started in 1943, the practice was discontinued from mid 1944.

Plates 1010-1015 (opposite page).
Plate 1010. Pz Kpfw III Ausf E or F with additional 30mm plates bolted on the upper and lower nose plates. A 30mm plate has also been attached to the front vertical plate.
Plate 1011. Pz Kpfw IV Ausf E with two supplementary 30mm armour plates bolted to the two sections of the front superstructure, and 20mm plates bolted to the superstructure sides.
Plate 1012. Pz Kpfw IV Ausf H with additional armour plate bolted to the nose plate.
Plate 1013. StuG III with Schürzen (skirts) and armour plates bolted on the nose.
Plate 1014. StuG40 on Pz Kpfw III chassis with additional frontal armour.
Plate 1015. 10.5cm Sturmhaubitze 42 mounted on the ge Sfl Ausf F. Platypus tracks have been attached to the normal track, and the additional frontal armour.

1010

1011

1012 / 1014

1013 / 1015

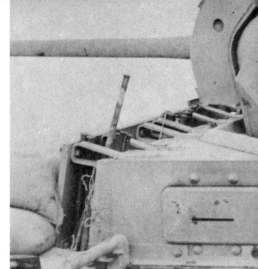

1016

1020

1018

1020

Plates 1016–1017. A Pz Kpfw III Ausf J or L with spaced armour in front of the front vertical plate and (Plate 1019) gun mantlet.
Plate 1018. Shows spaced armour on a Pz Kpfw III Ausf N.
Plate 1019. Front view of spaced armour on Pz Kpfw III J or L.
Plate 1020. Pz Kpfw III Ausf M with spaced armour over the gun mantlet and front vertical plate.
Plates 1021 and 1017. Pz Kpfw III Ausf L with spaced armour over the front vertical plate and a frame for spaced armour over the gun mantlet. (The curved plate that was intended for this frame was often omitted from this model.)
Plates 1022–1023. Spaced armour on the turret of a Pz Kpfw IV Ausf H showing the fixing brackets (Plate 1022) and the door in the plating for the left-side hatch (Plate 1023).

Plates 1024–1025. Side skirts (Schürzen). Plate 1024 shows the method of attaching the skirts on a Pz Kpfw IV; the Pz Kpfw III Ausf L in Plate 1025 demonstrates the rail for hanging the plates on; note that it also has spaced armour on the gun mantlet.

Plate 1026. Pz Kpfw IV Ausf J with heavy-gauge wire mesh protection.
Plate 1027. Pz Kpfw IV Ausf G with Schürzen and additional armour welded to the hull and superstructure front.

1023

1025

1027

1028

1029

1030

1031

Plate 1028. Pz Kpfw III Ausf J with sandbags and spare tracks for extra protection.
Plate 1029. A close-up showing how tracks were attached to the nose plate of a Pz Kpfw IV Ausf F$_1$.
Plate 1030. Pz Kpfw IV Ausf E with lengths of track on the top of the turret, the front vertical plate and the nose plates.
Plate 1031. Jgd Pz IV/70(r) covered in Zimmerit anti-magnetic paste.
Plate 1032. Stu G IV (7.5cm StuK40) showing Zimmerit and spare tracks, and concrete protection.

1032

VII. German AFV production

In the following table, for the first time, is summarized the production of all types of armoured vehicles manufactured for the German Army. With the exception of the Panzerkampfwagen I, production prior to 1937 was insignificant and therefore all annual figures are grouped under the heading 'to 1938'.

Throughout the war years, the Germans took possesion of armoured vehicles belonging to the armies of countries which they occupied. Many of these were used for a short time only or for unimportant tasks, and records do not indicate the total numbers involved. Where foreign equipment was officially issued to the Army, and recorded by the OKH, the figures are shown in square brackets [ ]. The production facilities of Czechoslovakia, Austria and Italy were all assimilated into the German war programme, and output of foreign designed vehicles at these factories is treated in the same way as new production of German vehicles.

During the course of the war, the Germans converted obsolete vehicles for different purposes so as to prolong their active life. Such rebuilds and conversions are indicated within parentheses ( ).

When looking at these following pages, showing German AFV production, it is worth considering a number of points so as to see the results in the context of world affairs of the time. By the end of 1939, when Hitler's Germany was already committed to the Second World War, only 5,420 armoured vehicles of all types had been delivered. During the same period (1934 to 1939), the Soviet Army received about 17,000 AFVs to add to the small number it already possesed. Even more surprising is that the 5,420 German vehicles included only 533 battle tanks equipped with 3.7cm and 7.5cm guns (Pz Kpfw III and IV). From this it must be clear just how significant the new 'Blitzkrieg' tactics employed by the Germans really were. The serviceable armoured vehicles, from both sides, which faced each other during the German invasion of France were approximately 4,000 British and French against 2,800 German, of which, the majority were Pz Kpfw I and Pz Kpfw II. The Czech industrial contribution to the production

of AFVs for the German Army was very significant throughout the war, representing nearly eight per cent of all vehicles delivered, but during the early years, the contribution was even more important because of the quality of the Czech tanks. In addition to the mere 533 German gun-armed tanks, available at the end of 1939, there were 219 Pz Kpfw 35(t) taken from the Czech Army, and 150 brand new Pz Kpfw 38(t) delivered by the Czech Praga factory, both of which, were excellent vehicles armed with 3.7cm guns.

The 'shoestring' production during the first three years of the war proved disastrous during the Invasion of Russia in 1941 and during 1942. Despite the tremendous victories achieved, the German armoured divisions were so weakened by loss of equipment that they never quite managed to function as satisfactorily as in the initial years. The victories could not be sustained and the disasters of late 1942 followed.

During late 1942, major changes were made and AFV production began to soar. In 1943, under the programme of Speer, deliveries (25,000) were nearly five times that of 1941. Production continued to rise during 1944 and, while not so dramatic an increase as in the previous year, it must be remembered that this figure includes more and more sophisticated vehicles which were both larger and more powerful. This production achievement is even more impressive when considered against the overall progress of the war and the total supremacy of Allied air power over Germany. Destruction of industrial facilities was met by diversification of location of plants producing sub-components, and by simplification of the manufacturing processes. Even during 1945, when communications and transport in Germany was virtually at a standstill, 5,592 AFVs were known to have been completed in three months (projected figure for the year, on this basis, would have been about 23,000). However, for all the 89,000 AFVs produced by Germany, estimates put Soviet production during the same period at 125,000, while the Americans built over 48,000 of their single best known tank, the M4 'Sherman'.

	to 1938	1938	1939	1940	1941	1942	1943	1944	1945	Total
Tanks										
Neubaufahrzeuge	3									3
Pz Kpfw I	1,493									1,493
Pz Kpfw I nA					40					40
Pz Kpfw I nA verst					30					30
Pz Kpfw II	332	669	246	9	233	291				1,780
Pz Kpfw II nA				3		9				12
Pz Kpfw II nA verst						22				22
Pz Kpfw 35(t)			[219]							[219]
Pz Kpfw 38(t)			150	370	698	193				1,411
Pz Kpfw III (3.7cm)	38	33	206	391(5)						673
Pz Kpfw III (5cm L/42)				467(53)	1,673(285)	251(85)	(1)			2,815
Pz Kpfw III (5cm L/60)					40	1,907	22			1,969
Pz Kpfw III (7.5cm)						450	213(29)	(8)		700
Pz Kpfw IV (7.5cm L/24)	13	102	141	278	467	124				1,125
Pz Kpfw IV (7.5cm L/43 or L/48)						870(25)	3,013	3,126	385	7,419
Pz Kpfw Panther							1,768	3,749	459	5,976
Pz Kpfw Tiger (P)						5				5
Pz Kpfw Tiger I						84	647	623		1,354
Pz Kpfw Tiger II								377	112	489
Pz Kpfw M13/40 u M14/41(i)							[23]			[23]
Pz Kpfw M15/42(i)							[92]			[92]
Pz Kpfw P40(i)							[5]	100		100[5]
Totals	1,879	804	743[219]	1,515(58)	3,114(285)	4,276(110)	5,663(30)[120]	7,975(8)	956	26,925(419)[339]
Command Vehicles										
kl Pz Bef Wg	190									190
gr Pz Bef Wg		26	44	34	132	14				250
Pz Bef Wg (5cm L/42)						81	(104)			185
Pz Bef Wg (5cm L/60)						36	14			50
Pz Bef Wg M41 u M42(i)							[16]	41		41[16]
Totals	190	26	44	34	132	131	14(104)[16]	41		612(104)[16]
Flame-thrower vehicles										
Pz Kpfw II(F)				44(43)	39	29				155
Pz Kpfw B-2(f) (Flamm)				[8]	[52]					[60]
Pz Kpfw III (Flamm)							100			100
StuG III (Flamm)							(10)			10
Jagdpz 38(t) (Flamm)								20		20
Totals				44(43)	39[8]	29[52]	100(10)	20		232(53)[60]
Assault guns										
StuK (7.5cm L/24)				184	548	90				822
StuG III (7.5cm L/43 or L/48)						699	3,011	3,840(173)	864	8,587
StuG IV							31	1,006	102	1,139
StuG L6 (4.7cm 47/32)							[78]			[78]
StuG M42(i) (7.5cm 75/18 or 75/34)							[159]	135		135[159]
StuG M43(i) (7.5cm 75/34 or 75/46)								18	22	40
Totals				184	548	789	3,042[237]	4,999(173)	988	10,550(173)[237]
Assault artillery										
15cm sIG 33B						24				24
StuH 42						10	204	903	95	1,212
Stu Pz IV							66(8)	215	17	306
Stu Mrs Tiger								(18)		18
StuG M43(i) (10.5cm 105/25)							[26]	91		91[26]
Totals						34	270(8)[26]	1,209(18)	112	1,625(26)[26]

	to 1938	1938	1939	1940	1941	1942	1943	1944	1945	Total
Tank destroyers										
Pz Jäg Ferdinand							90			90
Jagdpanzer 38(t)								1,457	1,127	2,584
Jagdpanzer IV								769		769
Pz IV/70(V)								560	370	930
Pz IV/70(A)								207	71	278
Jagdpanther								226	166	392
Jagdtiger								61	16	77
Totals							90	3,280	1,750	5,120
Self-propelled anti-tank guns										
4.7cm PaK(t) auf Pz Kpfw I				(171)	(31)					(202)
4.7cm PaK(t) auf Pz Kpfw 35-R(f)					[174]					[174]
5cm PaK38(Sf) auf Pz Sf 1c						2				2
5cm PaK38(Sf) auf Pz Sf 1a						2				2
7.5cm K (L/40.8) auf Pz Sf III			2							2
7.5cm PaK40(Sf) auf Pz Kpfw 38(t)					111		799(175)	308		1,393(175)
7.5cm PaK40(Sf) auf LrS(f)					[170]					[170]
7.5cm PaK40(Sf) auf FCM(f)							[10]			[10]
7.5cm PaK40(Sf) auf 39-H(f)						[24]				[24]
7.5cm PaK40(Sf) auf m SPW Somua (f)								[16]		[16]
7.5cm PaK40/1(Sf) auf RSO							60			60
7.5cm PaK40/2(Sf) auf Pz Kpfw II						372	204(75)			651(175)
7.62cm PaK36(r)(Sf) auf Zgkw 5t					9					9
7.62cm PaK36(r)(Sf) auf Pz Kpfw II					(193)		(8)			(201)
7.62cm PaK36(r)(Sf) auf Pz Kpfw 38(t)					344		(19)			363(19)
8.8cm PaK43/1(Sf) auf Pz Kpfw III/IV							345	133	16	494
10.5cm K 18(Sf) auf Pz Sf IV a						2				2
12.8cm K 40(Sf) auf VK3001(H)						2				2
Totals			2(171)		9(31)[174]	835(193)[194]	1,408(277)[10]	441[16]	16	2,711(672)[394]
Self-propelled artillery										
10.5cm leFH16(Sf) auf FCM (f)						[12]				[12]
10.5cm leFH18(Sf) auf 39-H (f)						[48]				[48]
10.5cm leFH18(Sf) auf LrS(f)						[12]				[12]
10.5cm leFH18/1(Sf) auf Pz Sf IVb						8				8
10.5cm leFH18/2(Sf) auf Pz Kpfw II							514	162		676
10.5cm leFH18/3(Sf) auf GW B-2(f)						[16]				[16]
15cm sIG33(Sf) auf Pz Kpfw I				(38)						(38)
15cm sIG33(Sf) auf Pz Kpfw II					12					12
15cm sIG33(Sf) auf Pz Kpfw 38(t)						1	224	148		373
15cm sIG33(Sf) auf Jagdpz 38(t)									24(6)	30(6)
15cm sFH13/1(Sf) auf LrS(f)						[94]				[94]
15cm sFH18/1(Sf) auf Pz Kpfw III/IV							368	289	57	714
15cm Pz Werfer 42 auf Maultier							248	52(19)		319(19)
60cm/54cm Gerät 040				2	4					6
Totals			2(38)		16	1[182]	1,362	651(19)	81(6)	2,113(63)[182]
Ammunition carriers										
Mun Schlepper (Pz Kpfw I)			(51)							(51)
Mun fahrzeuge Wespe							104	55		159
Mun fahrzeuge Grille								102		102
Mun träger für Ferdinand (Pz Kpfw III)							(6)			(6)
Mun träger für Karl (Pz Kpfw IV)				1	13(4)					18(4)
Mun fahrzeuge Hummel							96	61		157
Mun Schlepper Panther								(2)		(2)
VK302					22	6				28
Sd Kfz 252				54	359					413
Mun Kw für Pz Werfer (Maultier)							232	57		289
Totals			1(51)	54	394(4)	6	432(6)	275(2)		1,162(63)
Observation vehicles										
Sd Kfz 253				85	200					285
Sd Kfz 254				121	7					128
Pz Art Beob Wg III							(225)	(37)		(262)
Pz Art Beob Wg IV								(96)		(96)
Pz Art Beob wg Panther								(10)	(31)	(41)
Pz Art Beob wg LrS (f)						[39]				[39]
Totals				206	207	[39]	(225)	(143)	(31)	913(399)[39]
Self-propelled anti-aircraft guns										
2cm FlaK30 or 38 (Sf) auf Zgkw 1t										610
2cm FlaK38 (Sf) auf Pz Kpfw 38(t)							86(1)	54		141(1)
2cm Flakvierling 38 (Sf) auf Zgkw 8t										319
2cm Flakvierling 38 (Sf) auf Wirbelwind								(87)		(87)
3.7cm FlaK36 (Sf) auf Zgkw 5t										339
3.7cm FlaK36 (Sf) auf Zgkw 8t										123
3.7cm FlaK36 (Sf) auf FlaKpz IV								205	35	240
3.7cm FlaK43 (Sf) auf Ostwind I								(15)	7(22)	44(37)
8.8cm FlaK18 (Sf) auf Zgkw 12t or 18t		10	15							25
Totals		10	15				86(1)+	259(102)+	42(22)+	1,928(125)
Maintenance vehicles										
Instandsetzungswagen I	107	57								164
Bergewg III								(150)		(150)
Bergewg IV								(36)		(36)
Bergewg Jagdpz IV								26		26
Bergewg Hetzer								89	81	170
Bergepanther							82	227(8)	30	347(8)
Bergetiger (P)							3			3
Bergetiger (H)								(3)		(3)
Totals	107	57					85	342(197)	111	702(197)
Bridging vehicles										
Brükenleger I			(2)							(2)
Brükenleger II			(1)	(?)						1+
Brükenleger IV				20						20
Inf Stu Steg IV				2						2
Totals			(3)	22(?+)						22(3+)
Demolition vehicles										
Minenräumer B I		50								50
Ladungsleger I			(100)							100
s Ladungsträger B IV						238	651	304		1,193
le Ladungsträger Goliath (E-Motor)						850	1,731	69		2,650
le Ladungsträger Goliath (V-Motor)							2,112	2,694	123	4,929
m Ladungsträger Springer								35	15	50
Totals		50	(100)			1,088	4,494	3,102	138	8,872(100)
Semi-tracked armoured vehicles										
Sd Kfz 250					389	1,374	2,895	1,701	269	6,628
Sd Kfz 251			232	337	424	1,200	4,258	7,785	1,016	15,252
Totals			232	337	813	2,574	7,153	9,486	1,285	21,880

	to 1938	1938	1939	1940	1941	1942	1943	1944	1945	Total
Reconnaissance vehicles										
Kfz 13	147									147
Kfz 14	40									40
Sd Kfz 221	143	46	126	24						339
Sd Kfz 222	72	72	64	52	179	352	198			989
Sd Kfz 223	117		59	71	112	62	108	21		550
Sd Kfz 231/232 (6-Rad)	123									123
Sd Kfz 231/232 (8-Rad)	27	29	55	32	94	170	200			607
Sd Kfz 233						9(10)	100			119
Sd Kfz 234 Fgst								15		15
Sd Kfz 234/1								163	37	200
Sd Kfz 234/2							7	94		101
Sd Kfz 234/3								88		88
Sd Kfz 234/4								25	64	89
Sd Kfz 247 (6-Rad)	10									10
Sd Kfz 247 (4-Rad)					54	4				58
Sd Kfz 260/261				10	171	236	76			493
Sd Kfz 263 (6-Rad)	28									28
Sd Kfz 263 (8-Rad)			64	20	8	108	40			240
Pz Sp Wg Luchs						16	77(4)			104
Aufkl Pz 38(t) (2cm)								50		50
Aufkl Pz 38(t) (7.5cm L/24)								2		2
Pol Pz ADGZ		[27]				25				39
Pz Sp Wg 178-P(f)				[233]						233
Pz Sp Wg AB41 u AB41/43							20[37]	90	12	122[37]
Totals	707	211[27]	324	189[233]	618	982(10)	826(4)[37]	555	113	4,525(14)[284]
Overall Totals	2,883	1,158[27]	1,359(154)[219]	2,589(310)[233]	5,890(320)[182]	10,745(313)[467]	25,005(665)[232]	32,635(662)[16]	5,592(59)	89,254*(2,483)[1,590]**

*Includes 1,516 self-propelled anti-aircraft guns not shown in annual figures.
**Several hundred French tanks also issued.

VIII. Sonderkraftfahrzeug numbers

Sd Kfz was the abbreviation for Sonderkraftfahrzeug or special purpose motor vehicles. It was applied to armoured vehicles and vehicles that had been built and taken into service for a specific military purpose.

This designation did not indicate the purpose or nature of the vehicle, but merely served as a convenient reference number in the Ordnance list of special motor vehicles. Minor modifications to a vehicle were normally indicated by the original Sd Kfz number followed by an oblique stroke and a number. Further minor differences were indicated by the addition of a Roman numeral, e.g. Sd Kfz 251/3–IV.

Major modifications to a vehicle were normally allotted a new Sd Kfz number, e.g. the Pz Kpfw II was allotted Sd Kfz number 121, whereas the redesigned Pz Kpfw II incorporating torsion-bar suspension ('Luchs'), was allotted Sd Kfz number 123.

There were, however a number of inconsistencies in the allotment of Sd Kfz numbers. In the case of commander's tanks, different Sd Kfz numbers refer to the wireless equipment installed, irrespective of the basic type of tank. In the case of flame-throwing AFVs, the Germans allotted the Pz Kpfw II flame-throwing tank a new Sd Kfz number (122), whereas with the Pz Kpfw III flame-throwing tank, they were content to add an oblique stroke followed by a number to the basic Pz Kpfw III number, i.e. Sd Kfz 141/3. This may have been because the Pz Kpfw II (Fl) was conceived as a new basic weapon, and the Pz Kpfw III (Fl) consisted of the normal Pz Kpfw IIIs converted for the role and produced in limited quantities.

Sd Kfz No.	Vehicle	Remarks
2	kleines Kettenkraftrad (kl Kett Krad)	motor cycle tractor
2/1	kleines Kettenkraftrad für Feldfernkabel (kl Kett Krad f Feldfk)	motor cycle tractor for field cable laying
2/2	kleines Kettenkraftrad für schweres Feldkabel (kl Kett Krad f schw Fe Kab)	motor cycle tractor for heavy cable laying
3a	Gleiskettenlastkraftwagen 2t offen (Maultier) (m Gleisk LKW 2t Maultier (Opel))	2 ton semi-tracked lorry (Opel)
3b	Gleiskettenlastkraftwagen 2t offen (Maultier) (m Gleisk LKW 2t Maultier (Ford))	2 ton semi-tracked lorry (Ford)
3c	Gleiskettenlastkraftwagen 2t offen (Maultier) (m Gleisk LKW 2t Maultier (Klockner-Humbolt-Deutz))	2 ton semi-tracked diesel lorry (Klockner-Humbolt-Deutz)
4	schwere Gleiskettenlastkraftwagen 4½t offen (Maultier) (s Gleisk LKW 4½t Maultier)	4½ ton semi-tracked lorry
4/1	15cm Nebelwerfer-Zehnling 42 auf 2t Maultier (Opel) (15cm Pz NbW 42 auf 2t Maultier)	2 ton semi-tracked lorry mounting 10 barrelled 15cm Nebelwerfer projector
6	mittlere Zugkraftwagen 5t (m Zgkw 5t)Pi	5 ton semi-tracked tractor (Engineers' version)
6/1	mittlere Zugkraftwagen 5t (m Zgkw 5t)Art	5 ton semi-tracked tractor (Artillery version)
6/2	Selbstfahrlafette mit 3.7cm FlaK 36 (3.7cm FlaK 36 auf Zgkw 5t)	5 ton semi-tracked tractor mounting 3.7cm FlaK 36
7	mittlere Zugkraftwagen 8t (m Zgkw 8t)	8 ton semi-tracked tractor
7/1	Selbstfahrlafette mit 2cm Flakvierling (m Zgkw 8t mit 2cm Flakvierling)	8 ton semi-tracked tractor mounting quadruple 2cm FlaK guns
7/2	Selbstfahrlafette mit 3.7cm FlaK 36 (m Zgkw 8t mit 3.7cm FlaK 36)	8 ton semi-tracked tractor mounting 3.7cm FlaK 36
7/6	FlaKmesstruppkraftwagen (FlaKmesstr Kw)	8 ton semi-tracked tractor for AA range-finding
8	schwere Zugkraftwagen 12t (s Zgkw 12t)	12 ton semi-tracked tractor
9	schwere Zugkraftwagen 18t (s Zgkw 18t)	18 ton semi-tracked tractor
9/1	Drehkran (Hebekraft 6t) auf Fahrgestell des schweren Zugkraftwagen 18t (Drehkran Kw 6t)	18 ton semi-tracked tractor mounting 6 ton crane
9/2	Drehkran (Hebekraft 10t) auf Fahrgestell des schweren Zugkraftwagen 18t (Drehkran Kw 10t)	18 ton semi-tracked tractor mounting 10 ton petrol-electric crane
10	leichte Zugkraftwagen 1t (le Zgkw 1t)	1 ton semi-tracked tractor
10/1	leichte Gasspürkraftwagen (Gasspu Kw)	1 ton semi-tracked light gas-detector vehicle

Sd Kfz No.	Vehicle	Remarks
10/2	leichte Entgiftungskraftwagen (le Eg Kw)	1 ton semi-tracked decontamination vehicle
10/3	leichte Sprühkraftwagen (le Spruh Kw)	1 ton semi-tracked decontamination vehicle with spraying equipment
10/4	leichte Selbstfahrlafette (2cm FlaK30) (le Zgkw 1t mit 2cm Flak 30)	1 ton semi-tracked tractor mounting 2cm FlaK30
10/5	leichte Selbstfahrlafette (2cm FlaK38) (le Zgkw 1t mit 2cm Flak 30)	1 ton semi-tracked tractor mounting 2cm FlaK38 and armoured cab
11	leichte Zügkraftwagen 3t (le Zgkw 3t)	3 ton semi-tracked tractor
11/1	Nebelkraftwagen (Nb Kw)	3 ton semi-tracked smoke-generator vehicle, also used as ammunition-carrier for Nebelwerfer projectors
11/2	mittlere Entgiftungskraftwagen (m Eg Kw)	3 ton semi-tracked decontamination vehicle
11/3	mittlere Sprühkraftwagen (m Spruh Kw)	3 ton semi-tracked decontamination vehicle with spraying equipment
11/4	Nebelkraftwagen (Nb Kw)	3 ton semi-tracked smoke-generator vehicle
11/5	mittlere Gasspürkraftwagen (m Nb Kw als Gasspu Kw)	3 ton semi-tracked gas-detector vehicle
101	Panzerkampfwagen I, Ausf A und B (Pz Kpfw I)	Pz Kpfw I, models A and B
111	gepanzerter Munitionsschlepper auf Pz Kpfw I (gep Mun Schl)	Pz Kpfw I converted to munitions carrier
121	Panzerkampfwagen II, Ausf a1, a2, a3, b, A, B, C, D, E, F	Pz Kpfw II series
122	Panzerkampfwagen II (Flamm) (Pz Kpfw II (Fw))	Pz Kpfw II models D and E converted to flame-throwing tank
123	Panzerkampfwagen II Ausf L (Luchs) (Pz Kpfw II Ausf L/Pz Spg II)	reconnaissance vehicle, also known as Panzerspähwagen Luchs
124	leFH18/2 auf Fgst Pz Kpfw II(Sf) Wespe (leFH18/2(Sf) auf Gw II)	10.5cm leFH18/2 mounted on Pz Kpfw II chassis
131	7.5cm PaK40/2 auf Fgst Pz Kpfw II (Sf) (7.5cm PaK40/2 a Sf)	7.5cm anti-tank gun mounted on Pz Kpfw II chassis
132	7.62cm PaK (r) auf Fgst Pz Kpfw II (Sf) (Pz Sf 1f 7.62cm PaK36)	7.62cm Russian anti-tank gun mounted on Pz Kpfw II chassis D and E
135	7.5cm PaK40/1 auf Lorraine Schlepper (f) Marder I (7.5cm PaK40/1 auf Pz Jäg LrS)	7.5cm anti-tank gun mounted on French Lorraine tractor
135/1	15cm sFH13 Selbstfahrlafette Lorraine (15cm lg sFH13 auf GW LrS)	15cm howitzer mounted on Lorraine tractor
138	7.5cm PaK40/3 auf Pz Jäg 38(t) Marder III (7.5cm PaK40/3 auf Sf 38(t))	7.5cm PaK40 mounted on Czech tank chassis
138/1	15cm sIG33 auf Geschützwagen 38(t) (sIG33(Sf) auf GW 38)	15cm howitzer mounted on Czech tank chassis
139	Panzerselbstfahrlafette II für 7.62cm PaK 36(r) Marder III (7.62cm PaK36(r) auf Pz Jäg 38)	7.62cm Russian anti-tank gun mounted on Czech tank chassis
140	Flakpanzer 38(t) auf Selbstfahrlafette 38(t) (2cm 38(t) PanzerflaK)	2cm FlaK gun mounted on Czech tank chassis
140/1	Aufklärungspanzer 38(t) (Aufkl Pz 38(2cm))	tracked reconnaissance vehicle based on 38(t) tank chassis
141	Panzerkampfwagen III Ausf A, B, C, D, E, F, G, H	Pz Kpfw III series
141/1	Panzerkampfwagen III Ausf J, L, M	Pz Kpfw III series
141/2	Panzerkampfwagen III Ausf N	Pz Kpfw III armed with 7.5cm L/24
141/3	Panzerkampfwagen III (Fl) (Pz Kpfw III(Fl))	Pz Kpfw III Ausf M converted to flame-throwing tank
142	gep Sf für Sturmgeschütz 7.5cm Kanone Ausf A, B, C, D, E (StuGIII für 7.5cm Kan L/24)	various versions of assault guns based on the Pz Kpfw III chassis and armed with the short 7.5cm L/24
142/1	gep Sf für 7.5cm Sturmgeschütz 40 Ausf F, F/8, G (StuGIII Ausf F, F/8, G)	assault guns based on Pz Kpfw III and armed with the 7.5cm L/43 or L/48
142/2	gep Sf für 10.5cm Sturmhaubitze 42 (10.5cm StuH42)	assault howitzer based on Pz Kpfw III armed with 10.5cm StuH42 L/28
143	Artillerie-Panzerbeobachtungswagen (Pz Beob Wg III)	Pz Kpfw III converted to mobile observation post for artillery
161	Panzerkampfwagen IV Ausf A, B, C, D, E, F	Pz Kpfw IV series
161/1	Panzerkampfwagen IV Ausf F$_2$, G	Pz Kpfw IV series
161/2	Panzerkampfwagen IV Ausf H, J	Pz Kpfw IV series
161/3	3.7cm FlaK auf Fgst Pz Kpfw IV (Sf) (Möbelwagen)	3.7cm FlaK43 mounted on the chassis of Pz Kpfw IV
162	Sturmgeschütz nA mit 7.5cm PaK L/48 (Jagdpanzer IV)	tank destroyer based on the Pz Kpfw IV chassis, armed with 7.5cm PaK39 L/48
162/1	Panzer IV/70(V)	improved version of the Jagdpanzer IV to mount the 7.5cm L/70
164	8.8cm PaK43/1 (L/71) auf Fgst Pz Kpfw III und IV (Pz Jag III/IV—'Nashorn' (früher 'Hornisse')	8.8cm PaK43 mounted on the Pz Kpfw III/IV chassis as a tank destroyer
165	15cm schwere Panzer-Haubitze 18/1 auf Fgst Pz Kpfw III/IV (Sf) (sFH18/1(Sf) auf GW III/IV) 'Hummel'	self-propelled carriage for field howitzer sFH18
166	Sturmhaubitze 43(L/12) auf Fgst Pz Kpfw IV(Sf) (15cm Stu Pz 43) 'Brummbär'	self-propelled carriage for heavy infantry howitzer 15cm sIG33 modified and redesignated 15cm StuH43
167	Sturmgeschütz IV L/48 (StuG IV für 7.5cm StuK40(L/48))	assault gun based on Pz Kpfw IV chassis and armed with the 7.5cm L/48
171	Panzerkampfwagen V Ausf D, A, G ('Panther')	'Panther' series
172	Sturmgeschütz für 8.8cm StuK43 auf Fgst Panther I	assault gun project based on Pz Kpfw V chassis
173	8.8cm PaK43/3 L/71 auf Panzerjäger 'Panther' (Jagdpanther)	tank destroyer based on the Pz Kpfw V chassis, armed with the 8.8cm PaK43/3 L/71
179	Berge Pz Wg Panther	armoured tank-recovery vehicle based on Panther chassis
181	Panzerkampfwagen VI Ausf E ('Tiger I')	Tiger I model E, formerly model H
182	Panzerkampfwagen VI Ausf B ('Tiger II') (Königstiger/Royal Tiger)	Tiger II model B
184	Pz Jäg (Tiger)P 'Ferdinand' für 8.8cm PaK43/2 (Jagdpanzer 'Elefant' für 8.8cm PaK43/2 L/71)	tank destroyer based on the Porsche Tiger chassis, armed with the 8.8cm PaK43/2
185	Jagdtiger für 8.8cm PaK43 L/71	

Sd Kfz No.	Vehicle	Remarks
186	Jagdtiger für 12.8cm PaK44 L/55 (Jagdpanzer VI)	tank destroyer based on the Tiger II chassis and armed with 12.8cm PaK44
221	leichte Panzerspähwagen (MG) (le Pz Sp Wg (MG))	light 4-wheeled armoured car (1 x 7.92mm MG)
222	leichte Panzerspähwagen (2cm) (le Pz Sp Wg (2cm))	light 4-wheeled armoured car (2cm gun and 7.92mm MG)
223	leichte Panzerspähwagen (Fu) (le Pz Sp Wg (Fu))	light 4-wheeled armoured car, with radio equipment
231	schwere Panzerspähwagen 6-Rad (s Pz Sp Wg 6-Rad)	6-wheeled armoured car
231	schwere Panzerspähwagen 8-Rad (s Pz Sp Wg 8-Rad)	8-wheeled armoured car
232	schwere Panzerspähwagen 6-Rad (Fu) (s Pz Sp Wg 6-Rad (Fu))	6-wheeled armoured car, with radio equipment
232	schwere Panzerspähwagen 8-Rad (Fu) (s Pz Sp Wg 8-Rad (Fu))	8-wheeled armoured car, with radio equipment
233	schwere Panzerspähwagen (5cm) 'Puma' (s Pz Sp Wg (KwK37 L/24))	turretless 8-wheeled armoured car mounting 7.5cm KwK37
234/1	schwere Panzerspähwagen (2cm) (s Pz Sp Wg (2cm))	8-wheeled diesel engine armoured car mounting 2cm gun
234/2	schwere Panzerspähwagen (5cm) 'Puma' (s Pz Sp Wg (5cm KwK39/1 L/60))	8-wheeled armoured car mounting 5cm KwK39/ in turret
234/3	schwere Panzerspähwagen (7.5cm) (s Pz Sp Wg (7.5cm KwK51 L/24))	8-wheeled armoured car mounting short 7.5cm in open turret
234/4	schwere Panzerspähwagen (7.5cm) (s Pz Sp Wg (7.5cm PaK40 L/46))	8-wheeled armoured car mounting 7.5cm PaK40 L/46
247	geländegängiger gepanzerter Personenkraftwagen (s G1 Pkw)	armoured staff-car on 4 or 6 wheeled chassis
250	leichte Schützenpanzerwagen (le SPW)	light armoured semi-tracked personnel-carrier (basic type)
250/1-I	leichte Schützenpanzerwagen	with intercomm facilities
250/1-II	leichte Schützenpanzerwagen	with radio equipment
250/2	leichte Fernsprechwagen (le Fe Pz Wg)	telephone cable-laying vehicle
250/3-I	leichte Funkpanzer (le Fu Pz Wg)	wireless vehicle
250/3-II	leichte Funkpanzer (le Fu Pz Wg)	wireless vehicle
250/3-III	leichte Funkpanzer (le Fu Pz Wg)	wireless vehicle
250/3-IV	leichte Funkpanzer (le Fu Pz Wg)	wireless vehicles, differences in wireless equipment carried
250/4	Luftschütz Pz Wg	anti-aircraft vehicle armed with two MG34
250/5-I	leichte Beobachtungspanzerwagen (le Beob Pz Wg)	mobile armoured observation post
250/5-II	leichte Aufklärungspanzerwagen (le Aufkl Pz Wg)	differing from le Beob Pz Wg in radio equipment
250/6	leichte Munitionspanzerwagen Ausf A (le Mun Pz Wg)	ammunition-carrier for StuG
250/6	leichte Munitionspanzerwagen Ausf B (le Mun Pz Wg)	ammunition-carrier for StuG
250/7	leichte Schützenpanzerwagen (Schwerer Granatwerfer) (le Schtz Pz Wg-Gr W)	light armoured semi-tracked mortar vehicle
250/7	leichte Schützenpanzerwagen (Munitionsfahrzeug)	ammunition-carrier for mortar vehicle
250/8	leichte Schützenpanzerwagen mit 7.5cm KwK37 (le SPW (7.5cm))	light armoured semi-tracked vehicle mounting short 7.5cm K51 L/24
250/9	leichte Schützenpanzerwagen (2cm) (le SPW (2cm))	light armoured semi-tracked vehicle with 2cm KwK38 and MG34 mounted in turret
250/10	leichte Schützenpanzerwagen (3.7cm PaK) (le SPW (3.7cm PaK))	light armoured semi-tracked vehicle armed with 3.7cm PaK35/36
250/11	leichte Schützenpanzerwagen (s PzB41) (le SPW (s PzB41))	light armoured semi-tracked vehicle armed with the schwere Panzerbüchse 41
250/12	leichte Messtruppanzerwagen (le Schtz Messtrupp Pz Wg)	light armoured semi-tracked survey and range-plotting vehicle
251	mittlere Schützenpanzerwagen (m SPW)	medium armoured semi-tracked personnel-carrier (basic type)
251/1-I	mittlere Schützenpanzerwagen	with intercomm facilities
251/1-II	mittlere Schützenpanzerwagen	with radio equipment
251/2	mittlere Schützenpanzerwagen (Granatwerfer) (m SPW (GrW))	medium armoured semi-tracked mortar vehicle
251/3	mittlere Funkpanzerwagen (m Fu Pz Wg)	wireless vehicle
251/3-I	mittlere Funkpanzerwagen (m Fu Pz Wg)	wireless vehicle
251/3-II	mittlere Funkpanzerwagen (m Fu Pz Wg)	wireless vehicle
251/3-III	mittlere Funkpanzerwagen (m Fu Pz Wg)	wireless vehicle
251/3-IV	mittlere Funkpanzerwagen (m Fu Pz Wg (Kmdo Wg))	mobile command post
251/3-V	mittlere Funkpanzerwagen (m Fu Pz Wg)	wireless vehicle, differences in wireless equipment carried
251/4	mittlere Schützenpanzerwagen für Munition und Zubehör des leIG18 (m SPW (IG Mun))	ammunition-carrier and tractor for the IG18 infantry close-support gun
251/5	mittlere Schützenpanzerwagen für Pi Zug (m SPW (Pi))	command vehicle for engineers in armoured division
251/6	mittlere Kommandopanzerwagen (m Kmdo Pz Wg)	mobile command post
251/7-I	mittlere Pionierpanzerwagen (m Pi Pz Wg)	medium semi-tracked vehicle for engineering equipment

Sd Kfz No.	Vehicle	Remarks
251/7-II	mittlere Pionierpanzerwagen (m Pi Pz Wg)	this vehicle differed only in type of radio carried
251/8-I	mittlere Krankenpanzerwagen (m Kr Pz Wg)	medium semi-tracked armoured ambulance
251/8-II	mittlere Krankenpanzerwagen (m Kr Pz Wg)	medium semi-tracked armoured ambulance, differed from Sd Kfz 251/8-I only in radio carried
251/9	mittlere Schützenpanzerwagen (7.5cm KwK37) (m SPW (7.5cm K37))	medium semi-tracked vehicle mounting short 7.5cm K37
251/10	mittlere Schützenpanzerwagen (3.7cm PaK) (m SPW (3.7cm PaK))	medium semi-tracked vehicle mounting 3.7cm PaK35/36
251/11	mittlere Fernsprechpanzerwagen (m Fe Pz Wg)	medium semi-tracked armoured telephone vehicle
251/12	mittlere Messtrupp und Gerätpanzerwagen (m Messtrupp-u-Ger-Pz Wg)	medium semi-tracked armoured survey and instrument vehicle
251/13	mittlere Schallaufnahmepanzerwagen (m Schallaufn Pz Wg)	medium semi-tracked armoured artillery sound-recording vehicle
251/14	mittlere Schallauswertepanzerwagen (m Schallausw Pz Wg)	medium semi-tracked armoured artillery sound-ranging vehicle
251/15	mittlere Lichtauswertepanzerwagen (m Lichtausw Pz Wg)	medium semi-tracked armoured artillery flash-spotting vehicle
251/16	mittlere Flammpanzerwagen (m Flamm Pz Wg)	medium semi-tracked armoured flame-throwing vehicle
251/17	mittlere Schützenpanzerwagen mit 2cm FlaK38 (m SPW (2cm))	medium semi-tracked armoured vehicle mounting 2cm FlaK38
251/18-I	mittlere Beobachtungspanzerwagen (m Beob Pz Wg)	mobile armoured observation post
251/18-Ia	mittlere Beobachtungspanzerwagen	mobile armoured observation post
251/18-II	mittlere Beobachtungspanzerwagen	mobile armoured observation post
251/18-IIa	mittlere Beobachtungspanzerwagen	mobile armoured observation post, differences in wireless equipment carried
251/19	mittlere Fernsprechbetriebspanzerwagen (m Fe Betr Pz Wg)	mobile armoured telephone exchange
251/20	mittlere Schützenpanzerwagen (Infrarotsheinwerfer) UHU	medium semi-tracked armoured vehicle carrying infra-red searchlight
251/21	mittlere Schützenpanzerwagen mit Fla MG Drilling (m SPW (1.5 oder 2cm Drilling))	medium semi-tracked armoured vehicle mounting triple 15mm or 20mm AA MG151
251/22	7.5cm PaK40 L/46 auf Mittlerer Schützenpanzerwagen (7.5cm PaK40 auf m SPW)	medium semi-tracked armoured vehicle mounting 7.5cm PaK40 anti-tank gun
251/23	2cm Hängelafette 38 auf m SPW	medium semi-tracked reconnaissance vehicle
252	leichte Gepanzerter Munitionskraftwagen (le gep Mun Trsp Kw)	light semi-tracked armoured ammunition-carrier
253	leichte Gepanzerter Beobachtungskraftwagen (le gep Beob Kw)	light semi-tracked armoured observation vehicle
254	mittlere Gepanzerter Beobachtungskraftwagen (RK-7) (m gep Beob Kw auf RK7)	medium wheel and track armoured observation vehicle
260	kleine Panzerfunkwagen (kl Pz Fu Wg)	light 4-wheeled armoured car with radio equipment
261	kleine Panzerfunkwagen (kl Pz Fu Wg)	light 4-wheeled armoured car with radio equipment. This version had frame antenna
263	Panzerfunkwagen (6-Rad) (Pz Fu Wg) 6-Rad	6-wheeled armoured car with fixed turret and radio equipment
263	Panzerfunkwagen (8-Rad) (Pz Fu Wg) 8-Rad	8-wheeled armoured car with fixed turret and radio equipment
265	kleine Panzerbefehlswagen (kl Pz Bef Wg)	Pz Kpfw I converted to armoured command vehicle
266	Panzerbefehlswagen Ausf E (Pz Bef Wg)	Pz Kpfw III Ausf E converted to armoured command vehicle
266	Panzerbefehlswagen Ausf H (Pz Bef Wg)	Pz Kpfw III Ausf H converted to armoured command vehicle
266	Panzerbefehlswagen (5cm KwKL/42) (Pz Bef Wg)	Pz Kpfw III Ausf J converted to armoured command vehicle
266	Panzerbefehlswagen Ausf K (Pz Bef Wg)	Pz Kpfw III Ausf M converted to armoured command vehicle
267	Panzerbefehlswagen Ausf D[I] (Pz Bef Wg)	Pz Kpfw III Ausf D converted to armoured command vehicle
267	Panzerbefehlswagen 'Panther'	Pz Kpfw 'Panther' with additional radio equipment
267	Panzerbefehlswagen 'Tiger' (Pz Bef Wg 'Tiger')	Pz Kpfw 'Tiger' with additional radio equipment
268	Panzerbefehlswagen Ausf D[I] (Pz Bef Wg)	Pz Kpfw III Ausf D converted to armoured command vehicle
268	Panzerbefehlswagen Ausf E (Pz Bef Wg)	Pz Kpfw III Ausf E converted to armoured command vehicle
268	Panzerbefehlswagen Ausf H (Pz Bef Wg)	Pz Kpfw III Ausf H converted to armoured command vehicle
268	Panzerbefehlswagen (5cm KwK L/24) (Pz Bef Wg)	Pz Kpfw III Ausf J converted to armoured command vehicle
268	Panzerbefehlswagen Ausf K (Pz Bef Wg)	Pz Kpfw III Ausf M converted to armoured command vehicle
268	Panzerbefehlswagen 'Panther'	Pz Kpfw 'Panther' with additional radio equipment
268	Panzerbefehlswagen 'Tiger'	Pz Kpfw 'Tiger' with additional radio equipment

The 268 vehicles varied from the 266 and 267 versions in the different radio equipment carried

280	Gepanzerter Munitionsschlepper (VK 501)	
300	Minenräumwagen Ausf I und Ausf II (Borgward BI and BII)	radio-controlled minefield-clearance vehicle
301	schwere Ladungsträger Ausf A und B (Sonderschlepper BIV)	demolition vehicle
301	schwere Ladungsträger Ausf C (Sonderschlepper BIV)	demolition vehicle

Sd Kfz No.	Vehicle	Remarks
302	leichte Ladungsträger Ausf A ('Goliath')	demolition vehicle
303	leichte Ladungsträger Ausf B ('Goliath')	demolition vehicle
304	Mittlere Ladungsträger 'Springer' (NSU Springer)	demolition vehicle

IX. Fremdengerät numbers

Prior to the outbreak of war, the Heereswaffenamt (Army Ordnance Department) inaugurated a system for listing data on all known foreign weapons and equipment. This information was published in a series of illustrated loose-leaf books known as the *Kennblätter Fremdengerät* (D.50 series), which were periodically amended during the war as captured weapons and equipment came into German possession. The D.50 series consisted of 14 volumes, of which the following covered weapons:

D.50/1 Hand weapons (pistols, rifles, submachine-guns).
D.50/2 Machine-guns (light and heavy).
D.50/3 Mortars.
D.50/4 Light artillery.
D.50/5 Medium artillery.
D.50/6 Heavy artillery.
D.50/12 Motor vehicles (armoured cars, tanks, self-propelled guns, armoured tractors, artillery tractors, semi-tracked vehicles).
D.50/14 Engineer equipment (mines, grenades, fuzes, demolition charges).

The system consisted of the German nomenclature for the weapon or equipment involved, then a group number for the type of weapon or equipment, followed by the initial letter of the country of origin, in parentheses. From the very start of the war, the Germans made maximum use of every serviceable piece of artillery that came into their possession; normally the guns were used with their own ammunition, but in some cases they were modified to conform to German calibres. (Examples of this were the Russian 7.62cm and 8.5cm Flak guns that were bored out by the Germans to 8.8cm, this calibre

ammunition was more readily available. Artillery and small-arms taken into service with the German armed forces were identified by their Fremdgerät designation, and, in many cases, the German Army published and issued their own workshop manuals on these equipments.

Group series numbers for motor vehicles
200	armoured cars.
300	semi-tracked vehicles.
400	armoured semi-tracked vehicles.
600	fully-tracked artillery tractors.
630	armoured artillery tractors.
700	tanks (including British armoured carriers).
800	self-propelled guns.

Initial letter for country of origin
(a)	amerikanisch	American
(b)	belgisch	Belgium
(e)	englisch	British
(f)	französisch	French
(h)	holländisch	Dutch
(i)	italienisch	Italian
(ö)	österreichisch	Austrian
(p)	polnisch	Polish
(r)	russisch	Russian
(t)	tschechisch	Czechoslovakian

Selected list of Fremdgerät numbers

Series 200 (armoured cars)
leichter Panzerspähwagen Mk I 202(e)
(Scout Car Mk I Dingo)
leichter Panzerspähwagen Ir 204(e)
(Armoured Reconnaissance Car Ironside)
Panzerspähwagen Mo 205(e)
(Armoured Reconnaissance Car Morris)
Panzerspähwagen F 208(e)
(Armoured Reconnaissance Car Ford)
Panzerspähwagen G 209(e)
(Guy Light Tank Wheeled)
Panzerspähwagen Wh 201(f)
(AMD White-Laffly)
Panzerspähwagen Laf 202(f)
(AMD Laffly)
Panzerspähwagen TOE 203(f)
(AMD Panhard TOE)
Panzerspähwagen P 204(f)
(AMD Panhard)
Panzerspähwagen L 202(h)
(Landsverk)
Panzerspähwagen AB40 und 41 201(i)
(Autoblinda 40 und 41)
Panzerspähwagen Lince 202(i)
(Autoblinda Lince)
Panzerspähwagen AB43 203 (i)
(Autoblinda 43)
gepanzerter Mannschaftstransportwagen S 37 250(i)
(Autoprotetto S 37)
Panzerspähwagen BA 202(r)
(BA Bronieford)
Panzerspähwagen BAF 203(r)
(BA Ford)

Series 300 (semi-tracked vehicles)
Zugkraftwagen P302, 302(b)
(Panhard Kegresse Hinstin)
Zugkrafwagen P302, 302(f)
(Panhard Kegresse Hinstin)
Zugkraftwagen S303, 303(f)
(Tracteur Somua)
Zugkraftwagen P107, 304(f)
(Unic Kegresse P107)

Zugkraftwagen U305, 305(f)
(Unic TU1)
Zugkraftwagen Ci, 306(f)
(Citroen P14P)
Zugkraftwagen S307(f)
(Somua MCG)
gepanzerter Transportkraftwagen P380(f)
(Panhard Kegresse)

Series 700 (tanks)
Panzerkampfwagen M2A4 740(a)
(Light Tank M2A4)
Panzerkampfwagen M3 747(a)
(Medium Tank M3)
Panzerkampfwagen M4 748(a)
(Medium Tank M4)
Panzerspahwagen VCL 701(b)
(Char leger/Vickers Carden-Loyd)
gepanzerter MG Träger Br 731(e)
(Bren Gun Carrier)
gepanzerter MG Träger Br 732(e)
(Scout Carrier)
leichter Panzerkampfwagen Mk II 733(e)
(Light Tank Mk II)
leichter Panzerkampfwagen Mk IV 734(e)
(Light Tank Mk IV)
leichter Panzerkampfwagen Mk VIB 735(e)
(Light Tank Mk VIB)
leichter Panzerkampfwagen Mk VIC 736(e)
(Light Tank Mk VIC)
leichter Panzerkampfwagen Mk VII 737(e)
(Light Tank Mk VII)
Kreuzer Panzerkampfwagen Mk I 741(e)
(Cruiser Tank Mk I)
Kreuzer Panzerkampfwagen Mk II 742(e)
(Cruiser Tank Mk II)
Kreuzer Panzerkampfwagen Mk III 743(e)
(Cruiser Tank Mk III)
Kreuzer Panzerkampfwagen Mk IV 744(e)
(Cruiser Tank Mk IV)
Kreuzer Panzerkampfwagen Mk V 745(e)
(Cruiser Tank Mk V)

Kreuzer Panzerkampfwagen Mk VI 746(e)
(Cruiser Tank Mk VI)
Infanterie Panzerkampfwagen Mk I 747(e)
(Infantry Tank Mk I)
Infanterie Panzerkampfwagen Mk II 748(e)
(Infantry Tank Mk II)
Infanterie Panzerkampfwagen Mk III 749(e)
(Infantry Tank Mk III)
Panzerspähwagen VM 701(f)
(Renault VM, or AMR33)
Panzerspähwagen ZT I 702(f)
(Renault ZT, or AMR35)
Panzerkampfwagen 17R oder 18R 730(f)
(Renault FT)
Panzerkampfwagen 35R 731(f)
(Renault R-35)
Panzerkampfwagen D-1 732 (f)
(Char D-1)
Panzerkampfwagen D-2 733(f)
(Char d'Assaut D-2)
Panzerkampfwagen 35H 734(f)
(Hotchkiss H-35)
Panzerkampfwagen 38H 735(f)
(Hotchkiss H-38)
Panzerkampfwagen ZM 736(f)
(Char ZM)
Panzerkampfwagen FCM 737(f)
(Char de combat FCM)
Panzerkampfwagen AMC 738(f)
(AMC 1935 R)
Panzerkampfwagen 35 S 739(f)
(Char 1935 S)
Panzerkampfwagen B-1 740(f)
(Char B-1 bis)
Panzerkampfwagen 3-C 741(f)
(Char 3-C)
Panzerbefehlswagen 770(f)
(Voiture de Commandement YS)
Panzerkampfwagen FT 731(h)
(Renault FT)
Panzerkampfwagen L3/35 731(i)
(Carro Armato L3/35)

Panzerkampfwagen L3/33 (Flammenwerfer) 732(i)
(Carro Armato L3/331f)
Panzerkampfwagen L6 733(i)
(Carro Armato L6)
Panzerkampfwagen M11/39 734(i)
(Carro Armato M11/39)
Panzerkampfwagen M13/40 735(i)
(Carro Armato M13/40)
Panzerkampfwagen M14/41 736(i)
(Carro Armato M14/41)
Panzerkampfwagen P40, 737(i)
(Carro Armato P40)
Panzerkampfwagen M15/42 738(i)
(Carro Armato M15/42)

Panzerbefehlswagen 47/32, 770(i)
(Carro Commando Cômpagnia Semovente DA 47/32)
Panzerbefehlswagen M41 771(i)
(Carro Commando Semovente M41)
Panzerbefehlswagen M42 772(i)
(Carro Commando Semovente M42)
Schwimm-Panzerkampfwagen T-37 731(r)
Schwimm-Panzerkampfwagen T-38 732(r)
Schwimm-Panzerkampfwagen T-40 733(r)
Panzerkampfwagen T-27A 734(r)
(Tanketka T-27A)
Panzerkampfwagen T-26A 737(r)
Panzerkampfwagen T-26B 738(r)
Flammenwerfer Panzerkampfwagen T-26B 739(r)

Panzerkampfwagen T-26C 740(r)
Brüken-Panzerkampfwagen 741(r)
Panzerkampfwagen BT 742(r) (Bystrochodni Tank)
Panzerkampfwagen T-60 743(r)
Panzerkampfwagen T-28 746(r)
Panzerkampfwagen T-34 747(r)
Panzerkampfwagen T-28 V 748(r)
Panzerkampfwagen T-35A 751(r)
Panzerkampfwagen T-35C 752(r)
Panzerkampfwagen KVIa 753(r)
(Klim Voroschilow)
Panzerkampfwagen KVII 754(r)
(Klim Voroschilow)
Panzerkampfwagen KVIb 755(r)
(Klim Voroschilow)

1033

1034

1035

1036

Plate 1033. An Sd Kfz 252 ammunition carrier, being passed by a T-34 in German service (data page 168).
Plate 1034. Sd Kfz 221 mit 2.8cm sPzB41 (data page 191).
Plate 1035. 3.7cm FlaK36 auf Fgst Zg kw 8t, Sd Kfz 7/2 (data page 184).
Plate 1036. 2cm FlaK38 auf Fgst Zgkw 8t, Sd Kfz 7/1 (data page 184).
Plate 1037. Le SPW (3.7cm PaK), Sd Kfz 250/10 (data page 166).

Index
of vehicle names

SERIES NUMBERS